J.S.Black

D1206661

THE IRWIN SERIES IN ECONOMICS

BOOKS IN THE IRWIN SERIES IN ECONOMICS

Introduction to Mathematical Economics
  D. W. BUSHAW AND R. W. CLOWER STATE COLLEGE
  OF WASHINGTON

Economics
  JOHN A. GUTHRIE STATE COLLEGE OF WASHINGTON

Principles of Money and Banking
  HIRAM L. JOME DEPAUW UNIVERSITY

The American Economy: Principles, Practices, and Policies *Revised Edition*
  C. LOWELL HARRISS COLUMBIA UNIVERSITY

Public Policies Toward Business
  CLAIR WILCOX SWARTHMORE COLLEGE

Economic Fluctuations
  MAURICE W. LEE UNIVERSITY OF NORTH CAROLINA

Introduction to International Economics
  DELBERT A. SNIDER MIAMI UNIVERSITY

Government Finance: An Economic Analysis
  JOHN F. DUE UNIVERSITY OF ILLINOIS

Economics of Transportation *Fourth Edition*
  D. PHILIP LOCKLIN UNIVERSITY OF ILLINOIS

International Economics
  CHARLES P. KINDLEBERGER MASSACHUSETTS
  INSTITUTE OF TECHNOLOGY

Economic Policy: Readings in Political Economy *Revised Edition*
  WILLIAM D. GRAMPP UNIVERSITY OF ILLINOIS AND
  EMANUEL T. WEILER PURDUE UNIVERSITY (EDITORS)

Intermediate Economic Analysis *Third Edition*
  JOHN F. DUE UNIVERSITY OF ILLINOIS

Collective Bargaining: Principles and Cases *Revised Edition*
  JOHN T. DUNLOP AND JAMES J. HEALY
  HARVARD UNIVERSITY

Economics of Labor Relations
  FREDERIC MEYERS UNIVERSITY OF TEXAS

Money, Income, and Monetary Policy
  EDWARD S. SHAW STANFORD UNIVERSITY

Welfare and Competition: The Economics of a Fully Employed Economy
  TIBOR SCITOVSKY STANFORD UNIVERSITY

Economics of Money and Banking
  GEORGE N. HALM THE FLETCHER SCHOOL OF LAW
  AND DIPLOMACY TUFTS UNIVERSITY

INTRODUCTION TO MATHEMATICAL ECONOMICS

Introduction to
MATHEMATICAL
ECONOMICS

By D. W. BUSHAW

Assistant Professor of Mathematics
State College of Washington

and R. W. CLOWER

Assistant Professor of Economics
State College of Washington

"IF I HAVE A MESSAGE TO SEND, I PREFER
THE TELEGRAPH TO THE WHEELBARROW."
—*Emerson*

1957

RICHARD D. IRWIN, INC.

HOMEWOOD, ILLINOIS

© 1957 BY RICHARD D. IRWIN, INC.

ALL RIGHTS RESERVED. THIS BOOK OR ANY PART
THEREOF MAY NOT BE REPRODUCED WITHOUT
THE WRITTEN PERMISSION OF THE PUBLISHER

First Printing, April, 1957

PRINTED IN THE UNITED STATES OF AMERICA
Library of Congress Catalogue Card No. 57–7595

PREFACE

OUR purpose in this book is to provide an introductory account of mathematical methods of economic analysis which is accessible to persons with a limited training in mathematics. We believe that no previous book has been written with just this intention. There are countless books on economics which make use of mathematical ideas, numerous books on mathematics for economists, and a rapidly increasing number of books on such special subjects as econometrics, the theory of games, and the theory of linear programming; but all of these books have been written with aims rather different from ours.

The dearth of books comparable to this one is rather surprising, in view of the fact that mathematical economics is now well established as a branch of economic science. Mathematics is, among many other things, a language—a language which is especially well suited to the precise elaboration and unambiguous communication of knowledge. As such it has long played an important role in almost every discipline where exact quantitative data and relations are significant. A large part of economics falls within this realm; for example, the theory of price determination, to which nearly every other part of economics may be linked in one way or another, deals with measurable prices and measurable quantities of commodities, and is therefore an obvious candidate for mathematical treatment. We will not claim that a mathematical treatment is absolutely indispensable for a clear understanding of this theory; the fact that mathematics itself is developed by means of ordinary language suggests, as Professor Frisch has observed, that this claim would be extravagant. Nevertheless, it is safe to say that few people are ingenious enough to grasp the more complex parts of price theory *without* resorting to the language of mathematics, while most ordinary individuals can do so fairly easily *with* the aid of mathematics.

Unfortunately, mathematics is a foreign language for most economists and students of economics, and few works by mathematical economists make any serious attempt to alter this situation. On the contrary, it is usual either to relegate mathematical discussions to appendices, or else to confront the reader with such discussions in all their complicated glory, in both cases making uncompromising use of what is frequently difficult mathematics. In this way the mathematically unenlightened reader remains unenlightened, and is likely to yield to an honest despair or to a somewhat less than honest scorn for the use of mathematical methods in economics.

The present book attempts to meet these difficulties by a method closely resembling one (sometimes called the "inductive" method) often used in teaching foreign languages. From the very beginning, the reader is given a

vii

text in the unfamiliar language. Translations (into the language of literary economics in our case) are presented where they seem to clarify statements in the original language (mathematics); alternative formulations in the original language (graphs accompanying equations, for instance) are sometimes provided; and abundant information about the "grammar" and "vocabulary" of the language is assembled in special sections at the end of the book. At the outset, notes, explanations, paraphrases, and various other pieces of scaffolding are very much in evidence; but as the text proceeds they thin out, and by the time the end of the text is reached the reader finds himself proceeding without the aid of any "apparatus," and should be ready to go on independently.

For our "text" we have chosen a fairly systematic account of the modern theory of price determination. This is the content (except for an introductory chapter) of Part I. This choice recommends itself for several reasons: price theory is, as we have already remarked, an important and in many ways the central part of economic theory; it is well suited to mathematical treatment; it is, of all branches of economic theory, the branch in which the mathematical method has been most extensively and successfully exploited; and it provides occasion for the illustration of many (though by no means all) of the mathematical techniques that have become well established in the economic theorist's kit of tools.

Part II provides a mathematical glossary and grammar. It has been designed to provide just enough information about mathematics to enable the serious reader (who has already reached a tolerable level of accomplishment in elementary algebra) to understand the entire text and to work out a few simple exercises. Most of the mathematical topics treated in Part II can be developed to a much greater extent, both in the direction of closer attention to foundations and in the direction of further elaboration. Our policy throughout has been to omit such developments, confining ourselves to matters that meet our immediate needs.

We hope, however, that this book will so convince some readers of the utility of mathematical techniques in economic theory that they will be stimulated to undertake a further study of mathematics. Indeed, some such study is essential for those who wish to do research in mathematical economics or who intend to read widely in the literature.

We feel that our book is likely to be of value mainly to individuals who already have considerable training in economics; and it should be particularly useful to graduate students and teachers of economics who have only a moderate proficiency in mathematics and who wish to acquire a modest reading knowledge of mathematical economics. However, parts of it might serve in some schools as a basis for upper division courses; and since Part I of the book contains a number of ideas which have not been published elsewhere, it may be of interest to those who are already adept at mathematical economics.

Clower is primarily an economist, Bushaw a mathematician; and so we have certain feelings of separate responsibility for the economic and mathematical aspects of the text. But every section of the book in its final form has been revised and edited by both authors. The order in which our names appear on the title page has no significance beyond the alphabetical one.

STATE COLLEGE OF WASHINGTON   D. W. B.
       February, 1957   R. W. C.

TABLE OF CONTENTS

PART I. THE ECONOMICS

PART I

The Economics

Chapter One

INTRODUCTION

ONE cannot have a very precise or profound idea of what mathematical economics is about until he is familiar with some of the specific techniques and results which characterize the subject. Our object in this volume is to enable the reader to develop just such a familiarity. For this reason, no preliminary attempt to define the scope or the essence of the subject can be very satisfactory; nor is it necessary. There are, however, certain methodological issues on which a book of this kind must take a stand, and clarity and fairness require that the stand taken be made explicit. This is the purpose of the present introductory chapter. Without entering into a discussion of philosophical minutiae, we propose to give a brief statement of the methodological point of view from which the book has been written. This point of view appears to be consistent in all major respects with that implicit in most contemporary writings on mathematical economics.

We take it for granted that prospective readers, if they are not already convinced that mathematical methods are of some use in economics, are at least open to persuasion on the subject. Those who require initial or additional convincing are referred to P. A. Samuelson's excellent paper "Economic Theory and Mathematics—an Appraisal" in *Papers and Proceedings of the Sixty-fourth Annual Meeting of the American Economic Association, American Economic Review*, Vol. XLII, No. 2 (May, 1952), pp. 56–66.

1. Mathematical Economics. The term *mathematical economics* describes that part of economic theory which is formulated and developed using the symbols and methods of mathematics. As is true of all sciences, economic theory (and so mathematical economics) is based ultimately on observed facts. But observed facts are always subject to varying interpretations, depending on the investigator and the object of his investigation; thus the theorist is to some extent free to systematize and analyze raw empirical data in accordance with his own views concerning the probable fruitfulness of alternative arrangements and interpretations.

The precise nature of this theorizing process, like that of all mental operations, is a mysterious affair, and we need not discuss it here. For our purposes it is enough to know that somehow general statements (hypotheses, theories, "laws," etc.) are distilled from observations, and that these general statements have two important properties: they are always provisional, subject to test, revision, and rejection on both logical and empirical grounds; and they usually have many implications which are not immediately apparent to the investigator. The techniques of mathematics may accordingly be used by the theorist for at least three general reasons:

(*i*) To assist in expressing the definitions, postulates, and conclusions of a theory in a clear and consistent way;

(*ii*) To guide and facilitate the drawing of conclusions which are valuable in themselves;

(*iii*) To obtain conclusions which may be used to test the realism of the theory.

In this book we shall be concerned almost exclusively with the first two of these functions of mathematics in economics. The third, which begins to enter the domain of econometrics, will be excluded not only for this reason[1] but also because the statements whose implications we shall explore are either firmly entrenched in traditional economic theory or derived in an immediate way from everyday experience and are not likely to be seriously questioned in either case.

It is well to emphasize the abstract character of the argument in order to prevent later misunderstanding. Our immediate object is merely to organize certain widely accepted facts and ideas in a systematic way. On the other hand, the resulting analysis is ultimately intended to help in the examination and description of specialized economic problems. Although the book as a whole is therefore essentially theoretical, we have done our best to avoid sacrificing empirical and intuitive plausibility on the altar of formal logic.

2. Mathematical Models in Economics.   It is implicit in the preceding section that the typical theory in mathematical economics has the following constituents:

A set of assumptions, or *postulates*, which are based ultimately on observations of the real world, but which admit a wide variety of possible enunciations. (The particular assumptions chosen may thus be regarded as arbitrary, although in a useful theory they are always subject to direct or indirect tests of compatability with empirical evidence. Moreover, the set of postulates must be internally consistent.)

A set of *definitions*, describing either the terms appearing in the postulates or terms appearing subsequently in the theory.

A set of conclusions, or *theorems*, which are obtained from the postulates and the definitions in accordance with accepted mathematical and logical principles.

Such a theory is called a *model*, because it provides a simplified and idealized image of certain aspects of economic activity.

---

[1] In keeping with the usage of a majority of recent writers, we mean by *econometrics* that part of economic science which makes essential use of modern statistical ideas. This subject, together with the theory of games and that of linear programming, is excluded from this book—not because the topics we shall discuss are felt to be more important but as a matter of division of labor. The present book may thus be viewed as a comple. ment to such books as L. R. Klein, *Textbook of Econometrics* (Evanston: Row, Pe. terson & Co., 1953); J. C. C. McKinsey, *Introduction to the Theory of Games* (New York: McGraw-Hill Book Co., Inc., 1952); and A. Charnes, W. W. Cooper, and A. Henderson, *An Introduction to Linear Programming* (New York: John Wiley & Sons, Inc. 1953).

Economic theorists, by varying postulates and definitions, obtain various provisional models. By applying a process of selection involving comparison with empirical data and the use of certain other criteria (e.g., that of simplicity), these models are then modified to represent particular segments of "reality" in an ever more satisfactory way. This process may or may not lead to models having high predictive powers, but it is almost certain to give insight into the working of the economic system, and to provide a useful framework for the organization of economic knowledge.

Something more should be said about the constituents of the typical economic model. Regarding the nature of postulates, two further remarks are in order. The first remark is that in a pure model, once an assumption is adopted it is unnecessary to make further reference to the grounds on which it was chosen. From the standpoint of the model, postulates are the ultimate points of departure. If one goes "behind" them in the course of developing the model, he is effectively introducing new assumptions—and if this is done at all, it should be done explicitly. Within the model, the postulates are treated as "self-evident truths." This brings us to the second remark, which is that *axioms*, frequently characterized as "self-evident truths," are only postulates of a special kind, and there is no essential reason for distinguishing between the two. If one chooses to call certain postulates axioms, he may; but this will not affect the character of the model.

It has already been mentioned that definitions occur in two different ways: as definitions of terms appearing in the postulates, and as definitions of terms appearing subsequently in the model. In every model there are certain *primitive* terms the meaning of which is simply taken for granted so far as the model itself is concerned. Indeed, any attempt to define *every* term by the use of other terms within a given model would lead one in a circle.[2] Within the model, therefore, some terms *must* be left undefined. However, the model is likely to seem rather vague and of limited practical usefulness unless every term which it contains is assigned a meaning of one sort or another; so what invariably happens is that primitive terms are given "definitions" using concepts not properly belonging to the model. These definitions play no functional role within the model but merely serve to explain to the reader what "concrete" meaning may be assigned to the undefined terms in the model. They are *instructions for the interpretation of terms not defined within the model.*

The nature of the second kind of definition, the definition that is made within the model, is altogether different. Such a definition is, in a rather strict sense, an abbreviation. The users of the model agree to accept a certain convenient phrase A in place of a less convenient, usually longer, phrase B which is made up of primitive or previously defined terms of the model. The statement that this will be done is the definition of A. This kind

---

[2] For a sprightly discussion of this point, see J. L. Synge, *Science: Sense and Nonsense* (New York: Harcourt, Brace & Co., Inc., n.d.), chap. i.

of definition does not aid in the interpretation of the model but is introduced purely as a matter of convenience; one could refuse to accept a definition of this type, insisting on using the cumbersome phrase B and never the abbreviation A, and no fundamental harm would be done.

This distinction between the two kinds of definitions may be illustrated by means of two definitions from Book I of Euclid's *Elements:*

A *line* is length without breadth.

Parallel straight lines are straight lines which, being in the same plane and produced indefinitely in both directions, do not meet one another in either direction.

The first of these definitions, if one is willing to call it a definition at all, is of the first kind. "Line" is actually a primitive term of Euclidean geometry, for the "definition" serves merely to describe the real-world counterpart of one of the terms appearing in the postulates; it is not an abbreviation for any combination of terms appearing in the postulates. Euclid makes no use of this definition in his proofs; indeed, he scarcely could, for it is possible to imagine other things (e.g., "time") besides a line which have length without breadth; and Euclid's *Elements* would become nonsense if one replaced "line" by "time" wherever the former term occurred. On the other hand, the definition of parallel straight lines is a definition of the second kind; it supplies us with a long phrase involving the primitive terms of Euclid's model which could always be substituted for the phrase "parallel straight lines" wherever this phrase occurs. It will be observed that neither kind of definition affects the *logical* structure of a model; the first kind provides only an interpretation, and the second kind only a laborsaving device.

It is the theorems of a model which are its flesh and blood. A theorem is a proposition which is susceptible of proof within the model. More precisely, a proof of a proposition A within a given model is a sequence of propositions which has the following properties:

(*i*) Each proposition in the sequence is either (*a*) one of the postulates or (*b*) a proposition which can be obtained from one or more of the preceding propositions in the sequence in accordance with accepted logical and mathematical principles.

(*ii*) The last proposition in the sequence is A.

Sometimes certain theorems are called corollaries or lemmas. A *corollary* is simply a theorem whose proof can be obtained by making an easy extension of the proof of a theorem which has already been stated; in other words, it is a theorem that is all but proved as soon as a certain preceding theorem in proved. A *lemma* is a theorem which is stated and proved to facilitate giving a proof of another, normally more important, theorem. Corollaries and lemmas cannot be distinguished from other theorems on purely logical grounds because "easy" and "important" are not logical terms.

All of this may give the impression that a model is a formal, immaculately logical arrangement of postulates, definitions, and theorems with their proofs. A perfectly complete model would be precisely this; but in practice concessions are made to the fact that man is mortal. Setting out a complicated model with all of the logical steps included is a very dull and demanding task, and almost everyone is willing to settle for an abbreviated and informal account provided it seems clear that the model could be padded out to perfection if one were willing to expend the necessary time, labor, and tears. This applies especially to proofs, which almost always contain gaps which the reader is left to fill for himself. In describing a model, one should of course state theorems, definitions, and especially postulates carefully; but absolute completeness of detail is something no fair-minded critic requires.

The above remarks apply in full to the logical substructure of a model—to the "rules of inference" according to which one statement may be said to follow from another in the course of a proof. Fundamental logical principles are almost always left implicit on the assumption that there is essentially universal agreement regarding them. Similarly, the mathematical processes involved in a deduction, provided they are below a certain level of difficulty, are usually performed without explicit justification, on the assumption that readers can supply such justification for themselves.[3]

It might be added that, for our purposes, mathematics may be regarded as an extension of formal logic, so that the distinction between mathematical and logical principles which we have honored hitherto is more apparent than real.

3. The Theory of Price Determination. Beginning with the next chapter and continuing through the remainder of Part I, our task is to present a precise description of economic models embracing the factors which govern the production, consumption, and storage of commodities in an idealized capitalistic economy; i.e., we shall be dealing with the "pure" theory of price determination. This very general problem may be approached from two distinct points of view. One procedure is to begin by studying the behavior of various individual units of economic decision—consumers, firms, etc.—thereafter formulating a theory of market price determination which is consistent with this *microeconomic* foundation. Alternatively, one may begin by formulating a provisional theory of price determination, thereafter dealing with the microeconomic foundations of this *macroeconomic* superstructure.

The choice between these alternatives is largely a matter of convenience. In particular, it is not important that microeconomic analysis is, in a sense, logically prior to macroeconomic analysis; for results achieved along one

---

[3] It is possible to make errors of judgment in this regard. It is told that an eminent mathematician, in the course of one of his lectures, remarked that a certain inference in his argument was obvious. He paused at that point, meditated a moment, finally asked himself aloud, "It is, isn't it?" and then left the room. Some thirty minutes later he returned carrying a sheaf of hastily scribbled notes, said, "Yes, it's obvious," and proceeded with his lecture. In this connection, see the footnote on page 130 of G. H. Hardy's *Pure Mathematics* (10th ed.; New York: Cambridge University Press, 1952).

route must necessarily be made consistent with corresponding results obtained along the other. However, the macroeconomic approach is adopted in this book because it is initially less complex than the alternative procedure. Thus, throughout the first portion of our analysis we shall be dealing in an abstract fashion with the operation of, and interrelations among, commodity markets. As it happens, there is no definitive treatment of this subject in the existing economic literature. It is a field in which new results and new ideas are fairly common, so that no two treatments of the subject can be expected to have the same form or content. However, we shall at least begin on familiar ground by devoting the next chapter to a statement and appraisal of the central ideas of statical supply and demand analysis.

SUGGESTIONS FOR FURTHER READING

In order to understand why a particular methodology has gained general acceptance among scientists—indeed, in order to appreciate its acceptance at all—one should read a good book on the history of science. A recent and readable book of this kind is W. P. D. Wightman, *The Growth of Scientific Ideas* (New Haven: Yale University Press, 1951). A comprehensive account of one version of the philosophy underlying scientific method is given by Richard von Mises in his *Positivism* (Cambridge: Harvard University Press, 1951). For a treatment which goes less deeply into the relevant epistemological issues but provides a very clear description of the scientific method itself, see R. B. Braithwaite, *Scientific Explanation* (Cambridge: Cambridge University Press, 1953), especially chaps. i–iv. Still shorter discussions will be found in various sections of the *International Encyclopedia of Unified Science* (Chicago: University of Chicago Press, 1939–   ). For discussions of methodological questions by an economist, one may refer to the article by P. A. Samuelson mentioned in the first paragraph of this chapter, and to the first pages of the same author's *Foundations of Economic Analysis* (Cambridge: Harvard University Press, 1947). See also the early but still very excellent remarks by V. Pareto in *The Mind and Society* (New York: Harcourt, Brace & Co., 1935), Vol. I, chap. i.

Chapter Two

MACROECONOMIC STATICS

MACROECONOMIC statics is concerned largely with the concept of market equilibrium and its implications. Comparatively speaking, it is an extremely narrow field of study since its object is merely *to provide criteria to distinguish equilibrium from nonequilibrium situations.* The study of processes through which equilibrium situations are approached or attained, starting from nonequilibrium situations, involves separate problems requiring different methods of analysis. Because of its simplicity and its power to suggest promising approaches to the study of nonstatical adjustment processes, however, macroeconomic statics is a useful preliminary to the discussion of broader areas of price theory. And, as the subsequent argument will indicate, the subject is of considerable interest for its own sake, despite its evident limitations.

1. *Fundamental Definitions and Ideas* [Eight–Sec. 1 and 2].[1] In general we may suppose that an economy comprises n distinct markets for commodities (goods or services) denoted by the numbers $1, \ldots, n$, where any particular commodity may appear as a stock, as a flow, or as a stock and a flow simultaneously. That is to say, any given commodity may be a *stock commodity*, a *flow commodity*, or a *stock-flow commodity*. The general meaning of the terms "stock" and "flow" will be clear on common-sense grounds; e.g., capital value will be recognized as a stock whereas income will be recognized as a flow. However, since the distinction is basic to much of the subsequent argument, precise criteria are provided by the definitions which follow:

A stock *is a quantity measured at various instants of time* (e.g., so many tons of a specific grade of wheat held in storage at various dates; so many cans of a particular variety of beans in consumers' pantries at various dates; etc.).

A flow *is the rate at which a stock quantity changes per unit of time* (e.g., gross farm production of wheat *per day* at various dates; consumption *per year* of beans by consumers at various dates; the quantity of machinists' labor *per hour* utilized by business firms at various dates; etc.).

---

[1] Here, and throughout the remainder of Part I, the references in brackets following a section heading indicate the portion of Part II (The Mathematics) which will be used for the first time in the section, and with which the reader should be acquainted in order to follow the discussion.

Notice that the measurement of either a stock or a flow is always referred to a definite point in time. However, a flow quantity is characterized by a time *dimension* as well as a time reference, whereas a stock quantity is characterized by a time reference alone. In other words, both stock and flow quantities are "dated" (implicitly if not explicitly), but flow quantities are further distinguished by being measured in units involving time.

When we wish to refer subsequently only to flow aspects of a given market (i.e., when we wish to consider the production and/or consumption but not the holding of a commodity), we shall call the market a *flow market*. Similarly, when we wish to refer only to stock aspects of a given market (i.e., to consider the holding but not the production or consumption of a commodity), we shall call the market a *stock market*. Finally, if we wish to refer simultaneously to both stock and flow aspects of a given market (i.e., if we wish to consider simultaneously the production, consumption, and holding of a commodity), we shall call the market a *stock-flow market*. The theoretical and empirical significance of this classification of markets will become clear as we proceed. Meanwhile, the reader should be warned against regarding particular real-world commodity markets as counterparts of the above categories. It is one thing to analyze stock or flow *aspects* of a given market, quite another thing to describe a market as involving *only* commodity stocks or *only* commodity flows. At the same time, it may enhance one's intuitive grasp of the subsequent argument to fix in advance upon some particular stock-flow commodity (e.g., wheat or houses) for which the distinction between stock and flow aspects of the corresponding real-world market is relatively obvious.

In addition to the above market classification, it is convenient to characterize commodities further, for purposes of analysis, by associating each commodity with specific supply and demand relations. Here a problem arises: supply and demand relations may be defined to include explicitly every variable—economic, biological, psychological, political, institutional, religious, etc.—that might conceivably influence market behavior; or the same relations might be defined to include explicitly only a limited number of strictly "economic" variables (whatever this might mean). This general problem of selection—choosing certain factors for explicit treatment, ignoring other and perhaps equally significant factors—does not have a unique solution; the available alternatives are literally unlimited. However, the objectives of this text are sufficiently narrow to permit an easy initial solution of the problem. We shall suppose, provisionally, that the current output per unit of time of any given commodity is a function only of current market prices; and we shall call the functions thus defined *flow supply functions*. In symbols, the flow supply function for the ith commodity $(i = 1, \ldots, n)$ is denoted by

$$s_i = s_i(p_1, \ldots, p_n) \,,$$

where $p_1, \ldots, p_n$ represent the current market prices (in money) of the commodities $1, \ldots, n$, respectively. Similarly, we shall suppose that the quantity of any given commodity used currently as a productive input or for current consumption is also a function solely of current market prices; and we shall call the functions thus defined *flow demand functions*. In symbols, the flow demand function for the ith commodity is denoted by

$$d_i = d_i(p_1, \ldots, p_n) \, .$$

The flow quantity defined by

$$x_i \equiv d_i(p_1, \ldots, p_n) - s_i(p_1, \ldots, p_n)$$

is then called the *excess flow demand function* for the ith commodity. Excess flow demand represents, of course, the net amount by which the current use of a given commodity (i.e., physical destruction) exceeds or falls short of the current production of the same commodity.

In practice, few markets can be characterized simply in terms of flow supply and demand (or excess demand) relations because most commodities are normally acquired, in part, to be held for future disposal as well as to be used for current consumption. The quantity which persons in the aggregate desire to hold of any given good will depend, as a rule, upon a host of practical considerations including expected future market conditions, carrying costs, obsolescence rates, and so forth. However, taking these factors as given, we shall suppose that the current (aggregate) demand for stocks of any given commodity, to hold for future disposal, is again a function only of market prices; and we shall call the functions thus defined *stock demand functions*. In symbols, the stock demand function for the ith commodity is denoted by

$$D_i = D_i(p_1, \ldots, p_n) \, .$$

Similarly, it is necessary to recognize that quantities of various commodities may be made available for current use from existing stocks as well as from current production flows, and that current production flows may not be used (consumed) at precisely the same rate as they appear in the economy. At any given instant of time, however, commodity stocks represent a heritage from the past; current economic decisions may affect the immediate *distribution* of stocks among individual economic units and may also affect the *future level* of commodity stocks (via the influence of changes in distribution upon prices, for example), but the quantity of any given commodity currently in existence in the economy is necessarily a datum for the economy as a whole. Accordingly, the *stock supply* of the ith commodity at any given instant is independent of prices and, from a statical point of view, may be denoted simply by

$$S_i \quad (i = 1, \ldots, n) \, .$$

Finally, making further use of the concepts of stock demand and stock supply, we define *excess stock demand* (*and the excess stock demand function*) for the ith commodity by

$$X_i \equiv D_i(p_1, \ldots, p_n) - S_i \, .$$

It will be noticed that excess stock demand, since it is a *quantity as such*, is not directly commensurable with excess flow demand, which is measured as a *quantity per unit of time*.[2]

The above concepts may be clarified by illustrations drawn from a market for houses of a particular type. The stock supply of such houses (measured in appropriate units) is the aggregate of existing buildings at a particular instant; the aggregate of current demands for the ownership of existing houses represents stock demand; the aggregate quantity of *unsatisfied* demands for ownership represents excess stock demand; the gross rate at which houses are depreciated through current use in flow demand; the current (gross) rate of construction of new houses is flow supply; and the current *net* rate of depreciation of houses (real net disinvestment) is excess flow demand. It is important to notice that while a change in the ownership of existing commodities is represented by a flow quantity (to which we shall later assign the name *investment demand*), such a change *is not a flow demand or supply* in the sense defined above. Commodities must be newly produced or currently used up in a physical sense to qualify as flow supplies or flow demands.

A final word of explanation before proceeding: having adopted definitions of supply and demand which involve only market price and (aggregate) quantity variables, we must restrict the subsequent analysis accordingly. Many other possible economic variables—individual price expectations, individual incomes or asset holdings, social and institutional variables, etc.—might have been considered had we defined supply and demand relations in a broader manner. But as matters stand, factors other than market prices and aggregate quantities are taken as data and will not be considered explicitly in the subsequent argument except in special and clearly specified instances.

EXERCISES

1.1. Let flow demand for a given commodity be defined by the equation

$$d = -2p + 8 .$$

Draw the flow demand curve corresponding to this equation and indicate what restrictions should be placed upon the value of p in order for this curve to represent a "respectable" flow demand relation.

1.2. Does the function

$$d = 2p + 8$$

describe a relation which might plausibly be regarded as a flow demand curve? Why or why not?

1.3. Draw the flow supply curve corresponding to the equation

$$s_1 = 6p_1 - p_2 - 2 ,$$

---

[2] Where there is no risk of confusion, subscripts to variables will be omitted in the subsequent argument; e.g., in a one-commodity model the flow demand function will be written as $d = d(p)$, stock supply will be written as S, etc.

assuming initially that $p_2 = 1$. Illustrate graphically what happens to the flow supply curve as the value of p_2 is increased.

1.4. If, in a two-commodity market, the flow demand and supply functions for commodity 1 are given respectively by

$$d_1(p_1,p_2) = -2p_1 + 8 ,$$
$$s_1(p_1,p_2) = 6p_1 - p_2 - 2 ,$$

graph the excess flow demand function $x_1(p_1,p_2)$, assuming that $p_2 = 2$.

2. The Basic Assumption of Macroeconomic Statics. The notion of "equilibrium" is conventionally associated with "a state of rest." In reference to a commodity market, therefore, it is natural to adopt a definition of equilibrium which requires that all relevant price and quantity variables be constant over time, or, more shortly, motionless. The very concept of equilibrium is thus seen to involve reference to nonstatical considerations of some kind; for one cannot specify conditions under which prices and quantities will be lacking in motion unless one assumes something about the forces which give rise to motion. In the present connection, this means that no satisfactory justification can be provided for *any* set of equilibrium criteria within the framework of a purely statical argument. What we can and shall do, however, is to introduce equilibrium criteria which, for the time being, are to be regarded as *postulates*.

As a preliminary, let us define *market excess demand* for the ith commodity as *the total quantity of the ith commodity which prospective buyers offer to purchase per unit of time less the total quantity which prospective sellers offer to sell per unit of time.* In general, market excess demand will depend upon (be a function of) both excess flow demand and excess stock demand, although this may or may not be the case in particular instances (e.g., in a market for the services of barbers, market excess demand and excess flow demand are identical, for the stock aspect of this market does not exist). The relevance of this remark will become clear in a moment.

The fundamental postulate of macroeconomic statics may now be stated as follows:

Equilibrium exists if and only if prices and quantities are such that

(i) Market excess demand for each commodity is zero, and

(ii) Excess flow demand for each commodity is zero.

The rationale of these criteria for distinguishing equilibrium from nonequilibrium market situations will be considered later; meanwhile, we shall be concerned with the implications of (*i*) and (*ii*).

EXERCISES

2.1. Describe and clearly distinguish between the concepts excess flow demand, excess stock demand, and market excess demand, as applied to the commodity barley.

3. Isolated Flow Markets [Eight–Sec. 2 and 3]. Turning now to a specific illustration of statical analysis, we consider a flow market for a single commodity and suppose that the market is *isolated;* i.e., we suppose that the commodity is not held (or else that individuals do not alter their current holdings in response to changes in price), and we suppose that the flow supply and demand functions depend only upon the price of this commodity—all other prices are ignored. In this case, market excess demand and excess flow demand are identical so that the criteria (*i*) and (*ii*) given in Section 2 come to precisely the same thing. The basic criterion for equilibrium can be expressed, therefore, by saying that equilibrium occurs in the market if and only if price p satisfies the equation

$$(3.1) \quad x(p) \equiv d(p) - s(p) = 0 \,.$$

Given, however, that the values of p which satisfy (3.1)[3] are exactly the prices at which the market would be in equilibrium, there are three distinct possibilities:

1. The equation (3.1) has exactly one solution.
2. The equation has at least two distinct solutions.
3. The equation has no solution.

In case 1 the equilibrium price is unambiguously determined; the statement "the market is in equilibrium" implies that the price p of the commodity has this value. This is clearly the most satisfying of the three cases, for in case 2 the statement "the market is in equilibrium" leaves the value of p ambiguous, and one can select one of the possible values of p as the actual equilibrium price only upon the admission of additional assumptions about the behavior of the market; and in case 3 equilibrium is not possible (i.e., no equilibrium position is defined). For this reason economists have traditionally (though not always explicitly) confined their attention to case 1. This step is not as arbitrary as it may seem, for the occurrence of case 1 can be shown to follow from certain intuitively plausible assumptions about the character of the functions $d(p)$ and $s(p)$—i.e., about the shape and position of the supply and demand curves. But there is no *logical* reason for expecting case 1 to be more common than cases 2 or 3, nor is there anything to prevent us from considering case 2 as a subject for statical analysis; one can analyze any one equilibrium price as if others did not exist.[4] Once it has been established that case 3 occurs, however, statical theory can have nothing further to say; for statical theory is the theory of equilibrium states, and in the absence of such states it is an impotent intruder. Indeed, the determination of which of the three cases occurs and, in cases 1 and 2, the acquisition of further information about the values of the equilibrium prices is the sum and substance of the statical theory, in the strict sense, of a market of the type under consideration. This observa-

---

[3] In view of the interpretation of the variable p, only real and nonnegative solutions of (3.1) need to be considered.

[4] What one can say about equilibrium situations in these circumstances will be indicated in more detail in what follows (e.g., in Section 7 of this chapter).

tion applies, with appropriate changes in language, to any economic model.

We recall now the graphical meaning of the equation $d(p) - s(p) = 0$ in (3.1): the supply curve $q = s(p)$ and the demand curve $q = d(p)$ (q stands for "quantity") have been drawn on a single co-ordinate system (Fig. 3.1) with the co-ordinates p,q, and equation (3.1) is clearly satisfied at the point (or points—we have illustrated the simplest case) where the two curves intersect, and nowhere else. The values of p and q at this point may be denoted by $\bar{p}$ and $\bar{q}$, respectively; they represent the equilibrium price and quantity in this market.

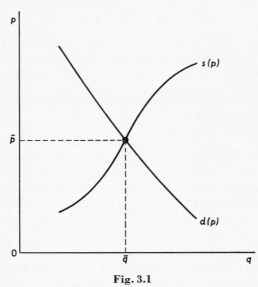

Fig. 3.1

EXERCISES

3.1. Draw excess flow demand curves on a co-ordinate system with the co-ordinates p,x, in such a way as to illustrate each of the three cases 1, 2, and 3 given in the text.

3.2. In what circumstances (in terms of the flow demand and supply curves) will the excess flow demand curve be downward sloping? Upward sloping?

3.3. What kinds of markets in the real world might be described reasonably well as pure flow markets?

3.4. Find the equilibrium price (or prices), if any, in the markets characterized by the following supply and demand functions:

a) $s = p + 1$, $d = 1 - p$.

b) $s = p^2$, $d = \dfrac{1}{p}$.

c) $s = 2 + p^2$, $d = 1 - p$.

d) $s = p(p - 1)$, $d = 4p - 4$.

3.5. Determine which of the following, if any, are equilibrium prices in a market characterized by the supply and demand functions:

$$\begin{cases} s = 18p^3 - 6p^2 + 2, \\ d = p^6 - 8p^5 + 16p^4 + 2. \end{cases}$$

a) $p = 0$

b) $p = 1$

c) $p = \dfrac{3}{2}$

d) $p = 4$

4. Isolated Stock Markets and Investment Demands. Consider next an isolated market for a stock commodity; i.e., a commodity which may be held by and exchanged among individuals but which is neither produced nor consumed (or else one for which production is always equal to consumption regardless of the level of price). In this case, excess flow demand is identically zero by hypothesis, and the condition (*ii*) given in Section 2 is gratuitous. Only the condition (*i*), requiring that market excess demand be zero in equilibrium, is relevant in these circumstances. However, the condition (*i*) has, as yet, no meaning with reference to a stock market since excess stock demand, $X \equiv D - S$, refers to desired increases in (aggregate) *stock holdings* rather than to a *flow* of market purchases (or sales).

To overcome this difficulty (i.e., to avoid dealing with incommensurable quantities), we now denote (aggregate) *investment demand* for the commodity by $x'(p)$ and we define the *investment demand function*

$$(4.1) \quad x'(p) = x'[X(p)],$$

by which the aggregate quantity of the commodity demanded per unit of time to be added to stocks is brought into functional relationship with the excess stock demand for the commodity. In words, this asserts that market demand for the commodity depends on the total quantity of unsatisfied demands to hold units of that commodity and is otherwise independent of the price and quantity variables explicitly considered in the model.

Now, if unsatisfied demands for stock holdings of a commodity vary, everyday experience indicates that current market purchases of the commodity will vary in the same direction. Also, if unsatisfied demands to hold stocks are nonzero, it is certainly true in practice that some individuals will attempt to increase (or decrease) stock holdings by making current purchases (sales) in the market. That such purchases (sales) will not occur if unsatisfied demands are zero is a more dubious proposition, but common sense suggests that it may be true in some circumstances. With these considerations in mind, therefore, we shall assume that x' is an *increasing* function of X, i.e., that whenever X increases, so does $x'(X)$, and that $x'(0) = 0$. These two assumptions are quite independent but together embody the suppositions just mentioned.

A typical relation between x' and X satisfying these assumptions is illustrated in Figure 4.1. The stock supply and demand curves are represented by S and D, respectively, in Figure 4.1(*a*), and the investment demand function is represented by x' in Figure 4.1(b) (two diagrams have to be used since the relevant quantities are of different dimensions). Since the stock supply curve is a vertical straight line in every instance (for stock supply is independent of price), the investment demand curve is upward or downward sloping at any given level of price according to whether the stock demand curve is upward or downward sloping at the corresponding price; and the investment demand curve intersects the price axis in Figure 4.1(b) at precisely the same value of price (viz., $p = \bar{p}$) as that for which the stock supply and stock demand curve intersect in Figure 4.1(a) (so that x' and X are always of the same sign).

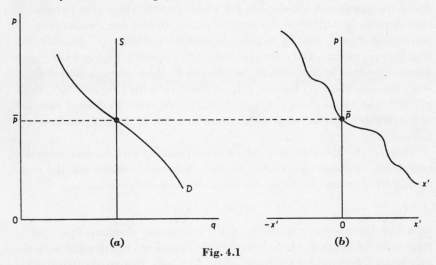

Fig. 4.1

As the preceding illustration suggests, there is in general no necessity for the investment demand curve to have the same form as the stock demand curve except that both must be upward or downward sloping for any given value of the price variable; e.g., market purchases of a commodity to add to stock may be proportionately greater the greater are (net) unsatisfied demands to hold units of the commodity. However, it simplifies the subsequent mathematics in significant respects and it facilitates later graphical exposition to deal with the special case in which the excess stock demand and investment demand functions *do* have precisely the same general form, viz., the case in which investment demand is constantly proportional to excess stock demand. This is represented symbolically by redefining the investment demand functions, replacing (4.1) by

$$(4.2) \quad x' = kX,$$

where k is a fixed positive constant called the *investment coefficient*. The functions (4.2) have the properties which were assigned to the investment demand functions (4.1); but the precise character of the functional relation between x' and X is specified in (4.2), whereas it is left open in (4.1). For all practical purposes, however, (4.2) may be regarded as an adequate approximation to (4.1); so *in what follows we shall have in mind the equations* *(4.2) whenever reference is made to investment demand functions*. With the judicious use of subscripts, these notions may be used for models involving any number of stock commodities.

Having defined the investment (demand) function x', we can apply the criterion (i) in Section 2 to an isolated stock market by requiring as a condition for equilibrium,

$$(4.3) \quad x' \equiv kX(p) = 0 \; ;$$

this is formally equivalent to the corresponding condition (3.1) for an isolated flow market. Since $k > 0$, however, the satisfaction of (4.3) is equiva-

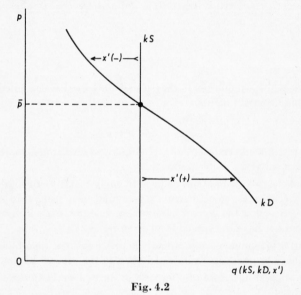

Fig. 4.2

lent to the satisfaction of the condition $D - S = 0$; i.e., for market equilibrium, price must be such that individuals in the aggregate are just willing to hold the given quantity of commodity stocks, S. In effect, therefore, market price variations serve as a device by which the *freedom* of each economic unit to hold such stocks of a given commodity as it desires to hold is reconciled with the *necessity* for units in the aggregate to hold precisely that quantity of the commodity which in fact exists. In this connection it is worth remarking that gross purchases and sales may both be zero in equilibrium since each and every owner of a portion of the total stock supply may be just satisfied to continue holding such quantities as he currently possesses. At first sight, it may seem a little curious that the equilibrium price might be one at which no current transactions occur, but a little reflection will indicate that this is not unreasonable under pure stock hypotheses.

The condition (4.3) is represented graphically in Figure 4.2, where the curve kS represents (gross) market supply from existing commodity stocks and the curve kD represents (gross) market demand for commodities to hold. Investment demand, x', is then measured by the (positive or negative) horizontal distance from the curve kS to the curve kD. (Notice that the relations among S, D, and x' could not be expressed so simply as in Figure 4.2 if we had retained the definition of x' given in [4.1].) The equilibrium price, $\bar{p}$, is then defined by the intersection of the curve kD with the line kS. The line kS might well be called the "effective" price axis in an isolated stock market since it is with reference to it that investment demand (which, in this case, is also—but for a constant factor—market excess demand) is measured. The "effective" price axis lies further to the right, relative to the "true" price axis defined by $q = 0$, the greater the value of S.

EXERCISES

4.1. What prices give equilibrium in the isolated stock market characterized by the supply and demand functions
$$S = 6,$$
$$D = p^3 - 6p^2 + 11p - 12,$$
and the investment coefficient $k = \frac{1}{4}$? Graph and give approximate answers if you cannot solve the problem directly.

4.2. Show that the two assumptions on page 16 imply that investment demand can be zero *only* if excess stock demand is zero; and then, using this fact, explain why $D - S = 0$ is the correct equilibrium condition even if investment demand does not have the special form given by (4.2).

4.3. As a matter of common sense, would you assign greater importance to one of the equilibrium prices in Exercise 4.1 than to the others? Explain carefully.

4.4. Can you suggest any close counterparts in the real world to the concept of a stock market?

4.5. What, if any, connection exists between the price at which units of a stock commodity can be purchased and the price at which such units can be rented?

4.6. Supposing a government issued a given quantity of bonds yielding a fixed annual money return in perpetuity to their holders, describe the determination of the equilibrium price of the bonds. What would be the relation between the fixed annual money return on the bonds, their current price, and their current market interest yield? What would happen to the current market interest yield if there were a sharp increase in the prices of other stock commodities? What would happen to the current interest yield if the government which issued the bonds were threatened with bankruptcy?

4.7. Suppose dealers hold positive stocks but wish to hold zero stocks of new cars in the month preceding the introduction of new models. Discuss the probable variation in the value of k (take a day as the relevant unit of time) and the factors giving rise to such variations as the date for sale of new models is approached.

5. *Isolated Stock-Flow Markets* [Eight–Sec. 5 and 6]. By hypothesis, the production, consumption, and holding of a commodity are all relevant in a stock-flow situation. Thus, to define market equilibrium in an isolated stock-flow market, both of the conditions (*i*) and (*ii*) given in Section 2 must be taken into account. On the one hand, the total quantity offered for sale must be equal to the total quantity demanded (market excess demand must be zero); on the other hand, the current rate at which quantities are produced must be equal to the rate at which quantities are currently used (excess flow demand must be zero). But market excess demand in this case is simply the sum of investment demand and excess flow demand at any given level of price; in symbols, therefore, market equilibrium in an isolated stock-flow market requires that the following system of two equations be satisfied:

$$(5.1)\begin{cases} x(p) + x'(p) = d(p) - s(p) + k[D(p) - S] = 0, \\ x(p) = d(p) - s(p) = 0. \end{cases}$$

Notice, however, that since the first condition involves the stock supply quantity S, which is independent of price, whereas the second condition involves quantities all of which depend upon price, the two conditions (5.1) are certainly independent (i.e., the satisfaction of one does not imply the satisfaction of the other). Hence, there is no reason to expect that a price which makes market excess demand zero will also suffice to equate flow demand to flow supply, or vice versa. That is to say, the system (5.1) appears, in general, to be inconsistent.

A graphical illustration may clarify the nature of this "inconsistency." The gross stock of a given commodity offered for current sale and the current (gross) demand for commodities to add to stocks are represented in Figure 5.1 by the curves kS (with superscripts ′, ″) and kD, respectively (compare Fig. 4.2). Excess flow demand at each alternative level of price (not shown separately) is then added to (gross) market demand for additions to stocks to obtain the *market demand curve* $q = x + kD$. Thus *market excess demand* is measured horizontally by the (positive or negative) distance from kS to $x + kD$, while *excess flow demand* is measured by the (positive or negative) horizontal distance from kD to $x + kD$. Two typical cases have to be examined:

Case I.   If stock supply is S', the price at which market excess demand is zero is p', defined by the intersection of kS' with the curve $x + kD$. However, if $p = p'$, excess flow demand is negative rather than zero, for the curve $x + kD$ lies to the left of the curve kD for this value of price. In this case, therefore, the market equilibrium conditions (5.1) are inconsistent.

Case II.   If stock supply is S'', then the price p'' satisfies the first equation in (5.1), and at this price excess flow demand is also zero (as indicated by the intersection of the curve kD with the curve $x + kD$ at this value of p). In Case II, therefore, the market equilibrium conditions (5.1) are consistent.

Now the only difference between Case I and Case II is that stock supply is S' in Case I and S'' in Case II; i.e., *whether the equilibrium conditions (5.1) are consistent or inconsistent depends solely upon the level of stock supply,* once the investment demand and excess flow demand functions are given. Thus, to establish equilibrium criteria for an isolated stock-flow market, not only price but also stock supply must be regarded as variable. If this is done, the conditions (5.1) constitute a system of two equations in the two unknowns p and S, solutions of which may be presumed to exist.

The procedure just suggested may appear to be nothing more than a bit of mathematical trickery. When it was convenient to take S as given (viz.,

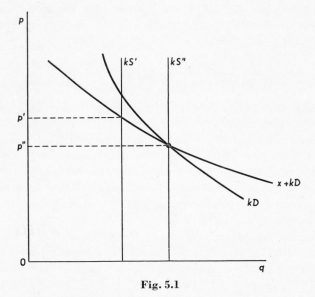

Fig. 5.1

in discussing an isolated stock market in Section 4), S was so considered; however, now that it is convenient to treat S as variable, our assumptions have been altered accordingly. But there is more to it than that. By hypothesis, a stock commodity is neither produced nor consumed, so that in examining a stock market it would not be legitimate to treat S as anything but a datum. But the quantity of a stock-flow commodity existing at any given instant can be changed subsequently through production or consumption. In this case, therefore, it is perfectly valid to treat S as variable.

The last point may be further clarified by noticing that the real significance of the excess flow demand condition in (5.1), $x = 0$, is to require that equilibrium stock supply does not change *over time*. For if $x \neq 0$, then by definition $s - d \neq 0$, and the difference between flow supply and flow demand represents a current addition to or depletion of existing commodity stocks (i.e., x represents current net investment if x is negative, current net disinvestment if x is positive); so S will certainly tend to vary with the passage of time. However, this is entirely consistent with the assumption that S is given independently of the level of current price; for although S will be *changing* at every instant of time during which $x(p) \neq 0$, S is nevertheless *fixed at any given instant* (i.e., net investment or disinvestment can bring about an actual change in existing commodity stocks only after the passage of a certain time interval).

The above considerations suggest the desirability of defining a set of stock supply *functions* relating stock supplies of various commodities to corresponding excess flow demands and to the variable *time*. Indeed, some such procedure is mandatory if one wishes to conduct a systematic inquiry into problems of "capital accumulation." However, stock supply functions, as distinct from stock supply variables, are relevant only in the analysis of nonequilibrium market situations and are therefore out of place in the present statical context.

EXERCISES

5.1. Describe briefly the factors which influence the pricing of urban real estate in your city, dealing with both stock and flow aspects of the problem.

5.2. Can you describe the pricing of British pounds in the New York foreign exchange "market" in stock-flow terms?

5.3. Link relevant aspects of a market for industrial securities with the notions of "productivity" and "thrift" and try to assign an appropriate role to each of these in the determination of the market interest yield of securities. (Hint: Excess flow demand is the difference between the retirement of outstanding issues and new issues.)

5.4. Which of the following stock supply and price combinations give(s) equilibrium in a stock-flow market represented by
$$\begin{cases} D(p) = 3 + p + 2p^4 - p^5 , \\ x(p) = d(p) - s(p) = 10 - 5p , \\ k = 1 ? \end{cases}$$
  a) $p = 2, S = 8.$
  b) $p = 1, S = 5.$
  c) $p = 2, S = 5.$

5.5. Find equilibrium price and stock supply (if they exist) in the following stock-flow systems (in each case, take $k = 1$):
  a) $D(p) = 7 - 4p$; $x(p) = -(p^2 + 1)$.
  b) $D(p) = 1 - 2p$; $x(p) = 4(p - 1) - p^2$.
  c) $D(p) = 2p^2 - p^3$; $x(p) = 4(p - 1) - p^2$.
  d) $D(p) = 3 - p^2$; $x(p) = 4p - 3 - p^2$.

6. *Price Setters and Price Setting.* Before proceeding further with the development of an abstract view of the pricing process, it may be helpful to inject a note of realism into the discussion by presenting a brief outline of the mechanics of price setting in the real world and indicating its relation to our analysis.

In speaking of the *determination* of prices, one is naturally led to look beyond supposedly efficacious systems of equations and unknowns and to inquire: (1) *Who* decides that the price of a particular commodity is to be set at a particular level at a particular time and place; (2) *Why* is one price decision adopted rather than another?

1. To the question, "Who sets price?," the answer is that *any individual is a price setter who offers to sell some (specified or unspecified) quantity of a commodity at a stated price per unit, or who offers to buy some quantity at a stated price per unit.* This remark incidentally leads to a definition of a market: *a market is a place where the transaction implicit in an offer to buy or sell is to occur.* (Notice that these definitions are purely interpretative; they do not affect the logical structure of our analysis in any immediate way.) Thus, a person who offers to sell or to buy (at a price) a secondhand car by advertising in the local weekly newspaper is a price setter; and in this case the market (being "unorganized") may be almost anywhere. Of more practical interest are relatively "organized" markets of the kind represented by local dealers in real estate, cars, secondhand furniture, groceries, gasoline, drugs, etc. Here, sale and/or purchase prices are announced in newspapers, on bulletin boards and signs, price tags, and so forth; and the markets in question are fixed in location (provided the price setter is sufficiently reputable!). The definitions given above may be extended from these cases, about which all of us have direct personal knowledge, to more exotic situations involving the setting of prices at wholesale houses, at auctions in large cities, at automobile factories in Detroit, at "markets" for agricultural commodities in Chicago, and in "markets" for securities and foreign currencies in New York.

In every instance it is individual owners or would-be owners of commodities who are price setters, acting for themselves in the case of small or unorganized "markets," acting through brokers or other middlemen in the case of large organized "markets" into which the general public is not permitted to penetrate directly (e.g., the New York Stock Exchange). And in almost every case the actual mechanics of price setting are substantially the same. The sale prices of various individuals are listed or announced, and if some would-be buyer is willing to part with cash at the lowest (of perhaps many) available quotations, a transaction occurs. When all sellers at one price have completed transactions with buyers, the next higher sale price governs subsequent transactions; or if new sale offers are received which are below previous offers, these govern the terms on which subsequent transactions occur. Alternatively, the purchase prices of various individuals are listed or announced, and if some would-be seller is willing to part with goods at the highest of the available quotations, a transaction occurs; if the lowest sale price exceeds the highest purchase price, no transaction occurs; etc. This description applies, of course, even if the sale or purchase prices in question are announced by a single individual (e.g., the local manager of the Texaco station); but the description of price *changes* requires more lengthy treatment in these cases.

As a general rule, markets are "one-sided" in the sense that a single price setter seldom stands ready to buy *and* to sell at a stated price (plus or minus a charge for marketing services and incidental transaction expenses), unless brokers and similar middlemen, rather than their principals, are regarded as price setters. However, the rule has many exceptions, notably among banks and other dealers in securities and foreign currencies. And in dealing with the *theory* of price determination, it is convenient to speak as if the exception were the rule, to talk about *the* price setter in a given market, a "person" who buys and sells, rather than to speak about many price *setters* some of whom buy and some of whom sell (as we should have to do if we wanted to stick closely to actual practice). To adopt the procedure suggested above is equivalent to assuming that one individual or agency acts as a clearing house for an aggregate of individual price setters, quoting one price for a commodity (i.e., either the lowest sale price or the highest purchase price of which it is currently apprised), and providing facilities for the conclusion of transactions which may occur at that price. In effect, "the price setter" in this case buys from sellers and sells to buyers at a single price (ignoring incidental marketing expenses). This description applies very well indeed to organized agricultural and securities markets and the like; and provided one were willing to postulate the payment of large "commissions" on purchases and sales, it would not be fanciful to apply it to local druggists, restaurateurs, and other small merchants. In any event, this is the view of the mechanics of price setting which we have adopted and shall retain in the subsequent argument. For the sake of simplicity, however, we shall ordinarily ignore the fact that net take-home prices to sellers may be less than the prices paid by buyers because of commissions, transport costs, insurance and storage fees, etc. The determination of "intervening" expenses of the latter kind is subject to analysis in precisely the same terms as are the prices of other "commodities," but we do not wish to deal explicitly with this problem.

2. *Why* a price setter decides to list or announce one price rather than another is a question to the deeper analysis of which most of Part I of this volume is devoted. Here, therefore, we shall merely offer a few remarks about the rationale of price setting and price adjustment.

The desire of individual price setters to arrive at prices which will equate quantity demanded to quantity supplied derives in practice from the natural desire to avoid the (money or subjective) expense of holding unwanted commodities (which can be done only if all "outputs" offered for sale at a given price are actually saleable at that price), or to avoid the expense of going without wanted commodities (which can be done only if all "inputs" demanded at a given price are purchaseable at that price). As a matter of principle, it might be desirable to explore this "market clearance" problem in greater detail. Price adjustment is only one of several possible means of equating actual with desired sales and actual with desired purchases; it might be supplemented or even replaced in some circumstances by direct adjustments in desired purchases, sales, and stock holdings, combined with advertising and other devices. To say anything about matters of this kind, however, would require reference to a variety of subjective factors including estimates by individuals of future prices and market conditions, liquidity considerations, and so forth. While it is as well to notice that the market clearance problem is not entirely straightforward, therefore, we shall not pursue the matter further at this time (see, however, Chapter Seven, Section 5 and 6). Our price setters are, in effect, commodity brokers who are paid by individual buyers and sellers (by commission or otherwise) to set price at such a level as will, in the price setter's opinion, equate quantity supplied to quantity demanded, *subject to the "rule" that price must be adjusted in an appropriate direction whenever a stated price is such that sales to the price setter exceed purchases from the price setter*. The latter "rule" imparts a definitely *mechanical* character to a process which would otherwise seem to be largely psychological in content. The resulting description of price determination, since it deals with definitely idealized price setters, undoubtedly distorts "reality" in certain respects; but the ultimate purpose of this distortion is to make important and otherwise mysterious complexities of "reality" more comprehensible.

7. Multiple Markets. We return now to the central theme of our argument. Equilibrium conditions for single markets having been established, it is natural to generalize these criteria to apply to two or more markets simultaneously. Let us begin by considering two markets: a flow market for the commodity 1, and a stock market for the commodity 2. Suppose that the two markets constitute an isolated system; i.e., suppose that the market for commodity 1 is isolated with respect to all markets other than that for commodity 2, and vice versa. For equilibrium in the first market, taken by itself, it is necessary that

$$d_1(p_1,p_2) - s_1(p_1,p_2) = 0 ;$$

for equilibrium in the second market taken by itself, we require that

$$k_2[D_2(p_1,p_2) - S_2] = 0.$$

For equilibrium to hold in the system consisting of both markets, therefore, p_1 and p_2 must assume values which satisfy the system of two equations:

$$(7.1)\begin{cases} x_1(p_1,p_2) = 0 , \\ k_2X_2(p_1,p_2) = 0 , \end{cases}$$

where

$$x_1(p_1,p_2) = d_1 - s_1 \text{ and } X_2(p_1,p_2) = D_2 - S_2$$

(S_2 being a fixed number in the present context); i.e., for equilibrium to exist in the system consisting of the two markets, price in each market must be such as to make both market excess demands zero. The nature of this requirement may be indicated graphically.

We may assume that for every particular value of p_2 there is at least one value of p_1 which will make market excess demand zero for commodity 1.

Allowing p_2 to vary, therefore, we obtain a curve such as P_1 in Figure 7.1 that depicts the set of all pairs of values of the prices p_1 and p_2 for which equilibrium will exist in the market for commodity 1. In other words, this curve is the graphic representation of the equation $x_1(p_1,p_2) = 0$. By a similar procedure, we can obtain a curve such as P_2 in Figure 7.1 representing the solutions of $k_2X_2(p_1,p_2) = 0$, i.e., pairs of values of the prices p_1 and p_2 which will give equilibrium in the market for commodity 2. At the intersection of the curves P_1 and P_2—and only there—the values $\bar{p}_1$ and $\bar{p}_2$ of p_1 and p_2 are such that excess demand is zero in both markets simultaneously. Accordingly the prices $\bar{p}_1$ and $\bar{p}_2$ constitute the equilibrium set of prices for the two-market system under consideration. If the curves inter-

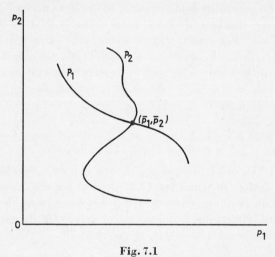

Fig. 7.1

sect more than once, there is a corresponding number of sets of equilibrium prices; if the curves do not intersect at all, equilibrium cannot occur.

Now consider an isolated system of three commodity markets, a flow market for the commodity 1, a stock market for the commodity 2, and a stock-flow market for the commodity 3. For equilibrium to exist in this system, p_1, p_2, p_3, and S_3 must assume values which simultaneously satisfy the system of four equations

$$(7.2)\begin{cases} x_1(p_1,p_2,p_3) = 0 \\ k_2X_2(p_1,p_2,p_3) = 0 \\ x_3(p_1,p_2,p_3) + k_3X_3(p_1,p_2,p_3,S_3) = 0 \\ x_3(p_1,p_2,p_3) = 0 \end{cases}$$

where

$$X_3(p_1,p_2,p_3,S_3) \ \ (\equiv D_3(p_1,p_2,p_3) - S_3)$$

is the excess stock demand function for the stock-flow commodity. The introduction of one stock-flow market into the problem increases by two the number of equilibrium conditions which have to be satisfied; but the number of unknowns is also increased by two, since for the third market S_3 as well as p_3 must be treated as variable. As for a two-market system, therefore, one may usually suppose that equilibrium values, $\bar{p}_1$, $\bar{p}_2$, $\bar{p}_3$, and $\bar{S}_3$ can be found for the variables p_1, p_2, p_3, and S_3 which cause the four conditions in (7.2) to be satisfied simultaneously.

The foregoing discussion indicates that from a formal point of view there is no difference, except in the *number* of variables involved, between a statical market system comprising a stock and a flow market and a system which also includes a stock-flow market. The same thing is true for a market system comprising any finite number of stock, flow, and stock-flow markets; the preceding equilibrium conditions for two- and three-commodity market systems may be generalized immediately to apply to an economy comprising, say, a flow markets, b stock markets, and c stock-flow markets $(a + b + c = n)$. For such an economy, the $a + b + 2c$ variables $p_1, \ldots, p_n$, $S_{a+b+1}, \ldots, S_n$ represent an equilibrium set of prices and commodity stocks if their values are such as to satisfy the system of $a + b + 2c$ equations:

$$(7.3) \begin{cases} x_i(p_1, \ldots, p_n) = 0 & (i = 1, \ldots, a) \\ X_j(p_1, \ldots, p_n) = 0 & (j = a + 1, \ldots, a + b) \\ x_m(p_1, \ldots, p_n) + k_m X_m(p_1, \ldots, p_n, S_m) = 0 & (m = a + b + 1, \ldots, n) \\ x_m(p_1, \ldots, p_n) = 0 & (m = a + b + 1, \ldots, n) . \end{cases}$$

Equations (3.1), (4.3), (7.1), and (7.2) are, of course, special cases of the more general system of equations (7.3). Just as for the one-equation systems (3.1), (4.3), however, there is no *a priori* reason why the general system (7.3) should determine a unique set of values for its variables rather than determining several such sets, or no set at all.

EXERCISES

7.1. Explain how the system of equations (7.3) can be replaced by an equivalent system in which the investment coefficients k do not appear—provided that these numbers are all positive. Describe your system in words.

7.2. Discuss how Figure 7.1 might be modified to provide a graphical interpretation of the system (7.2).

7.3. Find equilibrium values of the appropriate variables for the multiple market system governed by each of the following sets of excess demand functions. You may find it convenient to read Examples 6.1 and 6.2 in Chapter Eleven first.

a) $x_1 = 4 - p_1 + p_2$
    $x_2 = p_1 - 3p_2$
    $x_2 = 2p_1 - p_2 - S_3$.

b) $x_1 = -2p_1 + 2p_2 - 2p_3$
    $x_2 = 3p_1 - 7p_2 + 8p_3$
    $x_3 = 3p_1 + p_2 - 2p_3$.

c) $x_1 = p_2 - p_1$; $x_2 = p_3 - 4p_2$; $x_3 = -p_3 + 2p_4$;
    $x_4 = p_1 + p_2 - p_4$; $X_4 = 6p_3 - 2p_4 - S_4$.

d) $x_1 = 1 - p_1$; $x_2 = 2p_1 - 3p_2$; $X_1 = -p_1 + 9p_2 - S_1$;
    $X_2 = 20p_1^3 - S_2$.

8. *Money and Exchange.* That the general market economy described
by the system of equations (7.3) is, in some sense, a "money economy" is
implicit in the assumption that prices are quoted in money units. Even if
the presence of a money commodity is explicitly recognized in (7.3), however, little can be said about the specific economic functions or properties
of money on the present market level of analysis.[5] Nevertheless, it may be
worth while to pause at this point to see whether or not the assumption that
money is used as a medium of exchange requires us to qualify any of the
results obtained in preceding pages.

For the sake of realism and simplicity, let money be a stock commodity,
say commodity $n + 1$. Since the money price of a given commodity is the
number of money units required to purchase a unit of that commodity, the
money price of money is necessarily unity: $p_{n+1} \equiv 1$. Hence, the price of
money must be taken as a datum, not an unknown, in (7.3). On the other
hand, the excess demand functions in (7.3) describe only the "commodity
sector" of the economy; to describe a money economy explicitly, one should
augment (7.3) by the additional equation:

$$(8.1) \quad k_{n+1}X_{n+1} = x'_{n+1} = 0 \,,$$

x'_{n+1} being the investment demand for money. This yields a system of
$a + b + 2c + 1$ equations (viz., the $a + b + 2c$ equations of [7.3], plus
[8.1]), but involving only $a + b + 2c$ unknowns—the same unknowns as
occur in (7.3) itself. Accordingly, equilibrium values of prices and commodity stocks appear to be overdetermined; the explicit introduction of
money into (7.3) leads to an apparent inconsistency in the resulting system
(7.3)–(8.1). However, this difficulty is easily resolved.

If desire is to be translated into effective demand, an economic unit which
seeks to acquire additional quantities of one commodity must be willing to
dispose of quantities of at least one other commodity; thus, since there are
two sides to every exchange, the money value of quantities acquired
through exchange must necessarily equal the money value of the quantities
given up. Moreover, this must be true of the economy as a whole as well as
of individual members of the economy, so that (for example) if only two
commodities (say 1 and 2) are exchanged, we must have

$$p_1(x_1 + x'_1) + p_2(x_2 + x'_2) \equiv 0 \,;$$

i.e., whatever values are assigned to p_1 and p_2, the desire to sell quantities
of the first good implies a simultaneous desire to buy quantities of the
second good (and vice versa), and the value of the desired increment must
be precisely equal to the value of the desired decrement. This conclusion
may be extended immediately to apply to any number of commodities, including money. Thus, since $p_{n+1} \equiv 1$, we must have

$$(8.2) \quad x'_{n+1} \equiv - \sum_{i=1}^{n} p_i(x_i + x'_i) \,;$$

---

[5] We shall discuss this matter in more detail in Chapter Seven.

in other words, the sum of all nonmoney excess *supplies* (negative market excess demands), valued at any arbitrary set of prices, is identically equal to "market" excess demand for money.[6] (The quotation marks around "market" here are to emphasize that there is no specific place where this commodity is exchanged; it is involved in transactions in every market.) From (8.2) it is clear that if the market excess demands $x_i + x_i'$ $(i = 1, \ldots, n)$ are all zero, then x_{n+1}' must be zero also. Thus, in effect, to add the equation (8.1) to the system (7.3) is to add nothing; and if the system (7.3) is itself consistent, the augmented system (7.3)–(8.1) is also consistent.

The foregoing argument may be made more convincing from an intuitive standpoint if it is rephrased graphically. Suppose that the economy is com-

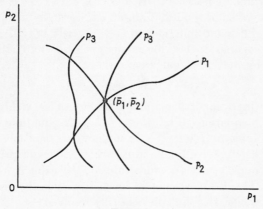

Fig. 8.1

posed of two flow markets whose equilibrium conditions are given by the equations:

$$x_1(p_1, p_2) = 0 , \quad x_2(p_1, p_2) = 0 ,$$

and assume that the investment (and so "market" excess) demand function for money is represented by $x_3'(p_1, p_2)$. As in Section 7, assume that each of the equations $x_1 = 0$ and $x_2 = 0$ has a set of solutions of the kind represented by the curves P_1 and P_2 in Figure 8.1. The intersection of P_1 and P_2 then determines certain values $\bar{p}_1$ and $\bar{p}_2$ for p_1 and p_2 which simultaneously satisfy the equations $x_1 = 0$ and $x_2 = 0$. However, one can also represent the equation $x_3' = 0$ by means of a similar graph, P_3, and in the absence of

---

[6] The condition (8.2) has been called *Walras' Law* (see O. Lange, "Say's Law: A Restatement and Criticism" in *Studies in Mathematical Economics and Econometrics*, edited by Lange *et al.* [Chicago: University of Chicago Press, 1942], pp. 49–68, especially p. 50). Walras' Law is very different from *Say's Law*, which asserts that

$$\sum_{i=1}^{n} p_i(x_i + x_i') \equiv 0 ;$$

taken together with Walras' Law, Say's Law states that $x_{n+1}' \equiv 0$. Cf. Chapter Seven, Section 4.

further information concerning the nature of the function x'_3, there is no reason to suppose that the curve P_3 will pass through the point $(\bar{p}_1, \bar{p}_2)$. This is the graphical meaning of the "apparent inconsistency" mentioned earlier. Fortunately, one can obtain further information about the function x'_3; specifically, one knows that it must satisfy the condition (8.2), which in this case becomes

$$x'_3 \equiv -(p_1 x_1 + p_2 x_2) \ .$$

But this implies that if p_1 and p_2 assume values such that x_1 and x_2 are zero, x'_3 must also be zero. That is to say, the equation $x'_3 = 0$ cannot be represented by the curve P_3 in Figure 8.1; rather, it must be represented by a curve such as P'_3, which passes through the intersection of P_1 and P_2, indicating that market excess demand for money is zero at that set of prices for which both commodity excess demands are zero.

The preceding argument suffices to show that the results obtained in previous sections are not directly affected by the assumption that money serves as a medium of exchange. However, this does not mean that "money" and "nonmoney" economies are substantially identical from a statical point of view; for we have not dealt, nor shall we deal, with any "nonmoney" models. All that we have done is to indicate that explicit recognition of a money commodity does not lead to conclusions which contradict findings which are valid in the case where recognition of a money commodity is merely tacit.

EXERCISES

8.1. In an economy made up of three stock markets, investment demand for commodities 1 and 2 is given by

$$x'_1 = 4 - (p_1 + p_2) \ , \quad x'_2 = p_1 - p_2 + p_3 - 4 \ ;$$

if the investment demand for money, x'_4, is $p_1^2 + p_2^2 + 3 p_2 p_3$, find a formula for the investment demand for commodity 3.

8.2. In terms of the example discussed in the last three paragraphs above, suppose that

$$x_1(p_1, p_2) = 10 - 2(p_1 + p_2) \ , \quad x_2(p_1, p_2) = 2p_1 - 1 \ .$$

Find x'_3, the investment demand for money, and graph the three equations $x_1 = 0$, $x_2 = 0$, $x'_3 = 0$, thus finding a specific example of Figure 8.1.

9. *Statical Systems and Comparative Statics.* A model for which no equilibrium state is defined does not lend itself to discussion on a statical level of analysis. Accordingly, models for which at least one equilibrium state is defined are given a special status and are called *statical systems* to distinguish them from models in which this requirement is not met. Thus, each of the models considered in the preceding sections is, when the system of equilibrium conditions has a solution, a particular example of a statical system. More generally, *a system of r functional relations*

$$(9.1) \quad f_i(u_1, \ldots, u_n; \ a_1, \ldots, a_m) = 0 \quad (i = 1, \ldots, r)$$

involving n variables $u_1, \ldots, u_n$ and also m parameters[7] $a_1, \ldots, a_m$, *represents a statical system if for given admissible values of the parameters there exists at least one set of admissible values of the variables which satisfies the equations (9.1).* If a statical system has the property that *only one* set of values of the variables satisfies (9.1) for each set of values of the parameters, the system is said to be *determinate*.

Statical systems are commonly associated with the physical sciences (where the concept has its origin); but such systems occur in many fields of knowledge. What the variables (u's) and parameters (a's) are chosen to represent in any particular case depends upon the decision of the investigator about which factors (variables) are to be given special consideration in the problem at hand and which factors (parameters) are to be given a subsidiary status or left over for later discussion. In the section of economics with which we are concerned, the u's will normally represent prices and/or commodity quantities; but certain prices and quantities may also appear as parameters together with factors such as "tastes," "techniques," and other psychological, social, and technical "quantities."

In constructing a statical system, one first chooses a set of variables and a set of parameters; this procedure defines the general scope of the subject matter to be represented in the system. Next, on the basis of observation and intuition, one selects various hypotheses relating the u's and a's to one another, these hypotheses being expressed in the form of a set of equations like (9.1). Additional restrictions on the u's and a's, restrictions which are either implicit in the premises defining the functions f_i or independently imposed, are then used to determine which particular sets of values of the u's and a's are admissible. Equation (8.2) is an example of such a restriction, as is the requirement that prices be real and nonnegative. The set of variables, parameters, equations, and restrictions set up in this way is then a statical system if the equations have the solubility property enunciated above. A set of values of the u's satisfying the equations (9.1) for a given set of values of the a's is called a set of *equilibrium values* of those variables corresponding to the given set of values of the parameters.[8]

For the sake of simplicity, we shall henceforth deal only with determinate statical systems. This is equivalent to making the assumption that every admissible set of values of the parameters determines a unique admissible

---

[7] Quantities such as tax rates, expected future prices, numbers which indicate the height of a supply or demand curve of a given shape, etc., are typical parameters in economics. The thing which distinguishes such parameters from ordinary variables (e.g., market prices and quantities) is that their values are determined outside the model and cannot be deduced from the model assumptions alone; they are, in a way, *contained* in the assumptions, different values of a given parameter leading to different models of the same general type. Needless to say, quantities which appear as parameters in one model frequently appear as ordinary variables in a different model.

[8] The terms "equilibrium" and "optimum" are sometimes used as virtual synonyms, particularly when the term "equilibrium" is given a normative interpretation. In general, however, this kind of interpretation is invalid, as will become clear when we examine the equilibrium concept more closely in Chapter Three.

set of values of the u's, namely, the corresponding equilibrium values of these variables. Hence, these values of the u's may be regarded as functions of the parameters:

$$(9.2) \quad \bar{u}_k = \bar{u}_k(a_1, \ldots, a_m), \quad (k = 1, \ldots, n)$$

where the bar over the u_k may be read as "the equilibrium value of." The determination of these functions is the ultimate goal of pure statical analysis in the strict sense. Once the existence of the functions (9.2) is granted, however, a whole new set of questions naturally arises—questions of the type: "If all of the a's but one are held fixed, and that one parameter varies, what is the effect of this variation on the $\bar{u}$'s?" In many cases it is possible to provide (partial or complete, qualitative or quantitative) answers to such questions on the basis of the equations (9.1) alone, without even knowing the functions (9.2) explicitly. And this is just as well, because these functions can be obtained explicitly in very few instances.

The general field of study generated by questions concerning the properties of the functions (9.2)—a field of study which extends far beyond the bounds of pure statical analysis as such—is called *comparative statics*. It has been described as ". . . the investigation of changes in a statical system from one position of equilibrium to another without regard to the transitional process involved in the adjustment."[9] That is to say, comparative statics deals with changes in the equilibrium values of the variables $u_1, \ldots, u_n$ resulting from given changes in the values of the parameters $a_1, \ldots, a_m$.

EXERCISES

9.1. Which of the following represent determinate statical systems? The variables are u and v, the parameters are a and b, and you should assume that all real values of a and b are to be admissible.

a) $u^2 - a^2 = 0, \quad u + v + b = 0$.

b) $u + v - a = 0, \quad u - v - b = 0$.

c) $u + v + v^2 - (a + b)^2 = 0, \quad u - 4ab = 0$.

d) $u + v + a + b = 0, \quad u + 2v + 3a + 4b = 0$.

9.2. Given the determinate statical system

$$u_1 + 2u_2 - 4a_1 = 0, \quad u_1 - 2u_2 + 4a_2 = 0,$$

find the equilibrium values of u_1 and u_2 as explicit functions of the parameters a_1 and a_2.

10. Methods of Comparative Statics [Nine–Sec. 1–6]. The comparative statics approach may now be illustrated by examining a few relatively simple examples.

Example 10.1. Consider first an isolated stock market. Suppose that stock supply, S, is given and that the stock demand function is $D(p, \alpha)$, where α is a parameter representing "tastes." We shall assume that, for

---

[9] P. A. Samuelson, *Foundations of Economic Analysis* (Cambridge: Harvard University Press, 1947), p. 8.

any given price, an increase in α would result in an increase in demand; in short, we shall assume $\partial D/\partial \alpha > 0$. Then, in terms of the general definition of a statical system (Section 9), $r = n = m = 1$, $u_1 = p$, $a_1 = \alpha$, and

$$f_1 = k(D - S) .$$

This statical system is thus embodied in the equation

$$k[D(p,\alpha) - S] = 0 \quad (k \neq 0) ;$$

and we shall suppose that the system is determinate, so that for every value of α this equation has a unique solution $\bar{p}(\alpha)$. By the definition of $\bar{p}(\alpha)$, the equation

$$(10.1) \quad k[D(\bar{p},\alpha) - S] = 0$$

is an identity. We shall now use this identity to answer the question: What will be the effect on $\bar{p}$ of a change in α?

First, we divide both sides of (10.1) by k, which is nonzero by hypothesis. Then we differentiate on both sides with respect to α. This gives

$$\frac{\partial D}{\partial \bar{p}} \frac{d\bar{p}}{d\alpha} + \frac{\partial D}{\partial \alpha} = 0 ,$$

from which it follows at once that

$$\frac{d\bar{p}}{d\alpha} = - \frac{\dfrac{\partial D}{\partial \alpha}}{\dfrac{\partial D}{\partial \bar{p}}} .$$

Since $\partial D/\partial \alpha > 0$ by hypothesis, this shows that $d\bar{p}/d\alpha$ and $\partial D/\partial \bar{p}$ have opposite signs. Now $\partial D/\partial \bar{p}$ represents, for any particular value of α, the slope of the stock demand curve; so if this curve (or, equivalently, the investment demand curve) is downward sloping at the equilibrium price, $\partial D/\partial \bar{p} < 0$, and therefore $d\bar{p}/d\alpha > 0$: a slight increase in α will entail an increase in $\bar{p}$, and a decrease in α will be accompanied by a decrease in $\bar{p}$. If $\partial D/\partial \bar{p} > 0$, the situation is reversed: a slight increase in α must produce a decrease in $\bar{p}$, etc. This provides only a conditional answer to our original question about $d\bar{p}/d\alpha$; but the analysis can be carried further only if additional information is furnished either from *a priori* or from empirical sources. This is fairly typical of the method of comparative statics, the usefulness of which lies not in its capacity to provide comprehensive and unconditional answers out of thin air but rather in its power to limit the field of possible answers and to determine what it is that the answer depends on.

Example 10.2. Next, we give a further illustration of the methods of comparative statics by analyzing certain properties of an isolated flow market. Suppose that the flow demand function and the flow supply function are, respectively, $d(p)$ and $s(p,\alpha)$, where α is now a parameter representing "technique." We shall assume that $\partial s/\partial \alpha > 0$; i.e., that an increase in

α, an "improvement" in technique, increases supply at any given price, or in other words shifts the supply curve to the right. Here $m = n = 1$, $u_1 = p$, $a_1 = \alpha$, $f_1 = d(p) - s(p,\alpha)$, and our statical system is represented by the equation

$$d(p) - s(p,\alpha) = 0 \ .$$

This equation may be solved to give the equilibrium price $\bar{p}$, as a function of α, whence equilibrium quantity, $\bar{q} = d(\bar{p}) = s(\bar{p},\alpha)$, may also be obtained as a function of α; i.e., $\bar{p} = \bar{p}(\alpha)$ and $\bar{q} = \bar{q}(\alpha)$. To discover how $\bar{p}$ and $\bar{q}$ change with small changes in α, differentiate both sides of the identity

$$(10.2) \quad d(\bar{p}) - s(\bar{p},\alpha) \equiv 0$$

with respect to α to obtain

$$\frac{\partial d}{\partial \bar{p}}\frac{d\bar{p}}{d\alpha} - \frac{\partial s}{\partial \bar{p}}\frac{d\bar{p}}{d\alpha} - \frac{\partial s}{\partial \alpha} = 0 \ ;$$

therefore

$$\frac{d\bar{p}}{d\alpha} = \frac{\dfrac{\partial s}{\partial \alpha}}{\dfrac{\partial d}{\partial \bar{p}} - \dfrac{\partial s}{\partial \bar{p}}} = \frac{\dfrac{\partial s}{\partial \alpha}}{\dfrac{\partial (d - s)}{\partial \bar{p}}} \ .$$

Also, since $\bar{q} = d(\bar{p})$,

$$\frac{d\bar{q}}{d\alpha} = \frac{\partial d}{\partial \bar{p}}\frac{d\bar{p}}{d\alpha} \ .$$

Now because $\partial s/\partial \alpha > 0$ by hypothesis, $d\bar{p}/d\alpha$ and $\partial(d - s)/\partial \bar{p}$ must have the same sign. Whether equilibrium price will increase or decrease with an improvement in technique is thus dependent upon the sign of $\partial(d - s)/\partial \bar{p}$, the slope of the excess flow demand curve at the equilibrium price $\bar{p}$. And given the sign of $d\bar{p}/d\alpha$, equilibrium quantity $\bar{q}$ may increase or decrease, depending on the sign of $\partial d/\partial \bar{p}$, the slope of the flow demand curve at the equilibrium price. As usual, further information is required to obtain unequivocal qualitative results or to obtain quantitative conclusions of any kind; but our analysis does specify the area of ignorance which has to be explored before such conclusions can be reached.

Example 10.3. Next, consider an isolated stock-flow market. Assume that the flow supply and demand functions are given, respectively, by $s(p)$ and $d(p,\alpha)$, where α is now a parameter representing "consumer tastes." We shall suppose that $\partial d/\partial \alpha > 0$, so that an "increase" in consumer tastes leads to an increase in demand at any price. Moreover, we suppose that the stock supply variable is S while the stock demand function is $D(p,\beta)$, where β is a parameter representing "expected future prices." By analogy with earlier assumptions of a similar kind, we assume that $\partial D/\partial \beta > 0$. Here, $m = n = 2$, $u_1 = p$, $u_2 = S$, $a_1 = \alpha$, $a_2 = \beta$, $f_1 = d(p,\alpha) - s(p)$, and

$f_2 = d(p,\alpha) - s(p) + k[D(p,\beta) - S]$. Our statical system is thus represented by the equations

$$(10.3)\begin{cases} d(p,\alpha) - s(p) = 0\,, \\ d(p,\alpha) - s(p) + k[D(p,\beta) - S] = 0\,. \end{cases}$$

In saying that this is a statical system, we imply that the system (10.3) may be solved for the equilibrium price $\bar{p}$ and the equilibrium stock supply $\bar{S}$. The flow equilibrium quantity is determined in turn: $\bar{q} = d(\bar{p},\alpha) = s(\bar{p})$. We may thus suppose that the variables $\bar{p}$, $\bar{S}$, and $\bar{q}$ are given by (10.3) as functions of α and β: $\bar{p} = \bar{p}(\alpha,\beta)$, $\bar{S} = \bar{S}(\alpha,\beta)$, $\bar{q} = \bar{q}(\alpha,\beta)$. We have then the system, identical in α and β,

$$d(\bar{p},\alpha) - s(\bar{p}) = 0\,,$$
$$d(\bar{p},\alpha) - s(\bar{p}) + k[D(\bar{p},\beta) - \bar{S}] = 0\,.$$

As usual, it will be convenient to deal with the equivalent system

$$(10.4)\begin{cases} d(\bar{p},\alpha) - s(\bar{p}) = 0\,, \\ D(\bar{p},\beta) - \bar{S} = 0\,. \end{cases}$$

To discover how $\bar{p}$, $\bar{S}$, and $\bar{q}$ vary with changes in α, differentiate on both sides of the equations in (10.4) with respect to α to obtain

$$\begin{cases} \dfrac{\partial d}{\partial \bar{p}} \dfrac{\partial \bar{p}}{\partial \alpha} - \dfrac{\partial s}{\partial \bar{p}} \dfrac{\partial \bar{p}}{\partial \alpha} = \dfrac{\partial d}{\partial \alpha} \\ \dfrac{\partial D}{\partial \bar{p}} \dfrac{\partial \bar{p}}{\partial \alpha} - \dfrac{\partial \bar{S}}{\partial \alpha} = 0\,. \end{cases}$$

The term $(\partial D/\partial \beta)(\partial \beta/\partial \alpha)$ does not appear in the second equation because $\partial \beta/\partial \alpha = 0$, β being independent of α. Therefore

$$\frac{\partial \bar{p}}{\partial \alpha} = -\frac{\dfrac{\partial d}{\partial \alpha}}{\dfrac{\partial (d - s)}{\partial \bar{p}}}$$

and

$$\frac{\partial s}{\partial \alpha} = \frac{\partial D}{\partial \bar{p}} \frac{\partial \bar{p}}{\partial \alpha}\,.$$

Also, since $\bar{q} = s(\bar{p})$,

$$\frac{\partial \bar{q}}{\partial \alpha} = \frac{ds}{d\bar{p}} \frac{\partial \bar{p}}{\partial \alpha}$$

by the simple chain rule. Because $\partial d/\partial \alpha > 0$ by hypothesis, $\partial \bar{p}/\partial \alpha$ and $\partial(d - s)/\partial \bar{p}$ must have opposite signs; hence, equilibrium price will increase with an increase in consumption demand if the excess flow demand curve is downward sloping, decrease if it is upward sloping. Moreover, if $\partial D/\partial \bar{p} < 0$ (the stock demand curve is downward sloping), $dS/d\alpha$ and $d\bar{p}/d\alpha$ are of opposite signs, so that the equilibrium stock supply $\bar{S}$ will rise with an increase in α if equilibrium price falls with an increase in α, and vice versa. Finally, the (flow) equilibrium quantity $\bar{q}$ will vary in the same direction as price if the flow supply curve is upward sloping, in the opposite direction to price if the flow supply curve is downward sloping.

To examine the variations in $\bar{p}$, $\bar{S}$, and $\bar{q}$ associated with changes in β, differentiate both sides of each equation in (10.4) with respect to β to obtain

$$\frac{\partial d}{\partial \bar{p}} \frac{\partial \bar{p}}{\partial \beta} - \frac{\partial s}{\partial \bar{p}} \frac{\partial \bar{p}}{\partial \beta} = 0$$

$$\frac{\partial D}{\partial \bar{p}} \frac{\partial \bar{p}}{\partial \beta} - \frac{\partial \bar{S}}{\partial \beta} = -\frac{\partial D}{\partial \beta};$$

then, if $\partial(d - s)/\partial \bar{p} \neq 0$, as may be assumed, the first of these equations implies

$$\frac{\partial \bar{p}}{\partial \beta} = 0,$$

and this result together with the second of the equations gives

$$\frac{\partial \bar{S}}{\partial \beta} = \frac{\partial D}{\partial \beta}.$$

Also, since $\bar{q} = s(\bar{p})$,

$$\frac{\partial \bar{q}}{\partial \beta} = \frac{\partial s}{\partial \bar{p}} \frac{\partial \bar{p}}{\partial \beta} = 0.$$

Accordingly, a rise in expected future prices (an upward shift in the stock demand curve and so an increase in the investment demand component of market demand) will alter neither the equilibrium price $\bar{p}$ nor the equilibrium (flow) quantity $\bar{q}$; while the equilibrium stock supply, $\bar{S}$, will change by the same amount and in the same direction as stock demand.

The preceding examples are special instances of a general approach which can be applied to any statical system. Thus, consider a statical system defined by

$$f_i(u_1, \ldots, u_n; a_1, \ldots, a_m) = 0 \quad (i = 1, \ldots, n),$$

which determines a set of equilibrium values of the variables $u_1, \ldots, u_n$ as functions of the parameters $a_1, a_2, \ldots, a_m$:

$$\bar{u}_i = \bar{u}_i(a_1, a_2, \ldots, a_m).$$

To study the effects of a change in, say, the parameter a_j, one can differentiate both sides of each of the identities

$$f_i(\bar{u}_1, \ldots, \bar{u}_n; a_1, \ldots, a_m) = 0 \quad (i = 1, \ldots, n)$$

with respect to a_j, thus obtaining

$$\sum_{k=1}^{n} \frac{\partial f_i}{\partial \bar{u}_k} \frac{\partial \bar{u}_k}{\partial a_j} \equiv \frac{\partial f_i}{\partial a_j} \quad (i = 1, \ldots, n).$$

This system of n linear equations may then usually be solved, perhaps under appropriate restrictions on the partial derivatives $\partial f_i/\partial \bar{u}_k$, for the n derivatives $\partial \bar{u}_i/\partial a_j$, and information about the signs and sizes of these derivatives may be obtained from assumptions about the partial derivatives $\partial f_i/\partial \bar{u}_k$, $\partial f_i/\partial a_j$ in terms of which they will be expressed. This process may involve great practical difficulties; but it is identical in principle with that used in Examples 10.1–10.3. Even more complicated problems may be raised by asking about the effect on the various variables of changes in two or more parameters simultaneously, and so on.

EXERCISES

10.1. Discuss the comparative statics of the following markets and market systems:
    a) The market for Roman coins, regarded as an isolated stock market. Assume that the stock demand is given by

$$D(p,\alpha) = A + \frac{\alpha}{p^2},$$

    where A is a constant and α is a parameter representing "current interest in numismatics."
    b) A stock-flow market for wheat, assumed to be isolated, where flow demand is an increasing function of a parameter α representing "population," and stock demand is an increasing function of a parameter β representing "storage capacity."
    c) A two-market system consisting of a stock-flow market for commodity 1 and a stock market for commodity 2, where the flow demand for commodity 1 is assumed to be a decreasing function of a parameter α representing "interest rates."

10.2. Consider a system consisting of two interrelated stock markets for commodities 1 and 2. It might be argued that instead of studying the statics of this system one could equally well study the comparative statics of the market for commodity 1, treating p_2 as a parameter. Discuss the strengths (if any) and the weaknesses (if any) of this argument.

10.3. Apply the reasoning of Example 10.3 to markets for tax-free municipal bonds to show that, *ceteris paribus*, the (equilibrium) market rate of interest from the bonds will be the same with or without the tax exemption feature, but that the stock of bonds outstanding will be larger if the income from bonds is tax exempt.

11. *Comparative Statics and Stability.* Using methods of the kind set out in Section 10, one can describe movements of equilibrium positions corresponding to changes in the data of any statical system. However, the relevance of such results for describing empirical market behavior remains to be established, because the fact that a certain price is a unique *equilibrium* price under given circumstances does not imply that it will be, even approximately, the *prevailing* price at any time. Indeed, everyday experience suggests that most markets are likely to be in *dis*equilibrium most of the time. On the other hand, the fact that a market is normally in disequilibrium will not be important for any practical purpose if the extent of disequilibrium is never very great. And this is the problem: to determine the circumstances in which markets will be in, or very nearly in, equilibrium most of the time. In circumstances other than these, the conclusions of equilibrium analysis generally, and of comparative statics in particular, are clearly irrelevant from an empirical standpoint.

A mechanical illustration may be helpful at this point. For a boulder that is free to roll about in a mountain range, summits of mountains as well as bottoms of valleys represent possible positions of equilibrium; but a boulder perched on a mountain peak is rightly regarded as a natural curiosity, for such a position of equilibrium is essentially *unstable*. Thus, even if all boulders were on mountain peaks at some time in the distant past, one would not expect to find them there still; the student of boulders is well advised to visit valley bottoms, where boulders are in *stable* equilibrium. Arguing by analogy, one might reason that "peak" positions of price equilibrium are of little empirical significance; i.e., that prices will normally seek "valley" positions of equilibrium into which they will move given sufficient time, so that positions of unstable equilibrium will seldom be of any practical importance. Actually, the analogy is rather incomplete, because the student of statical market systems is in the position of an observer who sees a boulder at rest without being able to see the surrounding terrain. The problem is to discover which positions of price equilibrium are analogous to mountain valleys and which positions are analogous to mountain peaks. A look will suffice to resolve the problem in "boulderology," but not in economics! Statical theory of course sheds no light on this subject; it merely describes the locations of "peaks or valleys," or (comparative statics) describes changes in the locations of equilibrium points resulting from "earthquakes" and other such phenomena (changes in data), but does nothing to classify the equilibrium points among themselves. The problem of the *stability of equilibrium* must be handled by other means. Indeed, it is impossible to make statements about the stability of an equilibrium position in an economic model unless the model contains assumptions which describe the behavior of the system when it is *not* in equilibrium; but as soon as a model contains assumptions of this kind, it lies outside the realm of pure statical theory and is a part of dynamical theory instead.

The close relationship between comparative statics and dynamics (or, more particularly, stability) will be illustrated here by referring to a simple dynamical model obtained from one of our statical systems, namely, the isolated flow market model of Example 10.2.

Let us suppose that the equilibrium price corresponding to a certain value α' of the parameter α is $\bar{p}'$. Moreover, assume that at a certain instant the prevailing price, p, is actually at the corresponding equilibrium position, $p = \bar{p}'$. If the parameter α now changes from α' to α'' (we may suppose, for the sake of simplicity, that this change occurs instantaneously), then a new equilibrium price, $\bar{p}''$, is determined, and certain general statements can be made—indeed, have been made—about how the relation of $\bar{p}''$ to $\bar{p}'$ depends on the slopes of the supply and demand curves and the relation of α'' to α'. At the instant the change is made, however, the prevailing price in the economic system is still at $\bar{p}'$; and in the absence of nonstatical assumptions one is powerless to say what the prevailing price will do after this change, even though one knows that the new equilibrium price is $\bar{p}''$. All that the statical theory itself can say is that if the prevailing price were now at $\bar{p}''$, it would stay there; but the prevailing price is not at $\bar{p}''$.

To break this deadlock, we shall introduce some specific nonstatical assumptions. On the basis of the discussion in Section 6 of this chapter, it is plausible to suppose that if excess demand is positive (i.e., if the amount of the commodity demanded exceeds the amount supplied at a given price), price will be set at a higher level. Similarly, it is natural to suppose that if excess demand is negative (i.e., if the quantity supplied exceeds the quantity demanded at a given price), price will be set at a lower level. Under these conditions, equilibrium price is defined by the condition that excess demand be zero, which is precisely the condition which we have used to define equilibrium price in statical flow models. Thus the statical model represented by (3.1) can be obtained as a special case of the *dynamical* model which is implicitly defined by the above assumptions.

There are now two cases to be distinguished:

Case I: $\partial x/\partial p > 0$, the derivative being evaluated for $\alpha = \alpha''$ (the inequality is assumed to hold for all relevant values of p). The inequality simply means that excess demand (for the given value of the parameter) is an increasing function of p; therefore, since $x(\bar{p}'') = 0$ by the definition of $\bar{p}''$, $x(p)$ is positive if $p > \bar{p}''$, negative if $p < \bar{p}''$. But this means that if the prevailing price p has any value but $\bar{p}''$, the market price will *move away* from $\bar{p}''$; for when $p > \bar{p}''$, excess demand is positive, and by our assumptions price will *increase*, and the situation for $p < \bar{p}''$ is similar. Thus, in this case, the equilibrium price $\bar{p}''$ is *unstable*.

Case II: $\partial x/\partial p < 0$. By a line of reasoning analogous to that given under Case I, it may be seen that here the prevailing market price, no matter where it starts, will tend to move *toward* $\bar{p}''$, and, indeed, will continue to move in that direction until it is so close to $\bar{p}''$ that the two prices are practically indistinguishable. Accordingly, in this case the equilibrium price is *stable*.[10]

Now in order for the comparative statics conclusions to be of any empirical relevance, Case II must occur; for unless the new equilibrium price is stable, the prevailing price will not move from $\bar{p}'$ toward $\bar{p}''$ but rather in some other direction; and being able to describe the relation of the

---

[10] Of course there are other cases possible besides those considered above, namely, the cases in which $\partial x/\partial p$ changes sign. However, these cases lead to niceties which it would be premature to consider at this point.

new equilibrium price to the old will be an empty victory. However, if $\bar{p}''$ is to be stable, we have $\partial x/\partial p < 0$; and from the comparative statics discussion in Section 10 we have

$$\frac{d\bar{p}}{d\alpha} = \frac{-\dfrac{\partial d}{\partial \alpha}}{\dfrac{\partial x}{\partial \bar{p}}}.$$

Thus if the new equilibrium position is stable (and this, we repeat, is necessary for the relevance of the statical theory) $d\bar{p}/d\alpha$ must be positive, since $\partial x/\partial \bar{p}$ is negative and $\partial d/\partial \alpha$ is assumed to be positive. In other words, a change in tastes which increases demand will raise the equilibrium price (and therefore the prevailing price) of the commodity, while a change in taste which decreases demand will lower price. This confirms what one would expect.

The foregoing example has little intrinsic significance, but it is instructive nevertheless, and for several reasons. First, it shows *that the task of justifying the equilibrium assumption in the applications of comparative statics is substantially equivalent to that of furnishing criteria for the stability of equilibrium in nonstatical models.* It should perhaps be emphasized that for this purpose no exact knowledge is required about the nature of the path which a system follows in moving from one position to another; it must only be shown that if the equilibrium position of a system is displaced, the system moves, after the lapse of a sufficiently long interval of time, to within any prescribed small distance of the new equilibrium position, and stays there.

Second, the example suggests an interesting liaison between the study of statical and nonstatical systems. We have already seen how a criterion for equilibrium may be obtained directly from the hypotheses of a nonstatical model. Reciprocally, *statical analysis, the conclusions of which are more readily grasped and extended by intuition and common sense, may act as a stimulus and guide in formulating nonstatical models.* Starting from the statical system (3.1), one is prompted to construct nonstatical systems, of which the one just considered is an example, in which the statical system represented by (3.1) is imbedded; and similarly for all the other statical systems considered in this chapter. This relationship between the study of statical and nonstatical systems will be illustrated more fully in subsequent chapters.

Finally, our example also indicates that *the use of nonstatical techniques may help to make the conclusions of comparative statics less equivocal by ruling out possibilities which imply instability.* However, this is more an exception than a rule. The stability condition in the example happens to involve only the sign of the slope of the excess flow demand curve, and so can be applied directly to the conclusions of comparative statics; but we shall meet few situations in subsequent chapters which are this simple. In fact, most of the stability criteria with which we shall deal are equivocal in the same sense, and to a similar degree, as the comparative statics conclusions they might otherwise be used to evaluate. Moreover, one may get from differing nonstatical models, all of which correspond to a given statical model, different and conflicting stability conditions. Accordingly, the empirical relevance of a *particular* nonstatical model is normally presupposed when stability conditions within it are used to refine the conclusions of comparative statics; and this presupposition may be very difficult to justify.

Taken as a whole, the preceding argument suggests that in order to develop useful statical theories, one must at the same time cultivate the study of nonstatical systems. In addition to the collateral reasons just enumerated, however, there are compelling grounds for studying nonstatical systems for their own sake: many aspects of economic reality which must be ignored in statics can be taken into account in nonstatical analyses; and few economic problems involving the behavior of commodity markets out of equilibrium can be easily or correctly resolved without explicit recourse to nonstatical techniques. It is with techniques of this kind that we shall be concerned in the next two chapters.

EXERCISES

11.1. Assuming that price normally increases when excess demand is positive and decreases when excess demand is negative, discuss the stability of equilibrium in each of the following situations:

  a) An isolated stock market in which excess stock demand is given by $X(p) = -3 + 4p - p^2$.

  b) An isolated stock-flow market in which excess flow demand is given by $x(p) = 4 - p^2$ and excess stock demand is given by $X(p) = 22 - p - S$.

  c) A two-market system composed of markets for the stock commodities 1 and 2, where
$$\begin{cases} D_1(p_1,p_2) = 15 - 3p_1\,, & S_1 = 6\,, \\ D_2(p_1,p_2) = 35 - (p_1 + p_2)^2\,, & S_2 = 10\,. \end{cases}$$

11.2. Given that equilibrium in an isolated stock market is stable if and only if $dX/dp < 0$, what can you say about the comparative statics of the model in Exercise 10.1(*a*)?

11.3. Given that equilibrium in an isolated stock-flow model is stable if and only if $dD/dp < 0$ and $dx/dp < 0$, what can you say about the comparative statics of the model in Exercise 10.1(*b*)?

SUGGESTIONS FOR FURTHER READING

The division of markets into flow, stock, and stock-flow categories is not usual in the economic literature. However, the distinction between flow markets (variable supplies) and stock markets (fixed supplies) is not uncommon, and this leads very naturally to the idea of a stock-flow market. The latter notion is also implicit in the Marshallian division of the theory of price determination into "market," "short-run," and "long-run" analyses. For further elucidation of the concept of a stock-flow market and its importance, see the two papers by R. W. Clower: "Business Investment and the Theory of Price," *Proceedings of the Twenty-eighth Annual Conference of the Western Economic Association* (1953), pp. 22–24; and "An Investigation into the Dynamics of Investment," *American Economic Review*, Vol. XLIV, No. 1 (March, 1954), pp. 64–81.

For a good example of the traditional approach and an excellent introduction to "supply and demand" analysis generally, see G. J. Stigler, *Theory of Price* (New York: Macmillan Co., 1952), chaps. i, ix, and x. The best modern treatment of equilibrium analysis—which includes a discussion of the statical theory of money—is to be found in J. R. Hicks, *Value and Capital* (2d ed.; London: Oxford University Press, 1946), Part II, particularly chap. iv. The classical study of *partial* equilibrium theory is, of course, Alfred Marshall's *Principles of Economics* (London and New York: Macmillan Co., many editions); the corresponding work in *general* equilibrium theory is the *Elements of Pure Economics* by Leon Walras (London: George Allen and Unwin, 1954).

The main theoretical content of most literary writings on economics—and of the usual principles' texts in particular—is comparative statics. There is no need here to give specific references to this literature; however, adequate attention is seldom given to the separation between theory and practice which results from discussing comparative statics without making explicit reference to dynamical considerations. An important exception to this rule is Erich Schneider's *Pricing and Equilibrium* (New York: Macmillan Co., 1952), which provides one of the best existing discussions of comparative statics as a whole.

Appendix

AGGREGATIVE MODELS:
THE KEYNESIAN SYSTEM

THE direct usefulness of general statical models is in practice greatly limited by their complexity. To the person who is in a hurry to do good, therefore, concern with n-commodity models may seem a waste of time; practical policy recommendations require reference to less cumbersome theories which can represent significant aspects of reality in a simple and striking manner, and yield definite conclusions on reasonably short order. On the other hand, isolated systems of the kind considered early in Chapter Two, while sufficiently manageable to meet these requirements in point of simplicity, are, as descriptions of reality, too narrow to be of much interest to students of the "larger problems" of life—too many factors must be submerged in sweeping *ceteris paribus* assumptions.

A compromise is to formulate and explore one-, two-, or few-commodity models obtained by lumping together certain of the variables and functional relations that would appear in a more general model, introducing appropriate simplifications in the process. The first difficulty encountered in following this approach is that of defining aggregative variables and relations which are capable of yielding meaningful interpretations of reality; for it is only too easy to define aggregative quantities in such a way as to *embody* precisely those obscurities which occur explicitly in more detailed models. In practice, this means that the aggregation process must be applied to individual variables which are known to vary roughly in unison in the real world, commodities which do not meet this criterion being treated as components of different aggregates.

Perhaps a more significant difficulty is that of going from a supposedly satisfactory general model to a specialized aggregative model that is logically and empirically consistent with it. Generally speaking, most aggregative models developed in the past have been formulated independently of, and without a careful examination of their consistency with, any acceptable general theory of price determination. To the extent that one has faith in the essential correctness of a particular general theory, however, it is important to reconcile any proposed aggregative model with it; for such an inquiry will almost always suggest fruitful amendments to one

43

or both systems. This task is unlikely to be easy in the best of cases, and may be impossible in some.

The purpose of this appendix is to illustrate various aspects of the problem of obtaining useful aggregative models. We shall proceed by discussing the derivation of what is undoubtedly the most influential of existing aggregative models, the so-called Keynesian system. An adequate treatment of the topic is impossible in the space available here;[1] but in view of the important role which the Keynesian system plays in modern economics, it is desirable to say something (even if it is little more than an outline) about its relation to the rest of our analysis. As it happens, the path from our own (or from any similar model) to the Keynesian system is rather tortuous; but our discussion will serve to show that a path (of sorts) exists, and to indicate the location of various slippery corners.

The basic Keynesian model involves four aggregative variables, one each for *consumer goods, capital goods, labor,* and *securities.* Securities are stock commodities, consumer goods and labor are flow commodities, and capital goods are stock-flow commodities. (It will be observed that this classification of commodities into groups and types, while it warps reality noticeably, describes very well popular ideas of over-all economic activity; and its factual validity is supported moderately well by available statistical data.) Thus, recalling (7.3) in Chapter Two, and denoting different variables by appropriate subscripts (a for capital goods [assets], b for securities [bonds], c for consumer goods, and L for labor), we may write

$$(A.1) \begin{cases} x_a(p_a,b_b,p_c,p_L) + x_a'(p_a,p_b,p_c,p_L,S_a) = 0 \,, \\ x_b'(p_a,p_b,p_c,p_L) = 0 \,, \\ x_c(p_a,p_b,p_c,p_L) = 0 \,, \\ x_L(p_a,p_b,p_c,p_L) = 0 \,, \end{cases}$$

to represent a multiple market model which is analogous to the Keynesian system. We shall have occasion later to distinguish supply and demand components of x_c and x_L, but the implicit form of the excess demand equations is more convenient here. We have omitted the usual requirement that $x_a = 0$ from the above set of equilibrium conditions in accord with accepted practice in dealing with the Keynesian model. From a logical point of view this is not an altogether satisfactory procedure, for since S_a is *not* fixed, $x_a = 0$ is definitely a relevant equilibrium condition; but it is a useful simplification, and made by Keynes himself in the *General Theory.* The stock of bonds, S_b, is of course assumed to be fixed.

Now (A.1) is not much of an improvement, as an instrument for predicting actual aggregative behavior, over the general n-commodity model (7.3) which underlies it—as working out the comparative statics properties of

---

[1] It is now over twenty years since *The General Theory of Employment, Interest, and Money* made its appearance. The reader's acquaintance with the basic elements of this famous book will accordingly be taken for granted, and we shall not give specific references to support our assertions about these elements.

(A.1) will show. One of the major difficulties in this connection is the presence in the model of price variables, changes in which may affect different commodity variables in different ways so that net effects are difficult to disentangle. Keynes partially circumvented this problem by dealing with aggregate expenditure and aggregate receipts variables in conjunction with (and partly in place of) prices. Following his lead, we first distinguish between the household (consumer) and business sectors of the economy and confine our attention to net market expenditures and receipts either within or between the two sectors.

Then the net money value of aggregate demand for (i.e., "planned" expenditure on) "outputs"—consumer goods, capital goods, and securities—is given by

$$E_0 = p_c d_c + p_a x_a' + p_b x_b' .$$

Similarly, the net money value of aggregate supply of (i.e., "planned" receipts from) "outputs" may be written

$$R_0 = p_c s_c - p_a x_a - p_b x_b' .$$

The net money value of aggregate demand for (i.e., "planned" expenditure on) "factors" is

$$E_f = p_L d_L + p_a x_a + p_b x_b' + P ,$$

where P represents aggregate business profits and similar nonwage elements of expense which accrue as "income" to the household sector. Finally, we write the net money value of the aggregate supply of (i.e., "planned" receipts from) "factors"

$$R_f = p_L s_L - p_a x_a' - p_b x_b' + P .$$

If equilibrium occurs in the model, however, then the equations (A.1) imply that

$$E_0 = R_0 , \quad E_f = R_f ;$$

moreover, provided net sales of securities from one sector of the economy to the other are zero, household expenditures on consumer goods must be equal to current receipts. That is to say, we have

$$(A.2) \quad p_c d_c = p_L s_L + P ;$$

and from this (since $p_b x_b' = 0$ and $p_a x_a = -p_a x_a'$ in equilibrium) it follows that

$$(A.3) \quad E_0 = E_f ,$$

so that indeed $E_0 = E_f = R_0 = R_f$.

If we now define *aggregate income* Y by

$$Y = E_f - p_b x_b'$$

(p_bx' is excluded from aggregate income in this definition because it represents a mere transfer of purchasing power from buyers to sellers of bonds), it follows from (A.2) that in equilibrium

$$Y = p_c d_c + p_a x'_a .$$

Writing $C = p_c d_c$, $I = p_a x'_a$, therefore, we obtain finally[2]

$$(A.4) \quad Y = C + I .$$

Condition (A.4), which is a necessary condition for equilibrium in the model (A.1), is the fundamental building block of the Keynesian system. It asserts that, in equilibrium, *the net value of business demands for "factors,"* Y, *must be equal to the sum of the net values of business and consumer demands for "outputs,"* $C + I$. This is essentially a condition for the equilibrium of the consumer and business sectors of the economy, so the condition (A.4) does not imply that the system of equations (A.1) is satisfied.

It remains to specify what the actual equilibrium values of the variables C and I will be under various conditions. Equation (A.4) in effect summarizes the aggregative content of all four of the equilibrium requirements in (A.1), but it says nothing definite about single conditions. Our next problem is therefore that of translating relevant aspects of the conditions in (A.1) into Keynesian terms.

We begin with the first equation in (A.1). The precise way in which equilibrium consumption (in physical terms) depends upon the price variables is a difficult thing to judge on the basis of everyday experience. The manner in which consumer expenditure C will vary *when prices vary in such a way as to change aggregate income* Y is another matter, however. Specifically, it seems plausible to suppose C is a function of Y,

$$(A.5) \quad C = C(Y) ,$$

with the property that $0 < dC/dY < 1$—when aggregate income increases consumption expenditure also increases, but not as fast. This is the Keynesian *consumption function* or *propensity to consume;* it corresponds to the first equation in (A.1).

The equations (A.4) and (A.5) lead immediately to the Keynesian theory of the *multiplier:* If (A.4) and (A.5) are viewed as a statical system involving the single parameter I, we may eliminate C and write

$$Y = C(Y) + I ,$$

whence by differentiating on both sides with respect to I and rearranging terms, we get

$$(A.6) \quad \frac{dY}{dI} = \frac{1}{1 - \dfrac{dC}{dY}} .$$

---

[2] If *aggregate saving* S is defined by $S = Y - C$, then by (A.4) $S = Y - C = I$ *in equilibrium.*

This is the Keynesian "instantaneous" (i.e., comparative statics) multiplier; it shows what effect a change in investment expenditure will have upon the equilibrium level of aggregate income.

Still working on the basis of the system (A.4)–(A.5), which may be considered to determine equilibrium values of C and Y for any given value of I, it is natural to ask next about the factors which determine the values of I. Here we must again refer back to the system (A.1). Just as one may have doubts about how changes in prices in general will influence consumption expenditure, so one may have even more serious misgivings about the effect of changes in p_c and p_L upon the supply and demand of capital goods and securities. To circumvent this problem, let us suppose that the functions in question depend upon the prices p_a and p_b and upon Y (the latter quantity being regarded as a pragmatic substitute for the prices p_c and p_L). Then on the basis of (A.1) we may write

$$(A.7) \begin{cases} x'_a(p_a,p_b,S_a,Y) + x_a(p_a,p_b,Y) = 0\,, \\ x'_b(p_a,p_b,S_b,Y) = 0\,. \end{cases}$$

This provides a system of two equations to determine p_a and p_b in terms of the aggregate income Y, since S_b is a constant and S_a is "nearly" a constant; and equilibrium investment demand is in turn determined by the investment function x'_a.

In the Keynesian system, however, it is not p_a and p_b which appear as variables but rather the *rate of interest* r and the *marginal efficiency of capital m;* but the difference between the Keynesian formulation and ours is minor in this respect. Thus, instead of assuming (as in [A.7]) that money units are offered in exchange for securities, one may look at the matter the other way around and assume that securities (i.e., offers to part with a fixed amount of *contract* interest per unit of time) are offered for units of money. The ratio of the total amount of contract interest paid per unit of time to the number of units of money acquired in an exchange is then the *market* rate of interest r (e.g., if three bonds, each paying $1 per year contract interest, are given in exchange for 100 one-dollar bills, the market rate of interest is $3 per $100, or 3 per cent). It is as well to emphasize that the demand for money in terms of securities is a very different thing from the demand for money as such; the latter refers to the demand for money in terms of *all* other commodities—that is,

$$x'_M = -(p_a x_a + p_a x'_a + p_b x'_b + p_c x_c + p_L x_L)\,,$$

where the subscript M denotes the money commodity. Accepting Keynes' view of the pricing of securities, we may (provisionally) replace the second equation in (A.7) by

$$r = f(p_a,Y,x'_b)\,;$$

and if we then assume that x'_b is related in a definite way to the demand for (and so to the stock of) money M, we have

$$(A.8) \quad r = g(p_a,Y,M)\,,$$

which *resembles* the Keynesian liquidity preference function.

Adopting a similar procedure in dealing with the pricing of capital goods by stating the problem in terms of the offer of a certain quantity of *prospective net returns* per unit of capital goods in exchange for each unit of money, we may replace the first equation in (A.7) by a relation analogous to (A.8),

$$(A.9) \quad m = h(r,Y,M) .$$

The marginal efficiency of capital is of course a subjective rate of return. Now if we use m in place of p_a in (A.8), we obtain a system of two equations

$$r = r(m,Y,M) \quad m = m(r,Y,M)$$

from which equilibrium values of the rate of interest and the marginal efficiency of capital may be found once Y and M are given. In this connection, however, Keynes supposes that in equilibrium the (subjective) rate of net return on capital goods must be equal to the (objective) rate of net return on securities. On this assumption, we may make one last replacement, replacing the equations (A.7) by the definitely Keynesian relations

$$(A.10) \quad I = I(r,Y) ,$$
$$(A.11) \quad M = M(r,Y) .$$

The first function is called the *schedule of the marginal efficiency of capital*, while the second is called the *liquidity preference function*. They state precisely as much (or as little) about the determination of the prices of capital goods and securities, and the demand for new capital goods, as do the equations (A.7).

This completes the translation of the first three equations in (A.1) into Keynesian terms. The satisfaction of the last condition, $x_L = 0$, is of course implicit in (A.4); but we still require some kind of function to specify what the *level of employment* will be in equilibrium, as well as what the wage will be. One might use either the demand or the supply aspect of x_L for this purpose; following Keynes again, however, we choose the second and write

$$N = s_L = s_L(p_a,p_b,p_c,p_L) ,$$

where N represents aggregate employment. But the equilibrium value of employment, like the equilibrium level of consumption expenditure, may be related in a very complex fashion to the variables p_c and p_L: so we again sidestep the issue by using Y to replace the two fickle price variables. In accordance with our discussion of asset pricing, we also replace p_a and p_b by the variables r and M. Thus the *employment function* may be finally written as

$$(A.12) \quad N = N(r,Y,M) .$$

The system of equations (A.4), (A.5), (A.10), (A.11), and (A.12) provides five conditions which can be used to determine the values of the five unknowns Y, C, I, r, and N, given the stock of money M. Provided that one supplies plausible assumptions about the form of the functions C, I, M, and N (and many persons think that this can be done despite the numerous concealed causal relations which enter into the definition of these functions), one can proceed to make statements about the behavior of the economy as a whole. Keynes was himself a master at this kind of game; but his peculiar talents are given to few economists.

Of course, one man's pork and beans is another man's caviar; so there are different views about the usefulness of the Keynesian system. Some economists like the system as it stands and are willing to make policy recommendations on the basis it provides; others prefer a system more like (A.1) which includes more price variables, and their public pronouncements are modified accordingly; still others think that a system as condensed as (A.1) is itself an ill-chosen oversimplification and prefer to make policy recommendations which are so vague as to be irrefutable, or none at all. We shall not join the debate on these matters. For our purposes it is enough to have illustrated some of the steps which must be taken in moving from a general, detailed system such as (7.3) in Chapter Two to a more specialized system like (A.1), and from this in turn to a highly rarified model like that afforded by the Keynesian system.

A number of questions of interpretation and emphasis that have been bypassed in the preceding discussion are listed below as exercises for the reader. In the subsequent analysis we shall not return to the explicit consideration of aggregative models as such, although many of our conclusions will have some bearing in this realm.

EXERCISES

A.1. Interpret equations (A.4) and (A.5) geometrically (using expenditure and receipts co-ordinates) to illustrate the determination of aggregate income in terms of alternative levels of investment expenditure. Also illustrate how alternative assumptions about the form of the consumption function influence the size of the multiplier.

A.2. "Sales and purchases in a market are always identical since they are merely different aspects of the same thing. Hence, $s(p) \equiv d(p)$ for all values of price, so demand and supply do not determine price. Similarly, since income is the sum of consumption expenditure and investment expenditure, and since saving is the difference between income and consumption, saving and investment are just different aspects of the same thing and cannot be said to determine the equilibrium level of income." What, if anything, is wrong with these statements?

A.3. Given the stock demand function $D_a(p_a, p_b)$, stock supply S_a, and the excess flow demand function $x_a(p_a)$, obtain a schedule relating the price of bonds, p_b, to net investment. Draw a similar graph to illustrate the Keynesian marginal efficiency of capital schedule. Upon what considerations does the form of the latter depend? Would it be correct to describe the schedule as an investment *demand* function rather than an investment *supply* function, or is either view appropriate?

A.4. "The 'liquidity preference' theory of the rate of interest is based upon the assumption that, in equilibrium, $X_b(p_b,S_b) = 0$, where S_b is a constant. In contrast, the 'loanable funds' theory rests on the assumption that, in equilibrium, $x_b(p_b) = 0$." Is this true? Would it be more correct to say that the loanable funds theory rests on the assumption that $x_b(p_b) + x_b'(p_b,S_b) = 0$? What is the practical significance, if any, of the last assumption as compared with the assumption $X_b = 0$? Of the assumption $X_b = 0$ as compared with the assumption $x_b = 0$? Of the assumption $x_b + x_b' = 0$ as compared with the assumption $x_b = 0$?

A.5. "Had Keynes described the determination of the rate of interest in a direct rather than an indirect way (i.e., in terms of the market for bonds rather than in terms of the demand for money in terms of bonds), his analysis of Transactions, Precautionary, and Speculative Motives for holding money would have been unnecessary." Is this correct? Explain carefully.

A.6. "Situations are likely to arise in practice in which the marginal efficiency of capital is negative; and since the rate of interest cannot fall below zero, this may give rise to prolonged periods of less than full employment." Do you agree or disagree? (What happens to the marginal efficiency of capital if the price of capital goods varies? Is the marginal efficiency of capital likely to be negative even if all capital goods can be had without payment? Answers to these questions are relevant in connection with the answer to the first.)

A.7. "If the supply function of labor is represented by the curve s in Figure A, a rise in demand will increase employment but will not affect wages; so there is

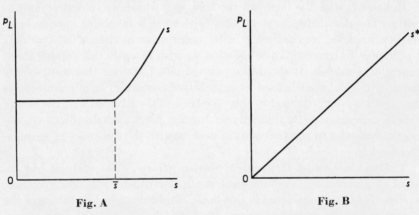

Fig. A   Fig. B

less than full employment so long as s is less than $\bar{s}$. If the labor supply function is represented by s^* in Figure B, however, then every level of employment is a level of full employment." Criticize these statements.

A.8. "The Keynesian system, since it deals explicitly both with the holding and with the production and consumption of capital goods, is a stock-flow model. Classical economics, on the other hand, dealt explicitly only with flow or with stock markets, never with stock-flow markets. Hence, there is no way in which an explicit reconciliation of 'Keynes' and 'Classics' can be effected." Can you refute this assertion?

Chapter Three

MACROECONOMIC DYNAMICS I:
ISOLATED MARKETS

IN this chapter we first discuss some fundamentals of dynamical analysis and then devote the remainder of the chapter to the construction and investigation of relatively simple dynamical extensions of some of the one-commodity statical models considered in Chapter Two. Our primary aim is to illustrate certain established methods for analyzing dynamical models· some of the models chosen for investigation are nevertheless of intrinsic interest and afford insights into the nature of economic processes in the real world. The latter aspect of these models is brought to the fore in the concluding section of the chapter.

In keeping with the theme of the book as a whole, we shall deal here, as well as in subsequent chapters, only with models involving specific commodity markets, as contrasted with aggregative models. The Appendix to Chapter Two contains most of what we wish to say in this volume about aggregative models. It should be pointed out, however, that most of the basic dynamical models used in aggregative economics have counterparts among the systems defined in this chapter and the next, so that the reader should experience little difficulty in turning his knowledge of macroeconomic dynamics to good account in dealing with the dynamics of aggregative models.

1. *Dynamics and Dynamical Assumptions.* The state at any instant of an economic system, more particularly of an idealized economic system like those considered in this book, can be described by means of the values of certain variables: prices, stock and flow quantities, and others. To each different state of the economic system there corresponds a different set of values of the variables, and to each different set of such values there corresponds a different state. It is therefore possible to identify each state of the system with a point of some abstract many-dimensional "space," the co-ordinates of any point in the space being merely a particular set of values of the variables which characterize the states of the system.[1] The

---

[1] Just as in ordinary co-ordinate geometry (see Chapter Eight, Section 3), where because one identifies pairs of numbers (x,y) with points in a plane these pairs of numbers may themselves be regarded as points in the plane, so sets of n numbers, $(x_1, x_2, \ldots, x_n)$,

transition from one state to another, if it is gradual, will be represented by motion along some "curve" in the "space" that links the initial state with the final state. This space, although it may be difficult to visualize in any but a vague way, is helpful for obtaining a mental picture of economic processes. Hence, we shall give it a name: borrowing a long-established term from the physical sciences, we call it the *phase space* of the economic system. A point in the phase space which represents the actual state of the economic system at some particular instant of time will be called a *representative point*. If all variables which are co-ordinates of points in the phase space are quantity variables, it may be more convenient to call the phase space a *commodity space;* or if all co-ordinate variables are price variables, it may be more convenient to call it a *price space;* but in every case the basic idea is the same.

From the present point of view, the statical theory developed in the last chapter may be regarded as dealing with the problem of singling out, within the phase space, certain special points representing equilibrium states—the points themselves can therefore be called, in a natural way, *equilibrium points*. These points have the characteristic property that once the economic system somehow arrives at one of them (say as the result of an exogenous shock), it must stay there indefinitely unless the assumptions underlying the model are relaxed or altered. Comparative statics, from this point of view, is the study of how equilibrium points shift in the phase space when assumptions are altered.

But what about points which are not equilibrium points? It is certainly conceivable that an economic system may be in a state which is not an equilibrium state; indeed, as we have observed, common sense and offhand observation would suggest that in any fairly realistic model the current state will seldom if even be an equilibrium state. The assumptions of a purely statical theory, however, have nothing to say about such nonequilibrium states except that they *are* nonequilibrium states. An economic system which behaved as if it knew nothing beyond the statical assumptions which it is asked to obey would not know what it should do if it suddenly found itself at a nonequilibrium point, except that it should keep moving.

In order for an economic model to be complete, therefore, some assumptions must be made which go beyond those of a statical character. Ideally (in what we shall call the *determinate* case) these additional assumptions will make it possible to say that, given the state of the system at any particular instant, the state of the system at any subsequent instant is uniquely determined thereby; and in the most favorable case, it will be possible explicitly to deduce subsequent states from the given initial state.

Under less than ideal circumstances, the system will not be determinate

---

can be regarded as points of an n-dimensional "space." The fact that this "space" cannot be drawn or visualized when $n > 3$ is an accidental feature of the physical environment in which we live, and does not impose any fundamental limitations on the usefulness of the concept for discussions such as ours.

in this sense, but there should still be assumptions that give *some* information about the movement of the system through the phase space.

A specific example may illuminate matters at this point.

Example 1.1. In the first model considered in Section 7 of Chapter Two, involving a system comprising two markets, all quantity variables are functions of prices; hence, the two prices themselves are adequate to define unequivocally the state of the system at any instant. For this model, therefore, the phase space may be represented by the plane made up of points with the price co-ordinates (p_1, p_2). This is the plane depicted in Figure 7.1 of Chapter Two. The point $(\bar{p}_1, \bar{p}_2)$ appearing in that figure is an equilibrium point; all of the other points in the figure (even those on the curves P_1 and P_2) represent nonequilibrium states of the model. In order to obtain a more complete model in the sense described above, it is necessary to impose further assumptions about the behavior of the system. Some very special assumptions of this kind would be provided, for instance, by the differential equations

$$(1.1) \begin{cases} \dfrac{dp_1}{dt} = p_2 - \bar{p}_2 \,, \\ \dfrac{dp_2}{dt} = -(p_1 - \bar{p}_1) \,, \end{cases}$$

which gives the rates of change of prices with respect to time (the "price velocities") at any point (p_1, p_2) in the price plane. It may be shown (this theory will be developed in Chapter Twelve) that the equations (1.1) completely determine the price movements of the system in the sense described above. In this case, indeed, it may be shown that the representative point of the system, starting from a certain initial point, will move in a clockwise direction along the circle which passes through the given initial point and which has its center at the equilibrium point. Notice that the only point in the plane at which both price velocities are zero is $(\bar{p}_1, \bar{p}_2)$, and this is as it should be; i.e., the assumption (1.1) is consistent with the equilibrium conditions (7.1) of Chapter Two.

Assumptions like (1.1), which enable one to say something about the behavior of the system when it is out of equilibrium, are called *dynamical assumptions*. In mathematical models of economic systems, dynamical assumptions usually take the form of differential equations (as above), difference equations, or in general *relations which establish some connection between (a) the manner in which the representative point tends to move at a certain point in the phase space and (b) the co-ordinates of that point*. A model which contains dynamical assumptions is a *dynamical model;* and the study of dynamical models in general is *dynamics*.

EXERCISES

1.1. Other things being equal, whether or not a model is determinate may depend on the choice of the phase space. Why? How might a model be *over*determinate?

1.2. Consider the model dealing with an isolated flow market in which time is measured discretely, $t = 0, 1, 2, \ldots$ (see Section 5 of this chapter), and which is governed by the dynamical assumption that the change in price from one value of t to the next is equal to one half of the number obtained by subtracting 2 from the price at the former instant. Symbolically,

$$p_{n+1} - p_n = \tfrac{1}{2}(p_n - 2),$$

where p_n is the price when $t = n$.

  a) How should the phase space be chosen so that this model will be determinate?

  b) In the phase space given in your answer to part (a), where is the representative point when $t = 4$ if $p_0 = 10$?

  c) There is an equilibrium point for this model. What is it?

1.3. It is sometimes claimed that it is quixotic to study *determinate* models of economic systems, because in fact economic systems are seldom if ever determinate, prey as they are to all kinds of imponderable and unaccountable influences. Discuss the merits of this claim.

1.4. Decide whether you would call each of the following assertions a dynamical assumption if it occurred among the assumptions in some model, and explain your decision in each case.

  a) The price of wheat is never greater than the price of bleached white flour.

  b) The size of bond issues of a certain type is larger the smaller the current rate of corporation taxation.

  c) The price of new automobiles is, *ceteris paribus*, proportional to the price of steel eight months before the date on which the price is set.

  d) The securities market is never in equilibrium.

2. Equilibrium and Stability in Dynamical Models. The discussion in the last section may seem to center about the concept of equilibrium; but this is merely an accident of the manner of exposition. In this section we restore the equilibrium concept to its proper place in dynamics.

For the sake of simplicity, we shall restrict ourselves to determinate dynamical models: to models, that is, in which once the representative point at some initial instant t_0 is given, the representative point is uniquely determined for every value of t satisfying $t \geqslant t_0$. This may be translated into other terms. Suppose the variables used to describe the various possible states of the economic system are u_i $(i = 1, 2, \ldots, N)$. Any set of values of the u's represents a certain conceivable state of the system or, equivalently, provides the co-ordinates of the corresponding point in the phase space. The statement that the model is a determinate dynamical model amounts to saying that, given any point with the co-ordinates u_i^0 $(i = 1, 2, \ldots, N)$ representing a possible state of the system, there exists a unique set of functions $u_i(t)$ (defined for all values of t such that $t \geqslant t_0$) satisfying the assumptions of the model and the further conditions

$$u_i(t_0) = u_i^0.$$

Here, of course, t_0 represents the "initial instant" at which the system is assumed to be in the state represented by the point whose co-ordinates are $u_i{}^0$, and the functions $u_i(t)$ give the state of the system at any time t after t_0. The numbers $u_i(t_0 + 1)$ give the co-ordinates of the point in the phase space which the system will have reached one time unit after t_0, etc. The set of functions $u_i(t)$ constitute the *solution* (and in the phase space give the co-ordinates of points on the *solution curve*[2]) determined by the initial state $u_i{}^0$ and the initial instant t_0.

It is now easy to characterize equilibrium points in the phase space of a determinate dynamical model. In the usual interpretation, a point is an equilibrium point if, as we have said, a system which somehow arrives at the point will remain there through all subsequent time, barring anomalous disturbances of the system. This leads directly to the definition: *The point whose co-ordinates are $u_i{}^0$ ($i = 1, 2, \ldots, N$) is an equilibrium point if the solution determined by it and any value t_0 of t consists of the constant functions $u_i(t) = u_i{}^0$.*

As we began to explain at the end of the last chapter, equilibrium points owe their empirical significance to considerations of *stability*. An equilibrium point which does not "attract" points from the region around it cannot have much empirical importance. Suppose that $\bar{u}_i (i = 1, 2, \ldots, N)$ are the co-ordinates of an equilibrium point in a certain determinate dynamical model. We shall say that this equilibrium point displays *perfect stability* if the solution corresponding to any point in the phase space approaches this point and remains arbitrarily close to it as time passes. More precisely, *the point with co-ordinates $\bar{u}_i (i = 1, 2, \ldots, N)$ is perfectly stable if, whenever $u_i(t)$ is a solution in the model, it follows that*

$$u_i(t) \to \bar{u}_i \quad as \ t \to \infty .$$

This definition implies that an equilibrium point cannot be perfectly stable if there is another equilibrium point in the phase space.

The use of the term "stability" arises from a certain natural interpretation of the above definition. Suppose that the economic system is at an equilibrium point in the phase space, but that the system receives a sudden shock of some kind (the assumptions of the model are momentarily violated) which displaces it from equilibrium; then once the shock has subsided, the system is likely to be at some nonequilibrium point, and its subsequent movement will be dictated by the dynamical assumptions of the model. The representative point will follow the solution curve determined by the point to which it was displaced, and if the original equilibrium point is perfectly stable, this solution curve must carry the system back toward the equilibrium point, so that after the lapse of a sufficiently long time interval the representative point will be back very near to its original (equilibrium) position, and will stay there at least until the next "shock." This self-restoring property of the equilibrium state corresponds very well to the everyday notion of stability.

---

[2] Thus, in Example 1.1, the solution curves are circles in the price plane with their centers at $(\bar{p}_1, \bar{p}_2)$. The words *path*, *trajectory*, and *orbit* are sometimes used instead of the term "solution curve."

The qualifying adjective "perfect" is used to emphasize the fact that no matter how far the system may be displaced from equilibrium by various shocks, it will nevertheless tend to return to equilibrium. This is a very strong kind of stability. The kind with which we shall actually be concerned most of the time is somewhat weaker. It is called *local stability* and is defined as follows: *the equilibrium point whose co-ordinates are* $\bar{u}_i(i = 1, 2, \ldots, N)$ *is locally stable if there exist fixed positive numbers* k_i *such that whenever*

$$(2.1) \quad |u_i^0 - \bar{u}_i| < k_i,$$

the solution made up of the functions $u_i(t)$ *determined by the point whose co-ordinates are* u_i^0 *(and any value* t_0 *of* t*) has the property*

$$u_i(t) \to \bar{u}_i \quad as \quad t \to \infty .$$

The inequalities (2.1) express the fact that the point with co-ordinates u_i^0 is not too far from the equilibrium point; so the definition could be expressed roughly by saying that an equilibrium point is locally stable if a *sufficiently small* displacement of the system from that point will be followed by an ultimate return to equilibrium.

Our special concern with local stability, as distinguished from perfect stability, is based on three considerations. First, the vast majority of realistic displacements from equilibrium may be expected to be small, so that the local stability of an equilibrium point is enough to assure its ability to preserve itself under conditions which are not too hectic. Second, the use of the term "perfect stability" implies that we have some confidence in the realism of our model over the entire phase space; but shortcomings of the model over such a vast domain could lead to such a large cumulative error that statements about long-range movements of the system—such as would be implicit in the imputation of perfect stability to an equilibrium point in the system—would be of doubtful relevance for the interpretation of real-world phenomena. The same objections apply to the study of local stability, but on a smaller scale; for by restricting attention to a small neighborhood of an equilibrium point, we are less likely to be biting off more than the model can chew. Third and finally, there exist sharp and powerful criteria for the local stability of an equilibrium point in all of the models we shall examine, while the problem of deciding whether an equilibrium point is perfectly stable is, in general, so difficult as to be practically insoluble. We shall therefore usually omit the adjective "local" and the adverb "locally," using the simple terms "stability" and "stable" for "local stability" and "locally stable." An equilibrium point which is not locally stable will be called *unstable*. It should be remembered that *stability* (perfect or local) *and instability are properties of equilibrium points.*

The concepts of equilibrium and stability just defined may now be illustrated by means of a familiar example outside economic theory. Imagine a rigid pendulum suspended from a not altogether frictionless support about which the pendulum is free to rotate. If the pendulum is lifted away from the vertical and released, it will oscillate in a more or less regular way around the downward position. Because of the friction at the point of support, however, the oscillations will gradually subside; and after a sufficiently long interval they will (for all practical purposes) vanish entirely. The pendulum will have reached a state of rest, hanging straight down. If the system is not disturbed again, the pendulum will remain in that position indefinitely. Such a state represents a constant solution of the dynamical model which describes the motion of the pendulum. However, the downward position is not the only possible equilibrium position for a pendulum; for if the pendulum is made to point exactly straight up and released, it will also remain in position indefinitely. This situation is virtually impossible to obtain experimentally, because the slightest error in placing the pendulum in the upward equilibrium position, or the slightest disturbance thereafter, will upset its balance and cause it to fall so that it will return eventually to the downward equilibrium position. Nevertheless, in principle the upward position of the pendulum is quite as much an equilibrium position as the other. The fact that the former position is difficult to realize experimentally while the latter is easy has nothing to do with the notion of equilibrium as such. Because there are two equilibrium positions, neither one is *perfectly stable;* moreover, the upward equilibrium position is definitely *unstable*, for even small displacements may cause the pendulum to fall. The downward equilibrium position, however, is (*locally*) *stable.*

In passing, it is perhaps as well to remark explicitly that since, as a general rule, there is no reason to give either abstract functional relations or arbitrary *ceteris paribus* clauses the status of value judgments, positions of stable equilibrium need have nothing in common with "optimal" situations in any normative sense. Whether it is pointing up or down is probably a matter of indifference to the pendulum, although the upward position may evoke some anxiety in the mind of a human spectator.

In a given dynamical model equilibrium points may or may not exist, and any equilibrium state which does occur may or may not be stable. In every case, however, the motions of a dynamical system are a legitimate object of inquiry.[3] On the other hand, it must be admitted that in most cases it is possible to obtain only a meagre picture of the behavior of a system which possesses no equilibrium states, whereas it is often possible to specify in a detailed and relatively concrete fashion the properties that a dynamical model must have if it is to possess, say, positions of stable equilibrium. Furthermore, while economic systems in the real world are

---

[3] It is misleading to suggest, as at least one writer has done, that unstable systems are uninteresting and that the establishment of their laws of change is a nonsense problem. Such a view is valid only as applied to models in comparative statics, where results can be used to interpret empirical data only if the satisfaction of certain stability criteria is presupposed.

never likely to be in stable equilibrium in any ultimate sense, because the data of society are constantly changing, one cannot help feeling that positions of stable equilibrium will exist in models which represent economic aspects of the real world rather faithfully. Finally, from a theoretical standpoint—taking comparative statics analysis into account, in particular —the stability problem is clearly of great interest. These considerations provide sufficient justification for the emphasis given to stability questions in subsequent pages.

EXERCISES

2.1. It is possible to imagine a model in whose phase space every point is an equilibrium point: the underlying system always tends to remain in whatever state it happens to have reached. Discuss the stability properties of such a model.

2.2. Consider a model for an isolated flow market in which the phase space is taken to be the positive half of the p-axis and all of the solution curves are given by the formula

$$p = 5 + \frac{p_0 - 5}{1 + (t - t_0)^2},$$

where p_0 is the (initial) price at the (initial) instant t_0. Find the equilibrium value of p and discuss its stability properties.

2.3. Find the general solution for the model of Exercise 1.2; i.e., find the solution with the property that p_0 (the value of p when $t = 0$) has an arbitrary prescribed value. Use your answer to verify your previous answer to part (c) of Exercise 1.2 and discuss the stability properties of the model.

3. *The Fundamental Assumption of Macrodynamics.* In dealing with dynamical problems concerning market price determination, it is possible to retain essentially the same definitions of supply and demand as were introduced in Chapter Two; all that is required is to alter our previous definitions slightly in order to make quantity variables functions of time. To do this, we regard each price as a function of time, but suppose that flow supply and stock and flow demand depend directly on prices only, so that these quantity variables are functions of t only via prices; i.e., if p_i is denoted by $p_i(t) (i = 1, \ldots, n)$, then the flow supply function for the ith commodity is written $s_i = s_i[p_1(t), p_2(t), \ldots, p_n(t)]$, and similarly for the other functions. However, where there is no risk of misunderstanding, we shall continue to write simply $s_i = s_i(p_1, \ldots, p_n)$, etc. Stock supply variables have to be generalized in a rather different way, but this will be done later.

Now, everyday observation naturally suggests that movements in market price and quantity variables occur when there is (positive or negative) excess demand in commodity markets; indeed, this can hardly fail to be true for aggregate stocks of any commodity if excess flow demand (i.e., net production, positive or negative) is not zero. Moreover, the operation of the forces of excess demand provides a convenient basis for the construction of dynamical models. Accordingly, we state the following as the *basic assumption of macroeconomic dynamics:*

Market price and quantity variables change over time if and only if the the excess demand for some commodity is not zero.

As will be apparent in the next few sections, this assumption may be embodied in a variety of different symbolic formulations representing different kinds of dynamical hypotheses.

EXERCISE

3.1. In Section 2 of Chapter Two, a basic criterion for equilibrium in a one- or multiple-market model was stated; in Section 2 of the present chapter, the relation between dynamical assumptions and equilibrium was defined. Explain how these two things are consistent with the basic assumption of macroeconomic dynamics stated above.

4. Model I: Continuous Flow or Stock Systems [Ten–Sec. 5, 6, 7; Twelve–Sec. 8]. Consider first an isolated market for a single flow commodity, a market characterized by the demand and supply relations $d = d[p(t)]$ and $s = s[p(t)]$. If trading in the market is continuous, i.e., if t is treated as a continuous variable,[4] and if the level of *current* excess demand alone is taken into account, then we may suppose that the behavior of price over time is governed by the relation

$$(4.1) \quad \frac{dp}{dt} = f\{d[p(t)] - s[p(t)]\} = f\{x[p(t)]\} ,$$

where $f(x) = 0$ if and only if $x = 0$; in words, the rate of change of price with respect to time at any instant is a function of excess flow demand at that instant. To obtain an explicit description of the behavior of price over time, it is necessary to deduce from (4.1) an expression giving price at any instant as a function of time; that is, one needs a *solution* of the differential equation (4.1).

In general, f may be so complicated a function that a solution may not be explicitly obtainable, even if it is known to exist. However, we need not attempt to find a solution for the general equation (4.1); instead we shall suppose that equation (4.1) has a constant solution given by some value $\bar{p}$ of p, and confine our attention to the behavior of price in the neighborhood of this equilibrium point. We assume (although it will be seen that this assumption is heavier than necessary) that f may be expanded as a Taylor series in p about the price $\bar{p}$. Thus (4.1) may be written as

$$(4.2) \quad \frac{dp}{dt} = \alpha a(p - \bar{p}) + [\ldots] ,$$

---

[4] This means that the market processes are to be thought of as occurring uninterruptedly, so that one must take as the range of the variable t some connected part of the t-axis. This notion is not to be confused with that of the continuity of *functions*, which is quite different.

where $\alpha = \partial f / \partial x$ and $a = \partial x / \partial p$, these derivatives being evaluated at $\bar{p}$, and [. . .] represents terms in the Taylor series of degree two or more. The number α, and other numbers which play analogous roles in similar models, will be called *adjustment coefficients*.

We are concerned only with the behavior of solutions of (4.2) very near the value $\bar{p}$ of p; but when p is very near $\bar{p}$, $(p - \bar{p})$ is a small quantity, and the terms occurring in [. . .], which are constant multiples of $(p - \bar{p})^n$ $(n \geqslant 2)$, are very small indeed. It would therefore seem safe to omit the small quantity [. . .] from (4.2), reasoning that near $\bar{p}$ the solutions of the simplified ("linearized") equation

$$(4.3) \quad \frac{dp}{dt} = \alpha a(p - \bar{p})$$

should behave like those of (4.2), because the right members of the two equations differ only very slightly near $\bar{p}$. In order for this line of reasoning to be valid, it should be assumed that neither a nor α is zero; we accordingly make this assumption. When this assumption is not made, results based on the linearized equation (4.3) are irrelevant to the study of (4.2); terms in [. . .] must be considered, and the whole investigation becomes much more difficult.

We shall therefore restrict our attention to (4.3) in the knowledge that qualitative conclusions about this equation will also apply to (4.2) for values of p near $\bar{p}$. In particular, the stability of $\bar{p}$ for (4.2) is equivalent to its stability for (4.3).

The general solution of (4.3) may be written

$$(4.4) \quad p(t) = \bar{p} + (p_0 - \bar{p})e^{\alpha a(t - t_0)},$$

where $p_0 = p(t_0)$.

It is not difficult to find criteria for the stability of equilibrium by a direct examination of (4.4). The equation gives p explicitly as a function of t, this function involving the five parameters p_0, $\bar{p}$, a, α, and t_0. Since t appears only in the exponent, we may expect that the behavior of $p(t)$ as $t \to \infty$ will depend entirely on the quantity αa; and this is correct. If $\alpha a > 0$, the exponent will approach infinity with t, so that the exponential term $(p_0 - \bar{p})e^{\alpha a(t - t_0)}$ will also approach infinity (positive or negative, depending on the sign of $p_0 - \bar{p}$—we can ignore the possibility $p_0 - \bar{p} = 0$, which would correspond to equilibrium). Thus, in this case, $\bar{p}$ is unstable. On the other hand, if $\alpha a < 0$, the exponential term will approach *zero* as $t \to \infty$, so that *irrespective of the values* of p_0 and t_0, we shall have $p(t) \to \bar{p}$ as $t \to \infty$; i.e., $\bar{p}$ is stable.

Now αa will be negative if and only if α and a have opposite signs. But α is the rate of change of dp/dt with respect to x at $\bar{x} = x(\bar{p})$, so if α is positive, dp/dt increases as excess demand increases, while if α is negative, dp/dt decreases as excess demand increases. Moreover, a is the slope of the excess flow demand curve (relative to price) at the equilibrium position and this in turn is the slope of the flow demand curve minus the slope of the flow supply curve; so a (which is nonzero by hypothesis) will be negative or positive according as the slope of the flow demand curve is smaller or larger than the slope of the flow supply curve. Thus, if the slope of the flow excess demand curve is negative, $\bar{p}$ will be stable if the price setter increases the rate of change of price as excess demand increases; and if the slope of the excess demand curve is positive, $\bar{p}$ will be stable if the price setter decreases the rate of change of price as excess demand increases. In other words, stability requires that the price setter gauge correctly the slope of

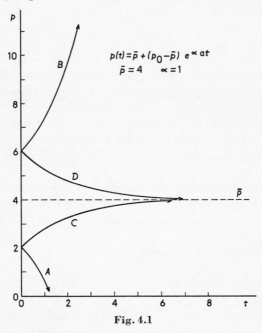

$$p(t) = \bar{p} + (p_0 - \bar{p})\, e^{\alpha\, at}$$
$$\bar{p} = 4 \qquad \alpha = 1$$

Fig. 4.1

the excess demand curve and adjust price accordingly. Everyday experience suggests that most excess demand curves may be downward sloping; but in any case a few "trials and errors" should permit the price setter to estimate correctly whether this is or is not the case (only the slope of the curve, not the curve itself, has to be determined). Since it is not to be supposed that a price setter will view continued one-directional movements in excess demand with complete equanimity, this means that, as a practical matter, one may take the stability of an *isolated* flow market for granted.

The various kinds of behavior possible in (4.1) are indicated in Figure 4.1. We assume that $\bar{p} = 4$, $\alpha = 1$ (the units need not be specified), and graph $p(t)$ in each of the four cases:

$$\text{(A)} \quad p_0 = 2, \quad a = \tfrac{1}{2}$$
$$\text{(B)} \quad p_0 = 6, \quad a = \tfrac{1}{2}$$
$$\text{(C)} \quad p_0 = 2, \quad a = -\tfrac{1}{2}$$
$$\text{(D)} \quad p_0 = 6, \quad a = -\tfrac{1}{2}$$

It is clear from the graph that $\bar{p}$ is unstable in cases (A) and (B), stable in cases (C) and (D). One may see what happens for negative values of α (say $\alpha = -1$) by permuting the cases $(A)-(D)$ in the appropriate way.

Since the stability of Model I depends upon the sign of the product αa, our conclusions are of little direct interest in connection with problems in comparative statics—for stability may occur whether a is positive or negative. Of course one may simply assume that the adjustment coefficient has a given sign, and in this case (since stability does not depend upon the *size* of α) one can say what the sign of a must be in order that the model should be stable. Then, following the same procedure as that illustrated in Section 11 of Chapter Two, this "knowledge" might be used to sharpen certain results in comparative statics. Strictly speaking, however, the determination of the signs of α and a is an empirical question the answer to which might vary from case to case; so the procedure just outlined would be difficult to justify. The business of the theorist is to provide pegs upon which to hang facts, not to provide moulds into which facts must be forced.

In passing (to explain why the heading of this section refers to flow *and* stock models), it should be noticed that the preceding analysis would be affected only in a notational sense if it were altered to apply to an isolated stock market. Specifically, one may substitute the investment demand function

$$k\{D[p(t)] - S\} = x'[p(t)]$$

(S is a constant) for the excess flow demand function $x[p(t)]$ in (4.1), re-interpret the coefficients a and α accordingly, and all conclusions which are valid for an isolated flow market remain valid for this isolated stock market.

EXERCISES

4.1. In an isolated flow market the demand and supply functions are given by

$$d(p) = \frac{6}{1 + p}, \quad s(p) = p,$$

and the "adjustment function" $f(x)$ is $x^2 + x$. Find the equilibrium price and determine whether it is stable.

4.2. In an isolated stock market the investment demand function is given by $x'(p) = \frac{1}{2}p^2 - 3p + 4$. If the "adjustment function" $f(x')$ is given by

$$f(x') = \frac{-1}{1 + (x')^2},$$

find the equilibrium prices and determine whether each one is stable.

4.3. Discuss the appropriateness of the term "adjustment coefficient."

4.4. Markets in which trading is strictly continuous are probably nonexistent. Does this mean that models in which continuous trading is assumed can be of no practical value? Explain.

5. *Model II: Discrete Stock-Flow Systems with Instantaneous Price Adjustment* [Twelve–Sec. 1–5, 7]. The role of time in dynamical models is open to various constructions; our assumption in Model I that trading occurred continuously (or, more precisely, that price could be treated as a differentiable function of time) represents one extreme. The opposite extreme is represented by the assumption that trading occurs at separate, equally spaced instants or, as we shall say, depends on a *discrete* time variable. This assumption would be realized approximately by a market in which trading occurs but briefly at regular intervals, say between noon and three o'clock on Wednesday afternoons. Likewise, a market in which price is set only at certain regularly spaced times, say at the beginning of each month, could be treated in the same way, even though trading itself might be more or less continuous. The essential feature common to these two situations is that price can be regarded as defined only for *whole* values of t, $t = 7$ corresponding to the seventh trading period, and so on. Needless to say, most real-world market situations lie somewhere between these two extremes, price setting being neither a strictly continuous nor a regularly scheduled activity; but one or the other may usually be taken as a valid approximation to reality. Which is better would normally depend on the relative magnitudes of the quantities involved, the violence of market fluctuations, and similar factors.

In this section we shall construct a model with discrete time. In other words, the domain of the function $p(t)$ is taken to be the set of nonnegative whole numbers. This will be interpreted to mean that price is actually defined at all times but is constant over successive intervals of unit length, so that one may without loss describe price at all times by describing it at one instant—say the initial instant—in each of the intervals over which it is constant. It should be remarked that in these circumstances each flow variable can be regarded as a flow per unit of time *multiplied by the unit of time;* this produces no numerical change but makes the flow variable into a quantity dimensionally. From this it follows that a per-period flow can always be treated as an end-of-period increment of stock, so that stock and flow variables are now commensurable, as they are not when t is a continuous variable.

Later in this chapter a discrete version of Model I will be obtained as a special case of another dynamical model; here, therefore, we shall formulate a discrete stock-flow model to illustrate the working of discontinuous market processes. As a rule the dynamical behavior of an isolated stock-flow market is more complicated than that of an isolated flow or stock market; however, the model outlined below is designed to avoid as many as possible of these complications.

Denote stock demand by $D = D[p(t)]$, excess flow demand by

$$x = x[p(t)] \,,$$

where $t = 0, 1, 2, \ldots$ Moreover, assume that commodity stocks cannot be depleted through accidental destruction, obsolescence, etc., nor augmented by waving a magic wand; then any change in stocks from one period to the next must be the result of an excess of total (new) production over total consumption (depreciation) during the period, or vice versa. Accordingly, for some initial value of stock supply, say $S(0)$, stock supply at time t is given by

$$S(t) = S(0) - \sum_{n=0}^{t-1} x[p(n)],$$

so that the market investment demand function may be written as

$$x^{\iota}(t) = k\{D[p(t)] - S(0) + \sum_{n=0}^{t-1} x[p(r)]\}.$$

Finally, drawing again upon the basic dynamical assumption of Section 3, suppose that changes in price occur in response to the existence of excess market demand, but assume for the sake of simplicity that $p(t)$ is such as to make market demand equal to market supply at the beginning of each period: in symbols,

$$(5.1) \quad x + x' = x[p(t)] + k\{D[p(t)] - S(0) + \sum_{n=0}^{t-1} x[p(n)]\} = 0.$$

This is a dynamical assumption.

A graphical analysis of this model may provide a helpful prelude to the subsequent mathematical treatment. We shall find it convenient to distinguish the function of price, $kD + x$, which we shall call the *market demand function* even though it is not strictly a demand function, involving as it does the flow supply function. Since excess market demand is obtained by subtracting kS from this function, we may accordingly call kS the *market supply function;* note that market supply does not depend on current price but represents a heritage from the past. In Figure 5.1(a) the market demand function is represented by the downward sloping curve, while market supply is represented by various vertical lines. Market *excess* demand at time t is then given by the horizontal distance from the market demand curve to the appropriate market supply line $kS(t)$. Finally, excess flow demand, multiplied by the factor k, in order to obtain the same horizontal scales in both figures, is represented by the curve kx in Figure 5.1(b). This curve indicates for each level of price the net *diminution* of market supply which will occur in any given period.

Now suppose that when $t = 0$, market supply is $kS(0)$. Since net production during the period 0 does not influence the market until the end of the period, price at the outset will be established at $p(0)$, the price at which market demand equals market supply (the market demand curve crosses the market supply line). At this price, however, excess flow demand, $x(0)$, is negative, and net investment will therefore occur during the initial period. Accordingly, at the beginning of period 1 market supply will increase from $kS(0)$ to $kS(1)$ [$= kS(0) - kx(0)$], and price will therefore fall instantaneously to $p(1)$. At this price net investment $(-x(1))$ remains positive, so that at the end of period 1 market supply will rise to $kS(2)$ $[kS(2) = kS(1) - kx(1)]$, price will fall instantaneously to $p(2)$, and so forth. This process will continue indefinitely unless and until price attains a value for which the excess flow demand x is zero; for if this happens market supply will not change over the subsequent period and equilibrium will have been attained. In the present example, a position of *stable* equilibrium will be approached more nearly in each succeeding period; that is to say, there will be a direct, if gradual, movement towards a situation in which market supply is $k\bar{S}$, price is $\bar{p}$, and x and $x + x'$ are both equal to zero. A little experimentation with different curves will show, however, that stability is not inevitable in this model. If the market demand curve

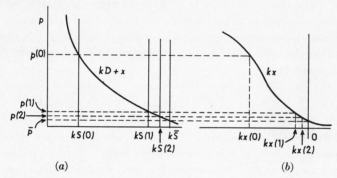

(a)   (b)

Fig. 5.1

were upward sloping, for example, price would move farther away from the equilibrium level in each succeeding period.

It is possible to use graphical methods to obtain a complete picture of price behavior in this model; but this procedure is distinctly pedestrian, and one could never be quite certain that all possibilities had been explored. A nongeometrical investigation is therefore in order.

We begin by expressing equation (5.1) in a form convenient for study. In the neighborhood of some equilibrium price, say $\bar{p}$, the excess flow demand function can be approximated, as in Model I, by the linear function $a(p - \bar{p})$, where a is the value of the derivative dx/dp when $p = \bar{p}$. There is no constant term because $x(\bar{p}) = 0$. Similarly, $D(p)$ may be approximated by the linear expression

$$D(\bar{p}) + b(p - \bar{p}),$$

where b is the value of dD/dp when $p = \bar{p}$. Substituting the above expressions into (5.1), we obtain

$$(5.2) \quad x(t) + x'(t) = a[p(t) - \bar{p}] + kD(\bar{p})$$
$$+ kb[p(t) - \bar{p}] - kS(0) + k\sum_{n=0}^{t-1}a[p(n) - \bar{p}] = 0.$$

Since (5.2) must hold for every value of t, the equation obtained by replacing t by $t + 1$ in (5.2), namely,

$$(5.3) \quad a[p(t + 1) - \bar{p}] + kD(\bar{p}) + kb[p(t + 1) - \bar{p}]$$

$$- kS(0) + k\sum_{n=0}^{t} a[p(n) - \bar{p}] = 0 ,$$

must also be valid. Subtracting the respective members of (5.2) from those of (5.3), one obtains

$$a[p(t + 1) - p(t)] + kb[p(t + 1) - p(t)] + ka[p(t) - \bar{p}] = 0 ;$$

or, upon rearranging terms,

$$(5.4) \quad p(t + 1) - \left(1 - \frac{ka}{a + kb}\right)p(t) = \frac{ka\bar{p}}{a + kb} .$$

This operation, which leads from the equation (5.2) to (5.4), is sometimes called *differencing* the equation; its primary value lies in the fact that certain inessential terms [e.g., $kD(\bar{p})$] are lost in the process. The equation (5.4) will be recognized as a difference equation.

Our next step is to solve the difference equation (5.4), i.e., to find a function $p = p(t)$ which, for some arbitrary initial value of price p_0, satisfies equation (5.4) for $t = 0, 1, 2, \ldots$ and has the further property that $p(0) = p_0$. Such a function is given by

$$(5.5) \quad p(t) = \bar{p} + (p_0 - \bar{p})\left(1 - \frac{ka}{a + kb}\right)^t .$$

For $\bar{p}$ to represent a position of stable equilibrium, it is necessary and sufficient that $p(t) \to \bar{p}$ as $t \to \infty$, irrespective of the value of p_0. This will occur if and only if the quantity raised to the tth power in (5.5) is less than one in absolute value: $|1 - ka/(a + kb)| < 1$. Equivalently,

$$(5.6) \quad 0 < \frac{ka}{a + kb} < 2 .$$

This is the *stability condition* for this model.

The quantity $a + kb$ is merely the slope of the market demand curve (the derivative of the market demand function $x + kD$) at $\bar{p}$; and since we may assume as usual that $k > 0$, the quantity ka, if not quite equal to, at least has the sign of the slope of the excess flow demand curve. Thus the first half of the stability condition (5.6) will be satisfied if and only if these two curves are both downward sloping or both upward sloping. The other half of the stability condition, the assertion that $ka/(a + kb) < 2$, does not allow so simple an interpretation, for it asserts a relation between the *magnitudes* of the two slopes. It is well to observe, however, that for given values of a and b ($a \neq 0$), *both* parts of (5.6) will be satisfied if k is sufficiently small; for $ka/(a + kb)$ is positive when k is small enough to give the denominator the sign of a, and $ka/(a + kb) \to 0$ as $k \to 0$.

The various ways in which price may behave are illustrated in Figure 5.2. Four distinct types of behavior are possible depending on the size and sign of $1 - ka/(a + kb)$. If this quantity is greater than one in absolute value, the market is unstable and the current price will move farther

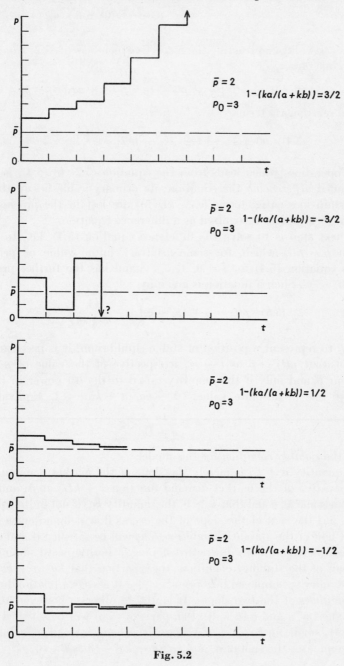

Fig. 5.2

away from the equilibrium price in each succeeding period. If the quantity is less than one in absolute value, the market is stable and the current price will move closer to the equilibrium price in each succeeding period. The mode of approach is "direct" [the quantity $p(t) - \bar{p}$ will have a constant sign] if this quantity is positive, but the path is "oscillatory" [the quantity $p(t) - \bar{p}$ changes sign from one period to the next] if the quantity is negative. In Figure 5.2 specific values have been given to $\bar{p}$, p_0, and

$$1 - \frac{ka}{a + kb}$$

to illustrate the four possibilities.

It should be remembered that these remarks apply literally only to the linearized model, the model obtained by replacing the excess flow demand and stock demand functions by the linear parts of their Taylor series. This linearization is permissible only so long as one wants merely a yes or no answer to the question of stability. The actual nature of the solutions for the nonlinearized model, particularly in the unstable cases, may be represented very imperfectly by Figure 5.2.

EXERCISES

5.1. What is the correct phase space for Model II?

5.2. The derivation of the difference equation (5.4) breaks down if it happens that $a + kb = 0$, since it involves division by this quantity. Assuming that the excess flow demand and stock demand functions are linear, discuss this case both graphically and using equation (5.2).

5.3. If $x(p) = 7 - p$ and $D(p) = 18$, while $k = 3$, find a formula for the solutions of Model II and investigate the stability of equilibrium. Graph a typical solution $p(t)$.

5.4. If $d(p) = 32/p$, $s(p) = 2p$, $D(p) = 1280/p^2$, find the equilibrium values of price and stock demand and determine whether the equilibrium state is stable if (a) $k = 0.0001$, (b) $k = 40$. For what values of k, if any, would this equilibrium be unstable?

5.5 Find verbal interpretations of the conditions for "direct" and "oscillatory" price movements obtained in the text.

6. Model III: Continuous Stock-Flow Systems [Nine–Sec. 7; Ten–Sec. 1–3; Twelve–Sec. 9]. We shall next consider a general isolated stock-flow market in which trading is continuous. As before, we denote excess flow demand by

$$x = x[p(t)]$$

and assume that commodity stocks can be increased only by new production and decreased only by physical consumption. This means that the net change in the stock of the commodity over any time interval is merely the integral over the interval of flow supply minus flow demand, i.e., the integral of the *negative* of excess flow demand. Stock supply as a function of time is therefore given by

$$(6.1) \quad S(t) = S(t_0) - \int_{t_0}^{t} x[p(t)]dt,$$

where t_0 is some initial reference time. Hence, excess stock demand at time t is given by

$$(6.2) \quad X(t) = D[p(t)] - S(t_0) + \int_{t_0}^{t} x[p(t)]dt.$$

Relations (6.1) and (6.2) follow from the definitions and the mild assumption made at the beginning of this paragraph. Our model will now be made into a *dynamical* one by introducing the dynamical assumption

$$(6.3) \quad \frac{dp}{dt} = f(x + x') = f(x + kX),$$

where f is again a function with the property that $f(0) = 0$. This assumption asserts that the "price velocity" dp/dt depends solely on the market excess demand $x + x'$.

For any fixed value $\bar{x} + k\bar{X}$ of market excess demand f can be approximated by the sum of the first three terms of its Taylor series:

$$f(\bar{x} + k\bar{X}) + \alpha(x - \bar{x}) + \alpha k(X - \bar{X}),$$

where α is a constant, namely, the value of the derivative of f with respect to its independent variable, evaluated when the latter is equal to $\bar{x} + k\bar{X}$. The error resulting from the substitution of this linear function for

$$f(x + kX)$$

can be made as small as one wishes by requiring that x and X be sufficiently near $\bar{x}$ and $\bar{X}$, respectively. We shall therefore replace (6.3) by the approximating equation

$$(6.4) \quad \frac{dp}{dt} = f(\bar{x} + k\bar{X}) + \alpha(x - \bar{x}) + \alpha k(X - \bar{X}),$$

and all of our subsequent discussion will apply to this equation. (6.4) can be regarded either as a simplified substitute for, or a local (near $\bar{x}, \bar{X}$) approximation to, the more general dynamical assumption (6.3).

The equation (6.4), as it stands, is still not very tractable, for the presence of the variable X, in view of (6.2), means that (6.4) involves not only a derivative of p (on the left side) but also an *integral* involving p, namely in the term αkX. (6.4) is therefore what is called an *integro-differential equation* for p; it can, however, be made into an ordinary differential equation by differentiating on both sides with respect to t:

$$(6.5) \quad \frac{d^2p}{dt^2} = \alpha\frac{dx}{dt} + \alpha k\frac{dX}{dt}.$$

Since

$$\frac{dx}{dt} = \frac{dx}{dp} \cdot \frac{dp}{dt} \,,$$

while, by (6.2), (see proposition [A] of Chapter Ten, Section 3),

$$\frac{dX}{dt} = \frac{dD}{dp} \cdot \frac{dp}{dt} + x(p) \,,$$

the equation (6.5) may be written

$$(6.6) \quad \frac{d^2p}{dt^2} = \left(\alpha \frac{dx}{dp} + \alpha k \frac{dD}{dp} \right) \frac{dp}{dt} + \alpha k x(p) \,.$$

Now suppose that $\bar{p}$ is a certain equilibrium price. It follows from the basic dynamical assumption that $x(\bar{p}) = 0$. Therefore, if $x(p)$ is expanded in a Taylor series about $\bar{p}$, one has

$$x(p) = a(p - \bar{p}) + [\dots] \,,$$

where a is the value of dx/dp (the slope of the excess flow demand curve) at $\bar{p}$ and $[\dots]$ represents the sum of all the terms involving $(p - \bar{p})$ raised to powers higher than the first. Similarly, the Taylor series about $\bar{p}$ of $D(p)$ may be written

$$D(p) = D(\bar{p}) + b(p - \bar{p}) + [\dots] \,,$$

where b is the value of dD/dp at $\bar{p}$; there is no reason to suppose that

$$D(\bar{p}) = 0 \,.$$

Replacing x and D by their Taylor series in (6.6) gives

$$(6.7) \quad \frac{d^2p}{dt^2} = (\alpha a + \alpha k b) \frac{dp}{dt} + \alpha k a (p - \bar{p}) + [\dots] \,,$$

where now $[\dots]$ is a sum of terms each of which, regarded as a monomial in the variables $p - \bar{p}$ and dp/dt, has a degree of at least two. By the same reasoning as before (Section 4), the solutions of (6.7) near $\bar{p}$ may be replaced by those of the linearized equation

$$(6.8) \quad \frac{d^2p}{dt^2} - (\alpha a + \alpha k b) \frac{dp}{dt} - \alpha k a p = k a \bar{p}$$

for the investigation of stability. If $\bar{p}$ is stable for (6.8), it will also be stable for (6.7), and similarly for instability.[5]

---

[5] This remark does not apply in the case $\alpha a + \alpha k b = 0$, $\alpha k a < 0$, for in this case the solutions of (6.8) are periodic; i.e., the solution curves in the p, dp/dt plane (which is the proper phase space for this model—the p line as a phase space would not give a determinate model) are ellipses, so that equilibrium for (6.8) is unstable. The corresponding solution curves of (6.7), however, may be ellipses or spirals *to* or *from* the equilibrium point, depending on the terms $[\dots]$. Thus, although the equilibrium point in this case is unstable for (6.8), it may be stable or unstable for (6.7). This case is sometimes said to represent "borderline instability."

According to the theory of differential equations (Chapter Twelve, Section 11), $\bar{p}$ is stable if and only if the two roots of the auxiliary equation

$$(6.9) \quad \lambda^2 - \alpha(a + kb)\lambda - \alpha ka = 0$$

have negative real parts. But according to Theorem 7.3, Chapter Eight, this will occur if and only if

$$(6.10) \quad \alpha(a + kb) < 0, \quad \alpha a < 0,$$

on the assumption that $k > 0$. The inequalities (6.10) are therefore the stability conditions for this model.

The adjustment coefficient α, like the coefficient α in Model I, may be either positive or negative. If it is positive, the second condition of (6.10) indicates that for stability the number a, which is the slope of the excess flow demand curve at $\bar{p}$ relative to the price axis, must be negative. This is a condition which we have encountered before. Similarly, the first condition in (6.10) requires that $a + kb$, the slope of the market demand curve at $\bar{p}$, be negative. This may happen even if b is positive. On the other hand, if α is negative, then the excess flow demand and market demand curves must be upward sloping at $\bar{p}$ in order for equilibrium to be stable. The inherent ambiguities in sign involved here indicate that a mere knowledge of market stability under the dynamical assumption (6.3) will not appreciably sharpen the comparative statics results of Example 10.3, Chapter Two.

The nature of the solution $p(t)$ in this model will depend upon the discriminant of the equation (6.9). There are two cases: if

$$\alpha^2(a + kb)^2 + 4\alpha ka \geqslant 0,$$

the roots of the auxiliary equation (6.9) are real and the motions of the system are necessarily direct; but if the discriminant is negative, the roots of the auxiliary equation are complex conjugates and the motions of the system are oscillatory. If the condition for real roots (direct motions) is rewritten in the form

$$\left(\frac{a}{k} + b\right)^2 + \frac{4a}{\alpha k} \geqslant 0,$$

one sees that for given values of a and b ($b \neq 0$), particularly when $a < 0$, the occurrence of direct motions is favored by the occurrence of relatively large values of α and/or k.

Illustrative time paths of price for Model III are shown in Figure 6.1. Curves A and B represent, respectively, unstable direct and unstable oscillatory motions, while curves C and D represent stable direct and stable oscillatory motions. Again it should be emphasized that these curves correspond to the linearized dynamical assumption (6.4); the curves for the nonlinearized equation (6.3), especially in the unstable cases, may be quite different.

In passing, it may be noticed that when $x' \equiv 0$, stocks disappear entirely from the model represented by (6.4) and we again have an isolated flow model. In this case linearization leads directly from (6.4) to the differential equation (4.3) of Model I; thus Model I may be regarded as a special case of Model III, obtainable (say) by putting $k = 0$.

Alternatively, suppose that $x \equiv 0$; i.e., either the commodity is neither produced nor consumed or else the production and consumption of the

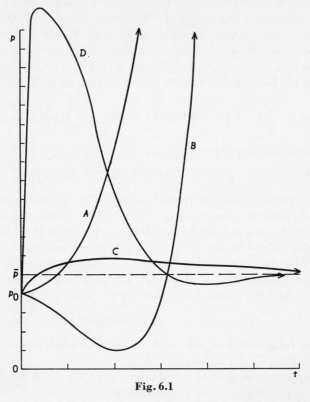

Fig. 6.1

commodity are always equal whatever the price level. This implies that stock supply is a constant S, so that equation (6.4) becomes

$$\frac{dp}{dt} = \alpha k b(p - \bar{p}) ,$$

which represents an isolated stock model and is again equivalent to Model I (cf. the last paragraph of Section 4).

EXERCISES

6.1. Given that $\alpha > 0$ and $b = 0$, state the stability condition for Model III as simply as possible.

6.2. Since Models II and III are both dynamical models of an isolated stock-flow market, there should be some connection between the stability conditions, however tenuous. Discuss their similarities and differences. How do you account for the differences?

6.3. Answer Exercise 5.4 for Model III, assuming that $\alpha = 1$.

6.4. Explain why (as stated in footnote 5) the correct phase space for Model III is the plane in which the co-ordinates are p and dp/dt.

7. *Model IV: Discrete Stock-Flow Systems* [Twelve–Sec. 7]. As a final example of an isolated dynamical model, we shall consider a discrete version of Model III, which may also be regarded as a version of Model II without instantaneous price adjustment. Here again price is assumed to be constant over successive time intervals of unit length, changing, if at all, only at the ends of these intervals. Under these circumstances, investment demand at the beginning of the tth period is given as in Model II by

$$(7.1) \quad kX(t) \equiv k\{D[p(t)] - S(0) + \sum_{n=0}^{t-1} x[p(n)]\} \,.$$

Our dynamical assumption now is that

$$(7.2) \quad p(t+1) - p(t) = f\{x[p(t)] + kX(t)\} \,,$$

where f is a function with the property that $f(0) = 0$, in accordance with the basic dynamical assumption of Section 3. In words, the assumption (7.2) asserts that the amount by which price changes at the end of the tth period is determined by the value of the market excess demand which has prevailed over the period; this is perhaps the simplest discrete analogue of the dynamical assumption of Model III. Precisely as in Section 6, we shall actually consider the model determined by the assumption

$$(7.3) \quad p(t+1) - p(t) = \alpha\{x[p(t)] + kX(t)\} \,,$$

which may be regarded as the result of approximating f in (7.2) by the linear part of its Taylor series about $\bar{x} = 0$, $\bar{X} = 0$.

Now suppose that $\bar{p}$ is an equilibrium price for (7.3). As before, we expand $x(p)$ and $D(p)$ in Taylor series about $\bar{p}$:

$$(7.4) \quad \begin{cases} x(p) = a(p - \bar{p}) + [\ldots] \\ D(p) = D(\bar{p}) + b(p - \bar{p}) + [\ldots] \,. \end{cases}$$

"Differencing" (7.3), i.e., subtracting both sides of (7.3) from the corresponding sides of·the equivalent equation

$$p(t+2) - p(t+1) = \alpha\{x[p(t+1)] + kX(t+1)\}$$

gives

$$(7.5) \quad p(t+2) - 2p(t+1) + p(t) = \alpha\{x[p(t+1)] - x[p(t)]\} \\ + k\alpha\{D[p(t+1)] - D[p(t)] + x[p(t)]\} \,.$$

However, by (7.4),

$$x[p(t+1)] - x[p(t)] = a[p(t+1) - p(t)] + [\ldots]$$

and

$$D[p(t + 1)] - D[p(t)] = b[p(t + 1) - p(t)] + [\ldots] .$$

Making the corresponding substitutions in (7.5) and collecting like terms gives

$$p(t + 2) - (\alpha a + \alpha kb + 2) \, p(t + 1) + (\alpha a + \alpha kb - \alpha ka + 1) \, p(t) =$$
$$- \alpha ka \bar{p} + [\ldots] .$$

Again, we strike off the terms [. . .], on the ground that (except in very special cases) this will have no effect on the stability of $\bar{p}$, and thus obtain

$$(7.6) \quad p(t + 2) - (\alpha a + \alpha kb + 2) \, p(t + 1) + (\alpha a + \alpha kb - \alpha ka + 1) \, p(t) =$$
$$- \alpha ka \bar{p} .$$

This is a second-order difference equation with constant coefficients, and as such is subject to the theory developed in Chapter Twelve. Before proceeding, we point out that (7.6) is a great improvement over (7.3); for not only is it linear but it is also free of the constants $S(0)$, $D(\bar{p})$ and the cumbersome sum appearing in (7.1), all of which are implicitly involved in (7.3). This was the object of the differencing operation.

According to the theory, p is stable for (7.6) if and only if the absolute values of both roots of the characteristic equation

$$\lambda^2 - [\alpha a + \alpha kb + 2]\lambda - [\alpha a + \alpha kb - \alpha ka + 1] = 0$$

are less than 1. This in turn will occur if and only if the following set of inequalities is satisfied:

$$(7.7) \begin{cases} \alpha(a + kb) > \alpha ka - 2 > 2\alpha(a + kb) , \\ \alpha ka > -2 . \end{cases}$$

These inequalities are rather difficult to interpret, for their satisfaction depends on the sizes as well as the signs of all four of the parameters α, k, a, b. This also means that these conditions can have no clear-cut consequences in comparative statics, where α does not appear. It should be noticed that the first condition in (7.7) implies (see Exercise 7.5 which follows) that $\alpha(a + kb) < 0$, which asserts that the market demand curve must be downward sloping if $\alpha > 0$, upward sloping if $\alpha < 0$, if stability is to occur; there is this much of an overlap with the stability conditions (6.10) of Model III. On the other hand, $\alpha ka < 0$ need not be satisfied when the conditions (7.7) hold; the condition on αka is rather that $|\alpha ka| < 2$, i.e., that the contribution of net production to market supply must not be unduly large in any period. This condition will be satisfied, *ceteris paribus*, if k is sufficiently small.

It can be shown that the motions of Model IV, whether stable or unstable, are direct if the roots of the auxiliary equation are real and the root with the larger absolute value is positive. Otherwise the motions will be oscillatory.

From a formal standpoint it is interesting to note that Model IV is identical with the basic model which underlies elementary discussions of "multiplier" and "accelerator" phenomena; and there is clearly more than a formal similarity involved. In effect, the present model provides a market (price adjustment) basis for aggregative models of the "multiplier-accelerator" variety.

To obtain a *discrete flow model* as a special case of Model IV, put $x' \equiv 0$; then equation (7.3) takes the form

$$p(t + 1) - p(t) = \alpha\{x[p(t)]\} ,$$

which, when linearized (there is now nothing to be gained by differencing, for there are no eliminable terms in the equation as it stands), may be written as

$$(7.8) \quad p(t + 1) - p(t) = \alpha a[p(t) - p] .$$

This equation is (except for the values of the coefficients) the same as equation (5.4) for Model II, and it may be solved in the same way. The general solution is

$$p(t) = \bar{p} + (p_0 - \bar{p})(1 + \alpha a)^t ,$$

where $p_0 = p(0)$. For $\bar{p}$ to represent a position of stable equilibrium, therefore, it is necessary and sufficient that $|1 + \alpha a| < 1$; i.e., that $-2 < \alpha a < 0$. Thus stability occurs if α and a have opposite signs and their product is not too far from 0.

A discrete stock model, formally equivalent to the special case of Model IV just analyzed, is obtained if one assumes instead that $x \equiv 0$.

EXERCISES

7.1. Write out a discussion of the discrete stock model mentioned in the last paragraph above.

7.2. Discuss the relative merits of Models II and IV as representations of isolated stock-flow markets in which trading is discontinuous.

7.3. Answer Exercise 5.4 for Model IV, assuming that $\alpha = \frac{1}{2}$.

7.4. The discrete flow model discussed above and Model I are both models intended to depict the dynamics of an isolated flow market. Compare their stability conditions, and explain the presence of the extra condition in the former.

7.5. Derive from the stability conditions (7.7) the following *necessary* conditions for stability in Model IV:

(a) $\alpha(a + kb) < 0$,   (b) $|\alpha ka| < 2$,   (c) $k^2 \alpha b < 2$.

8. Empirical Significance of Isolated Models. Now that we have examined the formal properties of several isolated dynamical models, something should be said about the possible application of such models to practical problems. Broadly speaking, an isolated dynamical model provides a generalized tool for dealing with problems which would normally be handled by partial equilibrium methods. This suggests that in practice the primary function of such models—like that of partial equilibrium models—will be to illustrate basic principles of price determination rather than to provide realistic descriptions of the behavior of actual markets; for the existence in the real world of even a single example of an isolated market is open to serious doubt. However, this does not mean that isolated dynamical models are of purely theoretical interest. Since economics is largely a qualitative science, a thorough grasp of fundamental principles and problems of price determination is of the greatest practical importance if economists are to be in a position to indicate the major implications and limitations of practical policy proposals—and this is, after all, the primary social function of economists at the present time. For such purposes, partial equilibrium analysis (more precisely, comparative statics investigations of partial equilibrium situations) is a powerful tool as far as it goes. The difficulty is that it goes such a very little way. The partial equilibrium method may be applied with good results to the study of isolated stock or flow markets, but, as indicated in Section 10 of Chapter Two, the method yields virtually no results (i.e., it yields no "short-run" results) if applied to the study of stock-flow markets. Yet, excepting markets for labor services, few real-world markets can be found in which a stock-flow commodity is not traded.

To take a concrete example, suppose that we wish to know what effect will follow from reversing a governmental policy of exempting from taxation incomes earned on holdings of municipal bonds. Such a change in policy would evidently have the immediate effect of lowering the demand to hold municipal bonds. However, according to the comparative statics analysis presented in Chapter Two, this will not affect the equilibrium level of municipal bond prices; on the contrary, the end result of such a policy change will be simply a reduction in the quantity of municipal bonds outstanding, with no change in price (and therefore, no change in interest rates). But to say just this is to distort the actual problem beyond recognition; for the short-run destabilizing effects which such a policy might have upon the securities market are left entirely out of account. In order to describe these short-run reactions, recourse must be had to a dynamical stock-flow analysis in terms of which the effects of reduced stock demand upon new municipal issues, and upon the retirement of outstanding issues, can be studied.

Examples of the kind just considered—examples involving problems in international trade, business investment, consumer purchases of durable goods, etc.—can be multiplied indefinitely. In every case it can be shown that unless ordinary partial equilibrium models are discarded in favor of "enlightened intuition"—a substitute of dubious value—or in favor of an explicit dynamical model, one's theoretical conclusions will be warped and misleading; these, in turn, may lead to economic disaster in practice if they should happen to be accepted by the public at large. Of course, this begs and then leaves undecided the delicate question as to how far it is worth while to pursue the analysis of dynamical models, a question to which reasonable people may be expected to give different answers. In the opinion of the authors, such investigations should be carried far beyond the level reached so far in this book, and we shall therefore deal with multiple market systems in the next chapter. However, we shall confine the subsequent discussion to systems which, in our opinion, provide a maximum "enlightenment-to-complexity ratio." We do not aim to obtain formal results for their own sake.

SUGGESTIONS FOR FURTHER READING

Very little has been written about the nature and methods of economic dynamics in general which we would recommend to the reader at this point. For concrete examples of dynamical models in economics, however, see P. A. Samuelson, *Foundations of Economic Analysis* (Cambridge: University Press, 1947), chap. ix; and M. Ezekiel, "The Cobweb Theorem," *Readings in Business Cycle Theory* (Philadelphia: Blakiston Co., 1944). Places in the literature where one can read of dynamical models relating to aggregative economics are cited at the end of Chapter Four.

$$\mathscr{C}hapter \ \mathscr{F}our$$

MACRODYNAMICS II:

MULTIPLE MARKETS

THE models constructed and discussed in Chapter Three all deal with isolated markets—with markets in which the conditions defining market behavior are assumed to be independent of prices in all other markets. Since it is doubtful, however, whether markets of this kind are likely to be found (even well approximated) in practice, it is natural to turn to more "realistic" models in which several interacting markets are considered simultaneously. The underlying concepts are the same here as in previous dynamical models—but there is an inevitable increase in difficulty because of increased technical detail. In order to keep the difficulties produced by these further technicalities within reasonable limits, therefore, we shall deal explicitly only with *pairs* of interacting (but otherwise isolated) markets. This very modest extension may seem to promise little improvement in practical applicability over the isolated market theory of Chapter Three; but the methods used and the results obtained in these two-commodity models are typical in almost every way of those for models involving any number of commodity markets. A consideration of general n-commodity models would be decidedly more difficult but only slightly more illuminating. This point will be further elaborated at the end of the chapter.

1. *Model V: The Continuous Flow or Stock Model* [Eleven–Sec. 1, 2, 3; Twelve–Sec. 10, 11]. First, consider a model involving two interdependent flow markets in which trading is continuous. Denote the price of the ith commodity by $p_i(i = 1$ or $2)$, and its excess flow demand function (which is also the market excess demand function in this case) by x_i as in Chapter Two; and assume, as before, that each excess flow demand is a function of *both* prices: $x_i = x_i(p_1, p_2)$. Our dynamical hypotheses are:

$$(1.1) \quad \frac{dp_i}{dt} = f_i[x_i(p_1, p_2)], \quad (i = 1, 2),$$

where each of the functions f_i has the property

$$f_i(0) = 0.$$

These hypotheses embody the basic dynamical assumption of Chapter Three, Section 3. They also imply that the price velocity dp_i/dt in each market depends directly on the excess flow demand *in that market only*—a condition imposed largely for the sake of simplicity; as concerns the question of plausibility, see Section 3 which follows.

Let us examine the behavior of the system (1.1) near an equilibrium set of prices $(\bar{p}_1,\bar{p}_2)$. In this region (1.1) may be closely approximated by the linearized system

$$(1.2) \quad \frac{dp_i}{dt} = \alpha_i a_{i1}(p_1 - \bar{p}_1) + \alpha_i a_{i2}(p_2 - \bar{p}_2), \quad (i = 1, 2),$$

where α_i is the value of df_i/dx_i when $x_i = 0$, and a_{ij} is the value of $\partial x_i/\partial p_j$ when both prices have their equilibrium values. This follows from a consideration of the Taylor series expansions for f_i and x_i:

$$f_i(x_i) = \alpha_i x_i + [\ldots]$$
$$x_i(p_1,p_2) = a_{i1}(p_1 - \bar{p}_1) + a_{i2}(p_2 - \bar{p}_2) + [\ldots].$$

Moreover, if one introduces the new variables $P_i = p_i - \bar{p}_i$, (1.2) can be written in the temporarily more convenient form

$$(1.3) \quad \frac{dP_i}{dt} = \alpha_i a_{i1}P_1 + \alpha_i a_{i2}P_2.$$

(Note that $dP_i/dt = dp_i/dt$, since $\bar{p}_i$ is a constant.) This is a system of first-order linear differential equations of precisely the kind discussed in Chapter Twelve, Sections 10 and 11; so using the theory developed there, we may at once say that the equilibrium point represented by $P_1 = 0$, $P_2 = 0$ (i.e., $p_1 = \bar{p}_1$, $p_2 = \bar{p}_2$) is stable if and only if the roots of the equation

$$(1.4) \quad \lambda^2 - (\alpha_1 a_{11} + \alpha_2 a_{22})\lambda + \alpha_1\alpha_2(a_{11}a_{22} - a_{12}a_{21}) = 0$$

have negative real parts. This is a necessary and sufficient condition for the stability of the equilibrium point $(\bar{p}_1,\bar{p}_2)$ in the linearized model; and since the quadratic equation (1.4) always can be solved explicitly, this criterion is completely satisfactory for any specific model involving just two commodities. When the number of commodities is larger than two, however, the auxiliary equation—the equation corresponding to (1.4)—is difficult to manage and may be practically impossible to solve explicitly and exactly. An alternative to this criterion which generalizes more smoothly to the case of more than two commodities is provided by Theorem 11.3, Chapter Twelve, which states that the equation (1.4) has only roots with negative real parts if the quadratic form

$$\Sigma_{ij}\alpha_i a_{ij}u_iu_j = \alpha_1 a_{11}u_1{}^2 + (\alpha_1 a_{12} + \alpha_2 a_{21})u_1u_2 + \alpha_2 a_{22}u_2{}^2$$

is negative definite; it should be emphasized that this is only a *sufficient* condition for stability. Moreover, since one can use the criterion for determining whether or not a given quadratic form with real coefficients is negative definite (Chapter Eleven, Theorem 7.3), this provides a stability condition which actually can be worked out for any specific model irrespective of the number of commodities. Unfortunately, however, stability may occur even though the quadratic form is not negative definite; the condition is not *necessary*. A further shortcoming of these conditions for stability is that it is in general difficult to extract their economic meaning—we can say little more than that the negative definiteness of the quadratic form generalizes the (economically plausible) condition encountered in the corresponding one-commodity model that the price setter estimates correctly whether the excess demand curve is downward or upward sloping. For the sake of definiteness, however, we shall assume henceforth that *all adjustment coefficients are positive*, and make use of this supposition whenever doing so enables us to simplify conclusions or clarify interpretations. The meaning of this assumption is that price velocities are increasing functions of excess demands, at least in a neighborhood of equilibrium; this is probably a fairly common thing in practice. In any case, whenever it is necessary to allow for the possibility that some adjustment coefficients may be negative, the appropriate conclusions can be obtained by allowing for changes in sign at the proper places in the conclusions which we shall describe.

EXERCISES

1.1. In Model V, assuming that $x_1(p_1,p_2) = -2p_1 + p_2 + 4$ and $x_2(p_1,p_2) = 20p_1 - p_2{}^2 + 56$, first find the equilibrium point and then determine whether it is stable or unstable under each of the following sets of further assumptions:

a) $\alpha_1 = 12$, $\alpha_2 = 1$.

b) $f_1(x_1) = 4x_1 + x_1{}^3$, $f_2(x_2) = x_2(x_2 - 1)$.

c) $\alpha_1 = \alpha_2 = \alpha$, where α is any positive number.

1.2. Set up the generalization of Model V in which the functions f_i ($i = 1$ or 2) are allowed to depend on *both* excess flow demands; assume that $f_i(0,0) = 0$ and carry your analysis at least far enough to obtain the auxiliary equation corresponding to (1.4). How do your results differ from those obtained for Model V in the text?

2. Model V: Further Observations. In the special case of two commodities it is a fairly simple matter to arrive at satisfactory conclusions about the economic significance of the relevant stability conditions. Acknowledging in advance that these conclusions cannot be extended to the general n-commodity model without considerable difficulty and qualification, we may still find it instructive to see what these conclusions are and how they may be obtained.

We first recall that stability of equilibrium in the linearized Model V represented by the equations (1.2) (and therefore, except for a few improbable cases, in the original nonlinearized model) will occur if and only if both of the roots of the equation (1.4) have negative real parts. What are the economic implications of this condition?

By Theorem 7.3 of Chapter Eight, we know that (1.4) will have roots with negative real parts if and only if

$$(2.1) \quad \alpha_1 a_{11} + \alpha_2 a_{22} < 0,$$
$$(2.2) \quad \alpha_1 \alpha_2 (a_{11}a_{22} - a_{12}a_{21}) > 0.$$

Unfortunately, these conditions (especially [2.1]) involve the adjustment coefficients α_1 and α_2 in a serious way, so that in any specific model it is necessary to take into account not only their signs (as in Chapter Three, Section 4) but also their actual values in order to test the equilibrium point for stability. It would be better if one could obtain conditions more or less equivalent to (2.1)–(2.2) but which did not involve adjustment coefficients in an essential way; for this would make it possible to decide whether or not the equilibrium is stable by simply inspecting the excess flow demand functions x_i. But this is not possible, for no matter what the excess demand functions may be, the inequalities (2.1) and (2.2) can be made either true or false by assigning appropriately chosen values to the adjustment coefficients. In other words, with given excess flow demand functions there will always be some values of the adjustment coefficients for which an equilibrium state is stable and other values for which it is unstable. In a weaker form, however, the problem can be solved. Without further preliminary remarks:

If the adjustment coefficients α_1 and α_2 are both positive, and if $a_{12}a_{21} \geqslant 0$, then the pair of conditions

$$(2.3) \quad a_{11} < 0, \quad a_{22} < 0,$$
$$(2.4) \quad a_{11}a_{22} - a_{12}a_{21} > 0,$$

is equivalent to the pair of conditions (2.1)–(2.2).

Proof. If α_1 and α_2 are both positive, (2.3) clearly implies (2.1), while (2.4) and (2.2) imply each other. We must show, then, that under the stated assumptions (2.1) and (2.2) together imply (2.3). By (2.1), at least one of the numbers a_{11} and a_{22} must be negative, since the adjustment coefficients are assumed to be positive; but if only *one* were negative, then $a_{11}a_{22} - a_{12}a_{21}$, being the sum of the two nonpositive terms $a_{11}a_{22}$ and $-a_{12}a_{21}$, could not be positive, and the condition (2.2) would be contradicted; i.e., (2.3) must be true.

The various conditions in this theorem can be given economic interpretations without difficulty. The positivity of the adjustment coefficients has already been discussed. The condition (2.3) is highly plausible, since it asserts that (at the point of equilibrium) each of the excess demand functions x_i is a decreasing function of the corresponding price, the other price being held fixed.

The other conditions involve the numbers a_{12} and a_{21}, which (reflecting as they do the interaction of markets) do not occur in any one-commodity models and therefore require closer attention at this, their initial appearance. If (for instance) $a_{12} > 0$, then a rise in p_2 (p_1 being kept fixed) will result in a rise in the excess demand for commodity 1. This would seem to indicate that commodity 1 is, in a certain sense,[1] a *substitute* for commodity 2. Similarly, if $a_{12} < 0$, a rise in p_2 will lead to a fall in the excess demand for commodity 1, so that commodity 1 is, in an analogous sense, a *complement* to commodity 2. The condition that $a_{12}a_{21} \geqq 0$, i.e., that either these two numbers have the same sign or at least one of them is zero, is therefore equivalent to the assumption that the two relations of being a substitute and being a complement are partially symmetrical; if commodity 1 is a substitute (in this special sense) for commodity 2, then commodity 2 is not a complement to commodity 1, etc. This, too, appears to be a reasonable assumption, although, as will be seen in Chapter Five, it does not necessarily follow from the usual assumptions in the theory of consumer behavior.

EXERCISES

2.1. Notice that the conditions (2.3)–(2.4), etc., are satisfied by the specific model in part (*a*) of Exercise 1.1. Write out an interpretation of the data of this model, giving particular attention to the meaning of the signs of the coefficients a_{ij}, the fact that α_1 is much larger than α_2, etc.

2.2. Briefly paraphrase the analysis of Section 1 and the first part of Section 2 so as to obtain an analysis of the "stock" version of Model V, as outlined at the end of Section 2. Then apply this analysis to the problem of determining the equilibrium point and deciding whether or not it is stable for the specific model in which

$$k_1 = \tfrac{1}{2} , \quad k_2 = 2 , \quad S_1 = 400 , \quad S_2 = 240 , \quad \alpha_1 = \alpha_2 = \tfrac{1}{2} ,$$

and

$$D_1(p_1,p_2) = 500 - 38p_1 + 3p_2 , \quad D_2(p_1,p_2) = 6{,}000 - 1{,}050p_1 - 170p_2 .$$

3. *Dynamical Dependence.*   Given a system like that represented by Model V, it is natural to ask: What is the effect of assuming that the time rate of change of price in one market depends on excess demands in *other* markets as well as upon excess demand in the given market? Indeed, the reader has been asked just this question in Exercise 1.2. Before proceeding to more complex models, however, we shall do well to settle this question once and for all.

As a rule, of course, one thinks of price in a given market as being dynamically dependent upon conditions in other markets, but only *via* the effect of these conditions upon excess demand in the given market. The assumption just suggested, however, posits the *direct* dynamical depend-

---

[1] This is not the usual sense, for we are dealing here with *excess* demands and with combined "substitution" and "income" effects, while in the usual sense one deals with the demand functions proper and with "substitution" effects only. Cf. Chapter Five, Section 6.

ence of markets. If this assumption is used to obtain a more general version of Model V, therefore, equation (1.1) gives way to

$$(3.1) \quad \frac{dp_i}{dt} = f\left[x_1(p_1,p_2),x_2(p_1,p_2)\right], \quad (i = 1, 2),$$

where $f_i(0,0) = 0$. The linearized version of (3.1) corresponding to (1.2) is then

$$(3.2) \quad \frac{dp_i}{dt} = \alpha_{i1}a_{11}(p_1 - \bar{p}_1) + \alpha_{i1}a_{12}(p_2 - \bar{p}_2) + \alpha_{i2}a_{21}(p_1 - \bar{p}_1) + \alpha_{i2}a_{22}(p_2 - \bar{p}_2),$$

where α_{ij} is the value of $\partial f_i/\partial x_j$ when both excess flow demands are zero.

Comparing equations (3.2) with equations (1.2), we see that both systems have the same over-all form, although the coefficients of $(p_1 - \bar{p}_1)$ and $(p_2 - \bar{p}_2)$ in (3.2) are more complicated. With suitable modifications, therefore, the preceding discussion of (1.2) can be applied to the present situation. In particular, the equilibrium state $(\bar{p}_1,\bar{p}_2)$ will be stable for (3.2) if the quadratic form

$$\Sigma_{ij}(\alpha_{i1}a_{1j} + \alpha_{i2}a_{2j})u_iu_j$$

is negative definite. However, in contrast to Model V (which involved the simpler stability condition that $\Sigma_{ij}\alpha_i a_{ij}u_iu_j$ be negative definite), it is not possible to express the economic implications of this condition in any simple way. While our original question is answered from a mathematical standpoint, therefore, the answer is hardly illuminating from a practical point of view. Before becoming discouraged by this fact, however, one should notice that the original hypotheses (3.1) lead directly to some unusual implications: specifically, price in a market may be changing over time even though supply is equal to demand in that market. In common-sense terms, this amounts to saying that one price setter may, on the basis of price changes in other markets, anticipate future changes in excess demand in his own market and act in advance, adjusting price in a way calculated to offset the anticipated changes. It would thus be wrong to exclude the possibility of the kind of price behavior described; it is senseless to argue that price in one market can vary *only* in response to changes in excess demand in that market. To estimate the empirical validity of the assumption of direct dynamical dependence it would be necessary to test (in this instance) the relative merits of the models represented by (1.1) and (3.1) against observations of real market phenomena; more specifically, one could assume the equations (3.2) and then attempt to evaluate the adjustment coefficients α_{ij}, and the amount of dynamical dependence could be judged to be significant or not according as the coefficients α_{12} and α_{21}, compared with the coefficients α_{11} and α_{22}, were or were not of a significant size. The delicacy of this task is more easily imagined than described.

Meanwhile, we may be content with the discovery that the model arising from (3.1) is formally the same as, though in details more complicated than, that arising from (1.1); for the same remarks can be shown to apply *mutatis mutandis* to subsequent models considered in this chapter. Accordingly, we shall henceforth exclude assumptions of direct dynamical dependence, assuming rather that all markets considered are *dynamically independent*.

EXERCISES

3.1. Discuss the effect of the assumption of dynamical dependence on equilibrium conditions.

3.2. Under what market conditions would you expect dynamical dependence to be especially pronounced? On general intuitive grounds would you expect a high degree of dynamical dependence to be conducive or inimical to market stability?

4. Model VI: The Discrete Stock-Flow Model with Instantaneous Price Adjustment [Twelve–Sec. 6]. Postponing further consideration of continuous models to a later section, we turn now to a discussion of multiple-market dynamical systems in which trading is discontinuous. The first model in this category will be that corresponding to Model II (Chapter Three, Section 5), but now covering the two-commodity case, which, as usual, may be taken as representative of the general n-commodity case. As in Model II, it is assumed that price in each market depends only upon *current* excess demand in that market, and that price adjustments occur instantaneously. More precisely, the model is governed by the equations

$$(4.1)\quad x_i[p_1(t),p_2(t)] + k_i\{D_i[p_1(t),p_2(t)] - S_i{}^0 + \sum_{n=0}^{t-1} x_i[p_1(n),p_2(n)]\} = 0 ,$$

$(i = 1, 2; t = 1, 2, \ldots)$, where D_i and x_i are, respectively, the stock demand and excess flow demand functions for commodity i, and $S_i{}^0$ is the stock supply of commodity i at the instant $t = 0$. This equation expresses the assumption that $p_1(t)$ and $p_2(t)$ assume values which make market

demand, $k_iD_i + x_i$, equal to market supply, $k_i\left\{S_i{}^0 - \sum_{n=0}^{t-1} x_i[p_1(n),p_2(n)]\right\}$, at

the beginning of each period. (Cf. equation [5.1], Chapter Three.) In order to arrive at stability conditions, we first difference the equations (4.1) by replacing t by $t + 1$ and subtracting, as before; this gives

$$(4.2)\quad x_i[p_1(t+1),p_2(t+1)] - x_i[p_1(t),p_2(t)] + k_iD_i[p_1(t+1),p_2(t+1)]$$
$$- k_iD_i[p_1(t),p_2(t)] + k_ix_i[p_1(t),p_2(t)] = 0 .$$

The meaning of this equation is that each price is determined at the end of any given period in such a way that market demand prevailing over the next period is equalized with the market demand prevailing over the given period plus the net change in stock supply over the period.

The next step is to linearize the equations (4.2) by replacing the stock demand and excess flow demand functions by the linear parts of their Taylor series about some pair of equilibrium prices $(\bar{p}_1,\bar{p}_2)$:

$$D_i = D_i(\bar{p}_1, \bar{p}_2) + b_{i1}(p_1 - \bar{p}_1) + b_{i2}(p_2 - \bar{p}_2) + \dots,$$
$$x_i = a_{i1}(p_1 - \bar{p}_1) + a_{i2}(p_2 - \bar{p}_2) + \dots.$$

This substitution yields the linearized equations:

$$(4.3) \quad a_{i1}p_1(t + 1) + a_{i2}p_2(t + 1) - a_{i1}p_1(t) - a_{i2}p_2(t) +$$
$$+ k_ib_{i1}p_1(t + 1) + k_ib_{i2}p_2(t + 1) - k_i(a_{i1} + b_{i1})p_1(t)$$
$$- k_i(a_{i2} + b_{i2})p_2(t) + k_ia_{i1}\bar{p}_1 + k_ia_{i2}\bar{p}_2 = 0 \quad (i = 1, 2).$$

This is a system of two linear first-order difference equations, and we know from Chapter Twelve, Section 7, that the equilibrium point $(\bar{p}_1, \bar{p}_2)$ will be stable if and only if the roots of the characteristic equation, which in this case is

$$(4.4) \quad \begin{vmatrix} A_{11} & A_{12} \\ A_{21} & A_{22} \end{vmatrix} = 0,$$

where $A_{ij} = k_i(a_{ij} + b_{ij}) - (a_{ij} + k_ib_{ij})\lambda$, are both less than 1 in absolute value. Here again, as in Model II, it appears that the stability condition depends on the numbers a_{ij}, b_{ij}, and k_i only; this was inevitable, for these are the only parameters in the linearized model. In particular, there are no adjustment coefficients because the assumption of instantaneous adjustment circumvents the point at which adjustment coefficients might have entered the model.

In the two-commodity model, the characteristic equation (4.4) is merely a quadratic equation for λ, so it can be explicitly solved by means of the familiar formula for such equations. But even in this especially favorable case the precise manner in which the roots depend on the parameters a_{ij}, b_{ij}, and k_i is very intricate, so that alternative stability conditions—preferably those admitting a direct economic interpretation—are not easy to come by. In the corresponding n-commodity model the outlook is even more bleak.

It is a mere exercise, albeit a complicated one, to formulate and analyze the multiple-market analogue of Model III (Chapter Three), where trading is again assumed to be discontinuous but price adjustment is not instantaneous. In form, the stability conditions would closely resemble those obtained for Model III; but since the stability conditions in Model III are already fairly complicated, there is little to be gained by making a general investigation of the n-commodity analogue of that model.[2]

EXERCISES

4.1. State the postulates of the two-commodity analogue of Model III, making the assumption of dynamical independence.

---

[2] One may analyze discrete systems by methods which are more powerful than those considered above (cf. P. A. Samuelson, *Foundations of Economic Analysis* [Cambridge: Harvard University Press, 1947], pp. 435–37); but the study of these methods is too specialized a topic, and too replete with mathematical complications, to be undertaken here.

4.2. Justify in detail the statement just following equations (4.2) in the text. To what extent, or in what sense, do (4.1) and (4.2) say the same thing?

4.3. In a certain specific instance of Model VI, stock and excess flow demand functions are as given below. Assuming that $k_1 = k_2 = 2$, determine whether the equilibrium state is stable.

$$D_1 = 20 - p_1 + p_2$$
$$D_2 = 100 - p_1 - 9p_2$$
$$x_1 = p_2 - p_1$$
$$x_2 = 1 + p_1 - 2p_2$$

5. Model VII: The Continuous Stock-Flow Model (Definition and Equilibrium Conditions).

We conclude our investigation of general dynamical models of market behavior by considering a system comprising two interdependent stock-flow markets in which trading is continuous. As before, stock demand for the commodity $i(i = 1$ or $2)$ will be denoted by $D_i(p_1,p_2)$, and excess flow demand for that commodity by $x_i(p_1,p_2)$. If the possibility of loss of commodity stocks through accidental destruction, obsolescence, etc., is ruled out, the stock supply of the commodity at the time t is given by

$$(5.1) \quad S_i(t) = S_i^0 - \int_{t_0}^t x_i dt \,,$$

where $S_i^0 = S_i(t_0)$, t_0 being some suitable initial value of t. Investment demand for the commodity i is then given by

$$(5.2) \quad k_i X_i(p_1,p_2,t) = k_i D_i(p_1,p_2) - k_i S_i(t) \,.$$

Our dynamical hypotheses for this model are embodied in the differential equations

$$(5.3) \quad \frac{dp_i}{dt} = f_i(x_i + k_i X_i) \,,$$

where (in line with the basic assumption of Chapter Three, Section 3) we assume that $f_i(u) = 0$ if and only if $u = 0$. We shall also assume that the derivative of each function f_i is positive; or, in other words, that for any fixed value of excess flow or investment demand for the commodity i, an increase in the other component of market demand will produce an increase in the corresponding price velocity dp_i/dt. This implies that the market adjustment coefficients in the model are positive; for the adjustment coefficients are precisely the values of these derivatives at an equilibrium point. It should be noticed that $f_i = 0$ implies directly $x_i + k_i X_i = 0$, but not $x_i = k_i X_i = 0$; hence we are not immediately able to say that the conditions

$$x_i = 0 \,, \quad X_i = 0 \,, \quad (i = 1, 2)$$

are necessary for equilibrium, although we shall see presently that such is the case.

We now denote by $\bar{x}_i$ and $\bar{X}_i$ equilibrium values of the variables x_i and X_i, and proceed to linearize the equations (5.3) in a neighborhood of these values. This gives first

$$(5.4) \quad \frac{dp_i}{dt} = \alpha_i[(x - \bar{x}_i) + k_i(X_i - \bar{X}_i)] \quad (i = 1, 2),$$

where α_i is the derivative of f_i with respect to $x_i + k_iX_i$ at $(\bar{x}_i, \bar{X}_i)$. By hypothesis, moreover,

$$(5.5) \quad \alpha_i > 0.$$

Strictly speaking, (5.4) is only a *partially* linearized form of (5.3)— "partially" because x_i and X_i themselves have not yet been linearized as functions of p_1 and p_2. However, a close connection between X_i and x_i is expressed by the equations (5.1) and (5.2), and the use of this fact enables us to complete the linearization of (5.4) in a satisfactory way. Differentiating both sides of (5.1) and (5.2) with respect to t (using the chain rule), and then eliminating dS_i/dt gives the equation

$$(5.6) \quad \frac{dX_i}{dt} = \frac{\partial D_i}{\partial p_1} \frac{dp_1}{dt} + \frac{\partial D_i}{\partial p_2} \frac{dp_2}{dt} + x_i.$$

At the same time, differentiating (5.4) with respect to t gives

$$(5.7) \quad \frac{d^2p_i}{dt^2} = \alpha_i\left(\frac{dx_i}{dt} + k_i\frac{dX_i}{dt}\right),$$

and using (5.6) to eliminate dX_i/dt from (5.7) gives

$$(5.8) \quad \frac{d^2p_i}{dt^2} = \alpha_i\left[\frac{dx_i}{dt} + k_i\left(\frac{\partial D_i}{\partial p_1}\frac{dp_1}{dt} + \frac{\partial D_i}{\partial p_2}\frac{dp_2}{dt} + x_i\right)\right].$$

Superficially, it would seem doubtful that (5.8) is an improvement over (5.4): the order of the differential equations has been raised from one to two, the right members are more cumbrous, some partial derivatives have appeared, etc. But these are negligible disadvantages compared with the advantage that the functions X_i do not appear in (5.8), so that the equations (5.8) can be written out explicitly as soon as the functions x_i and D_i and the adjustment coefficients are given.

The differential equations are still not linear, but we are already able to determine the equilibrium conditions. In order for $(\bar{p}_1, \bar{p}_2)$ to be equilibrium prices in this model, it must happen that $dp_i/dt = 0$ and $d^2p_i/dt^2 = 0$ when $p_1 = \bar{p}_1$ and $p_2 = \bar{p}_2$. This condition is both necessary and sufficient for equilibrium. It is necessary, for if $\bar{p}_1$ and $\bar{p}_2$ are equilibrium prices, once p_1 and p_2 somehow attain these values they must maintain them, are therefore constant, and so have all derivatives with respect to time, and in particular the first two, equal to zero. On the other hand, the condition is sufficient; for if $dp_i/dt = 0$ and $d^2p_i/dt^2 = 0$ when $p_1 = \bar{p}_1$ and $p_2 = \bar{p}_2$, all higher derivatives of p_i (which may be computed by differentiating

[5.8] a suitable number of times) will also be zero, and the corresponding solution must be a constant—i.e., an equilibrium solution.

Now when $p_1 = \bar{p}_1$ and $p_2 = \bar{p}_2$, while $dp_i/dt = d^2p_i/dt^2 = 0$, the equations (5.8) reduce to

$$\alpha_i k_i \bar{x}_i = 0 ,$$

which, because of (5.5) ($k_i > 0$ in every instance) is equivalent to

$$(5.9) \quad \bar{x}_i = 0 .$$

This is therefore a necessary condition for equilibrium. This implies, moreover, that

$$(5.10) \quad \bar{X}_i = 0$$

is also necessary for equilibrium; for $f_i = 0$ is obviously necessary for equilibrium (cf. [5.3]), and since $f_i(0) = 0$, it follows from the requirement $x_i + k_i X_i = 0$ that the *only* value of $\bar{X}_i$ that together with (5.9) will allow equilibrium to occur is zero. On the other hand, it is easy to see that the conditions (5.9) and (5.10) are sufficient for equilibrium, for (according to equations [5.4] and [5.8]) when these conditions are satisfied both dp_i/dt and d^2p_i/dt^2 are zero. We may therefore say that the four equations

$$(5.11) \quad x_i = 0 , \quad X_i = 0 , \quad (i = 1, 2) ,$$

viewed as equations to be solved for the equilibrium prices $\bar{p}_1$ and $\bar{p}_2$, are the equilibrium conditions for this model.

At first sight, the equilibrium conditions (5.11) may seem to "overdetermine" equilibrium, for there are twice as many equations as unknowns, and this normally (though not always; cf. Chapter Eight, Section 6) means that the system is inconsistent: *two* equations normally suffice to determine the values of two unknowns.

But this apparent difficulty dissolves under closer scrutiny. Suppose, for instance, that the prices $\bar{p}_1$ and $\bar{p}_2$ are such that $x_1 = x_2 = 0$, but at least one of the excess stock demands X_i is different from zero at a certain instant. Then not both of the functions f_i can be zero (for when $x_i = 0$, f_i equals zero if and only if $X_i = 0$), so that, by (5.3), at least one of the prices p_i will be changing at that instant. This shows that the prices $\bar{p}_1, \bar{p}_2$ certainly do not represent equilibrium. Whether or not the moving prices determined by these initial prices (and their velocities at the initial instant) will eventually approach equilibrium is another question, whose answer depends upon stability considerations. Similarly, if the prices $\bar{p}_1$ and $\bar{p}_2$ cause both X_1 and X_2 to vanish at a certain instant, while at least one of the numbers $x_i(\bar{p}_1,\bar{p}_2)$ is different from zero, then at least one of the functions f_i has a nonzero value for those prices at that instant, so that there cannot be equilibrium.

Briefly, the conditions (5.12) do not "overdetermine" equilibrium because the conditions $X_i = 0$ involve not only prices but also t [via stock supply, $S_i(t)$]; and if, at a certain instant, a given set of prices does not satisfy all four conditions, it may at some other instant. But prices determined by any pair of equations chosen from (5.12) which do not also satisfy the other two equations will not persist.

Now we shall complete the linearization of the differential equations in order to clear the ground for a study of stability in this model. Suppose that $(\bar{p}_1, \bar{p}_2)$ is a pair of equilibrium prices, and that the Taylor series of the functions x_i and D_i are written as in Section 4:

$$D_i = D_i(\bar{p}_1, \bar{p}_2) + b_{i1}(p_1 - \bar{p}_1) + b_{i2}(p_2 - \bar{p}_2) + [\ldots],$$
$$x_i = a_{i1}(p_1 - \bar{p}_1) + a_{i2}(p_2 - \bar{p}_2) + [\ldots].$$

Since we are dealing with an equilibrium point, the omission of the constant term in the Taylor series for x_i is justified—it is zero by (5.9). Differentiation of these equations gives

$$\frac{\partial D_i}{\partial p_j} = b_{ij} + \{\ldots\},$$
$$\frac{dx_i}{dt} = a_{i1}\frac{dp_1}{dt} + a_{i2}\frac{dp_2}{dt} + [\ldots],$$

where $\{\ldots\}$ stands for terms of *first* and higher degrees in the variables $p_1 - \bar{p}_1, p_2 - \bar{p}_2$, and $[\ldots]$ stands for the terms of *second* degree and higher in the four variables

$$(5.12) \quad p_1 - \bar{p}_1, \quad p_2 - \bar{p}_2, \quad \frac{dp_1}{dt}, \quad \frac{dp_2}{dt}.$$

Substituting the above Taylor series into (5.8) and omitting all nonlinear terms, i.e., all terms whose degree in the four variables (5.12) is greater than 1, gives finally

$$(5.13) \quad \frac{d^2p_i}{dt^2} = \alpha_i k_i a_{i1}(p_1 - \bar{p}_1) + \alpha_i k_i a_{i2}(p_2 - \bar{p}_2)$$
$$+ (\alpha_i a_{i1} + \alpha_i k_i b_{i1})\frac{dp_1}{dt} + (\alpha_i a_{i2} + \alpha_i k_i b_{i2})\frac{dp_2}{dt}.$$

The two equations represented by (5.13) are the fully linearized differential equations for this model, and for purposes of stability theory may be regarded as equivalent to the basic dynamical hypothesis (5.3) in some neighborhood of the equilibrium state.

It will be expedient, however, to carry the simplification a bit further. If the variables P_i and Q_i and the constants A_{ij} and B_{ij} are defined by the equations

$$P_i = p_i - \bar{p}_i,$$
$$Q_i = \frac{dP_i}{dt},$$
$$A_{ij} = \alpha_i k_i a_{ij},$$
$$B_{ij} = \alpha_i(a_{ij} + k_i b_{ij}),$$

then (5.13) is equivalent to the system

$$(5.14) \begin{cases} \dfrac{dP_i}{dt} = Q_i \\[2mm] \dfrac{dQ_i}{dt} = A_{i1}P_1 + A_{i2}P_2 + B_{i1}Q_1 + B_{i2}Q_2, \quad (i = 1, 2) . \end{cases}$$

This is a system of four first-order differential equations; the equilibrium point (in view of the previous definitions and remarks) is that at which the four quantities P_i, Q_i all equal zero. We now turn to the investigation of the stability of this equilibrium point.

EXERCISES

5.1. The coefficient $\alpha_i k_i$, which we may denote by β_i, occurs in equations (5.4), (5.8), (5.13), and elsewhere. Find an economic interpretation for this coefficient. What would be a good name for β_i?

5.2. Given the demand functions and investment coefficients of Exercise 4.3, and given that $\alpha_1 = 0.01$, $\alpha_2 = 4.5$, find the constants A_{ij} and B_{ij} defined above.

5.3. For what phase space is the linearized Model VII, as represented by the equations (5.14), determinate?

6. Model VII: Derivation of Stability Conditions [Eleven–Sec. 4, 5, 6]. We are dealing now with the system of first-order differential equations (5.14). According to the account given in Chapter Twelve, the equilibrium point $P_1 = P_2 = Q_1 = Q_2 = 0$ will be stable if and only if all of the roots of the characteristic equation

$$(6.1) \quad \begin{vmatrix} -\lambda & 0 & 1 & 0 \\ 0 & -\lambda & 0 & 1 \\ A_{11} & A_{12} & B_{11} - \lambda & B_{12} \\ A_{21} & A_{22} & B_{21} & B_{22} - \lambda \end{vmatrix} = 0$$

have negative real parts. This is a fourth-degree polynomial equation; and although there do exist formulas for solving such equations,[3] these formulas shed little or no light on the question of what simple conditions the coefficients A_{ij} and B_{ij} may be required to satisfy in order to guarantee stability, and such light as they do shed does not illuminate the n-commodity case. We shall therefore approach the matter indirectly, obtaining some *sufficient* conditions for stability which do not depend upon the possibility of solving (6.1) explicitly. Their economic interpretation will be discussed later.

We shall use the notations

$$A(u) = \Sigma_{ij}A_{ij}u_iu_j, \quad B(u) = \Sigma_{ij}B_{ij}u_iu_j .$$

The stability conditions will involve the symmetry and negative definiteness of these quadratic forms.

---

[3] See Burnside and Panton, *Theory of Equations* (Dublin: Hodges, Figgis, & Co., 1918), Vol. I, chap. vi.

Furthermore, it is a routine matter to verify that the equation (6.1) is the same as the equation

$$(6.2) \quad \begin{vmatrix} \lambda^2 - B_{11}\lambda - A_{11} & -B_{12}\lambda - A_{12} \\ -B_{21}\lambda - A_{21} & \lambda^2 - B_{22}\lambda - A_{22} \end{vmatrix} = 0$$

—by expanding both determinants and comparing the resulting equations, if in no other way. The form (6.2) will be more convenient for our purposes.

Now let λ be a *real* root of (6.2). This implies (cf. Chapter Eleven, Theorem 6.3) that there exists a (real) solution (x_1, x_2) of the equations

$$(6.3) \quad \begin{cases} (\lambda^2 - B_{11}\lambda - A_{11})x_1 + (-B_{12}\lambda - A_{12})x_2 = 0, \\ (-B_{21}\lambda - A_{21})x_1 + (\lambda^2 - B_{22}\lambda - A_{22})x_2 = 0, \end{cases}$$

where at least one of the numbers x_i is not zero. If the first of these equations is multiplied on both sides by x_1, the second by x_2, and the results are added, one obtains

$$(6.4) \quad (x_1^2 + x_2^2)\lambda^2 - B(x)\lambda - A(x) = 0.$$

Now if $A(u)$ and $B(u)$ are both negative definite quadratic forms, all of the coefficients in (6.4) are positive. However, any real root of a quadratic equation whose coefficients are all positive must be negative (by Theorem 7.2, Chapter Eight). It follows that λ, being by assumption a real root of (6.2) and therefore of (6.4), is negative. This proves the theorem:

Theorem 6.1.   If $A(u)$ and $B(u)$ are both negative definite, every real root of (6.1) is negative.

Corollary 6.1.   If $A(u)$ and $B(u)$ are both negative definite, and all roots of the characteristic equation (6.1) are real, the equilibrium point is stable.

The same approach yields corresponding conditions for complex roots of (6.2), but somewhat more calculation is required. Again let λ be a given root of (6.2), but now possibly complex: say $\lambda = \sigma + \tau i$, where σ and τ are real numbers. Our object is to obtain conditions under which σ must be negative. When λ has the value $\sigma + \tau i$, the system (6.3) has a solution (x_1, x_2), where now x_1 and x_2 may not be real: say $x_i = s_i + t_i i$; but at least one of the numbers can be assumed to be different from zero. Multiply the first equation in (6.3) by $s_1 - t_1 i$, the second by $s_2 - t_2 i$, and add; the result, after simplification, is

$$(6.5) \quad (s_1^2 + t_1^2 + s_2^2 + t_2^2)\lambda^2 - [B(s) + B(t) - i\Sigma_{ij}B_{ij}(s_i t_j - s_j t_i)]\lambda$$
$$- [A(s) + A(t) - i\Sigma_{ij}A_{ij}(s_i t_j - s_j t_i)] = 0.$$

The equation (6.5), despite its intricacy, merely states that a certain complex number is equal to zero. If, therefore, we replace i by $-i$ throughout the left side, the resulting equation will also be true, for the effect of this replacement is to replace the left side of (6.5) by the corresponding conjugate complex number, and the number conjugate to 0 is 0. Therefore

$$(6.6) \quad (s_1^2 + t_1^2 + s_2^2 + t_2^2)\bar{\lambda}^2 - [B(s) + B(t) + i\Sigma_{ij}B_{ij}(s_i t_j - s_j t_i)]\bar{\lambda}$$
$$- [A(s) + A(t) + i\Sigma_{ij}A_{ij}(s_i t_j - s_j t_i)] = 0,$$

where $\bar{\lambda} = \sigma - \tau i$, i.e., the conjugate of λ. Assume for the moment that $\lambda \neq 0$ (this assumption will be justified later); assume also that the quadratic form $A(u)$ is *symmetric*: $A_{12} = A_{21}$. Then dividing through by 2λ in (6.5), by $2\bar{\lambda}$ in (6.6), and adding the resulting equations gives, after simplification,

$$(6.7) \quad (s_1{}^2 + t_1{}^2 + s_2{}^2 + t_2{}^2)\sigma - [B(s) + B(t)] - [A(s) + A(t)]\frac{\sigma}{\sigma^2 + \tau^2} = 0.$$

Now if both of the quadratic forms $A(u)$ and $B(u)$ are negative definite, all of the coefficients in (6.7) are positive, and it follows that the number σ must be negative. This proves:

Theorem 6.2. If $A(u)$ and $B(u)$ are both negative definite, and $A(u)$ is also symmetric, then every root (real or complex) of (6.1) has a negative real part.

Corollary 6.2. Under the conditions stated in Theorem 6.2, the equilibrium point is stable.

Now we shall re-examine the possibility $\lambda = 0$, which was rather arbitrarily assumed aside in the course of proving Theorem 6.2. Suppose that 0 *were* a root of (6.1), or, in other words, of (6.2); then the system (6.3) with $\lambda = 0$ would have a nontrivial solution: there would exist real numbers x_1 and x_2, not both zero, such that

$$A_{11}x_1 + A_{12}x_2 = 0,$$
$$A_{21}x_1 + A_{22}x_2 = 0.$$

Multiply the first of these equations by x_1, the second by x_2, and add; the resulting equation is $A(x) = 0$. But this is impossible when $A(u)$ is a negative definite quadratic form, and this contradiction shows that 0 cannot be a root of (6.1) under the hypotheses of Theorem 6.2.

There is one more theorem in the same class which now may be proved very easily.

Theorem 6.3. If the quadratic forms $A(u)$ and $B(u)$ are both symmetric, and $B(u)$ is negative definite, then every root of (6.1) which is not real has a negative real part.

PROOF: Let λ, x_1, and x_2 be the same as in the proof of Theorem 6.2. The equation (6.5) is also valid here, but because of the assumed symmetry of the quadratic forms, the terms involving i vanish and the equation reduces to

$$(6.8) \quad (s_1{}^2 + t_1{}^2 + s_2{}^2 + t_2{}^2)\lambda^2 - [B(s) + B(t)]\lambda - [A(s) + A(t)] = 0.$$

In this equation, all of the coefficients are real; it therefore follows, by Theorem 7.7, Chapter Eight, that since λ is a (nonreal) root of this quadratic equation, $\bar{\lambda}$ (the conjugate of λ) must be the other. Another elementary theorem (which is easy to derive directly from the "quadratic formula") states that the sum of the two roots of an equation

$$a\lambda^2 + b\lambda + c = 0$$

is equal to $- b/a$. Applied to (6.8), this fact yields the equation

$$\lambda + \bar{\lambda} = (\sigma + \tau i) + (\sigma - \tau i) = 2\sigma = \frac{B(s) + B(t)}{s_1{}^2 + t_1{}^2 + s_2{}^2 + t_2{}^2} \cdot$$

Since $B(u)$ is negative definite, the numerator in this fraction is negative; since the denominator is certainly positive, σ must be negative, as was to be proved.

Corollary 6.3. If no roots of (6.1) are real, the hypotheses in Theorem 6.3 imply that the equilibrium point is stable.

EXERCISES

6.1. Corollary 6.1 gives stability conditions for the case in which *all* roots of the characteristic equation are real; Corollary 6.3, when *no* roots of the characteristic equation are real. On *a priori* grounds, which of these situations is more probable?

6.2. Using the results of Exercise 5.2, determine whether the instance of Model VII with the given demand functions, investment coefficients, and adjustment coefficients can be said to have stable equilibrium on the basis of some of the criteria proved in this section. (Hint: Use Theorem 3.1 of Chapter Eleven to decide whether the quadratic forms involved are negative definite.)

7. *Model VII: Discussion of the Stability Conditions.* The Corollaries 6.1, 6.2, and 6.3 provide the stability criteria which we set out to establish. It should be noted that Corollary 6.2 is, in a way, the result of widest applicability, for it is the only one of the three which makes no assumption about the nature of the roots of the characteristic equation (6.1). Nevertheless, the other two corollaries are of some interest. For instance, Corollary 6.3 applies when *no* roots of the characteristic equation are real, and this is precisely the condition under which all possible price paths near the equilibrium point in the price plane are oscillatory, i.e., (in the stable case) spiral in towards the equilibrium point (see Figure 7.1). On the other hand, Corollary 6.1 governs the case in which all roots are real, which cor-

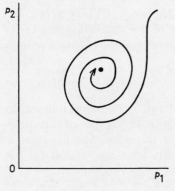

Fig. 7.1

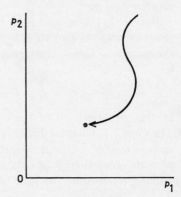

Fig. 7.2

responds to the geometrical situation where all price paths near the equilibrium point move (in the stable case) directly towards that point, without spiraling around it (Figure 7.2). These are the extreme cases, though not necessarily improbable because of that. In the intermediate case, when (6.1) has some roots real and some not, price paths of both types will occur.

We now turn to the interpretation of the stability conditions proper— the conditions on the quadratic forms $A(u)$ and $B(u)$ which occur in the three corollaries. These conditions are of two types: (a) negative definiteness, and (b) symmetry.

It should be recalled that the numbers A_{ij} and B_{ij} were defined at the end of Section 5 by the formulas

$$(7.1) \quad A_{ij} = \alpha_i k_i a_{ij}, \quad B_{ij} = \alpha_i(a_{ij} + k_i b_{ij}), \quad (i = 1, 2; \quad j = 1, 2),$$

where α_i is the adjustment coefficient, and k_i the investment coefficient for commodity i, and the a's and b's are partial derivatives of the excess flow demand and stock demand functions evaluated at the equilibrium point: b_{12}, for instance, is the value of $\partial D_1/\partial p_2$ at $(\bar{p}_1, \bar{p}_2)$, and therefore indicates the direction (up or down) and speed with which the stock demand for commodity 1 will change in response to a change in the price of commodity 2 when both prices have their equilibrium values. The numbers $A_{ij} = \alpha_i k_i a_{ij}$ may be regarded as the numbers a_{ij} *weighted* by the positive quantities $\alpha_i k_i$. This weighting of flow quantities by investment and adjustment coefficients is typical of stock-flow models. The numbers B_{ij} are of course the slopes of the *market* demand curves weighted by the adjustment coefficients α_i.

There is an alternative point of view which may prove instructive. The equations (5.14), the linearized differential equations for Model VII written as a first-order system, can be put in the form:

$$(7.2) \quad \frac{d^2P_i}{dt^2} = A_{i1}P_1 + A_{i2}P_2 + B_{i1}\frac{dP_1}{dt} + B_{i2}\frac{dP_2}{dt}, \quad (i = 1, 2),$$

where $P_i = p_i - \bar{p}_i$, so that P_i merely represents the price of commodity i as measured from equilibrium. The second derivative d^2P_i/dt, may be called without undue artificiality the "price acceleration" for commodity i.[4] Equations (7.2) may then be viewed as expressions which show how price accelerations depend upon price velocities and prices themselves, and the coefficients A_{ij} and B_{ij} assume a certain significance accordingly. For example, the coefficient $A_{12} = \alpha_1 k_1 a_{12}$ measures the sensitivity of the dependence, via changes in the stock supply of commodity 1, of the price acceleration for commodity 1 on the price of commodity 2: *ceteris paribus*, for given values of P_2 and a_{12} the price acceleration d^2P_1/dt^2 will be greater (one way or the other, depending on signs) the larger the value of $\alpha_1 k_1$. Similarly, $B_{12} = \alpha_1(a_{12} + k_1 b_{12})$ measures the response of the price acceleration for commodity 1 to changes in P_2, acting via changes in market

---

[4] In dynamics generally, acceleration is defined as the derivative with respect to time of velocity.

demand; this will be greater the greater the value of α_1. This viewpoint may perhaps justify our calling the numbers A_{ij} and B_{ij} *sensitivity coefficients* at the given equilibrium point.

We return now to the stability conditions. To say that the quadratic form $A(u)$ is negative definite is to say, first of all, that A_{11} and A_{22}, and therefore $\alpha_1 a_{11}$ and $\alpha_2 a_{22}$, are both negative, so that (as we may now say) each price is negatively sensitive to itself: when the actual price of commodity i is above its equilibrium value, its acceleration (to the extent that the acceleration of the given price depends on that price) is negative and its velocity is decreasing. This in turn means that if (say) the velocity is positive, so that the price is moving away from equilibrium, its rate of departure is decreasing; while if the velocity is negative, so that the price is already approaching equilibrium, its rate of approach is increasing. This is certainly the sort of behavior one would expect to find associated with stability, the tendency to return to equilibrium.

However, the negativeness of A_{11} and A_{22} is not enough to assure the negative definiteness of $A(u)$; it is also necessary that A_{12} and A_{21} be relatively small (more precisely, that $A_{12}A_{21} < A_{11}A_{22}$; see Chapter Eleven, Theorem 3.1), which means that the *cross*-sensitivities, for instance the sensitivity of P_1 to P_2, must be small when compared with the *direct* sensitivities A_{11} and A_{22}.

Altogether, then, we may say that the assumption that $A(u)$ is negative definite is equivalent to the assumption that the direct sensitivity coefficients A_{11} and A_{22} are negative and predominate over the cross-sensitivity coefficients A_{12} and A_{21}. The same interpretation applies to the negative definiteness of $B(u)$, and one may argue for the plausibility of this condition as for $A(u)$ above. In view of these remarks, then, it should appear that the negative definiteness conditions occurring in the three corollaries of Section 6 are rather natural ones. This is not to be taken as saying that they are *necessary* conditions; we shall see very soon that they are not.

The symmetry conditions are less natural, and their roles are best seen by comparing the corollaries themselves. In Corollary 6.1, where all roots are assumed to be real, no symmetry conditions are imposed. In Corollary 6.2, the roots *may* fail to be real, and *one* symmetry condition is imposed. In Corollary 6.3, the roots *must* not be real, and *two* symmetry conditions are imposed. It thus appears that in a general way symmetry conditions are substitutes for assumptions about the reality of the roots; symmetry of the quadratic forms and reality of the roots are somehow related.[5]

---

[5] This relation is illustrated by a classical theorem in algebra: if $c_{ij} = c_{ji}$ ($i, j = 1, \ldots, n$), *then all roots of the equation*

$$(*) \quad \begin{vmatrix} c_{11} - \lambda & c_{12} & \ldots & c_{1n} \\ c_{21} & c_{22} - \lambda & \ldots & c_{2n} \\ \ldots & \ldots & \ldots & \ldots \\ c_{n1} & c_{n2} & \ldots & c_{nn} - \lambda \end{vmatrix} = 0$$

are real. This theorem cannot be applied directly to the present problem, since it is not the symmetry of the *whole* determinant corresponding to (*), but only of *parts* of it, that is involved; but the theorem is suggestive.

Nevertheless, the symmetry conditions seem unduly restrictive, and it seems reasonable to guess that Corollaries 6.1–6.3 should remain true if those conditions were replaced by certain suitable less demanding ones. In particular, one might be led by Model V, where negative definiteness alone was sufficient for stability, to suspect that the same may be true here; i.e., that the mere negative definiteness of the quadratic forms $A(u)$ and $B(u)$ may imply stability. That this cannot be the case in general is shown by the following example:

Example 7.1.   Let $A_{11} = A_{22} = -5$, $B_{11} = B_{22} = -10$, $A_{12} = 1$, $A_{21} = 9$, $B_{12} = 11$, $B_{21} = 2$. Then it is easy to verify, using Theorem 3.1 of Chapter Eleven, that both of the quadratic forms $A(u)$ and $B(u)$ are negative definite; but the characteristic equation (6.1) is

$$\lambda^4 + 20\lambda^3 + 88\lambda^2 - \lambda + 16 = 0 .$$

Since this equation has a negative coefficient (-1) in it, there must be at least one root with a positive real part, and stability therefore cannot occur (cf. Theorem 7.5, Chapter Eight).

On the other hand, neither the symmetry conditions nor the negative definiteness conditions occurring in Corollaries 6.1–6.3 are *necessary* for stability; stability may obtain even though some or all of those conditions are not fulfilled. This is demonstrated by the two following examples.

Example 7.2.   Suppose that $A_{11} = A_{22} = -1$, $A_{12} = 3$, $A_{21} = 0$, $B_{11} = B_{22} = -2$, $B_{12} = 6$, $B_{21} = 0$. Then (6.2) is

$$\begin{vmatrix} \lambda^2 + 2\lambda + 1 & -6\lambda - 3 \\ 0 & \lambda^2 + 2\lambda + 1 \end{vmatrix} = 0 ,$$

or

$$(\lambda + 1)^4 = 0 ,$$

all four roots of which are equal to -1. Thus stability of a strong (non-oscillatory) type is indicated. Nevertheless, the quadratic forms

$$A(u) = -u_1^2 + 3u_1u_2 - u_2^2 ,$$
$$B(u) = -2u_1^2 + 6u_1u_2 - 2u_2^2 ,$$

are neither symmetric nor negative definite. This shows that none of the conditions in Corollaries 6.1 and 6.2 are necessary for stability.

Example 7.3.   Now let $A_{11} = A_{22} = -2$, $A_{12} = 6$, $A_{21} = 0$, $B_{11} = B_{22} = -1$, $B_{12} = 3$, $B_{21} = 0$. Then (6.2) becomes

$$\begin{vmatrix} \lambda^2 + \lambda + 2 & 3\lambda + 6 \\ 0 & \lambda^2 + \lambda + 2 \end{vmatrix} = 0 ,$$

or

$$(\lambda^2 + \lambda + 2)^2 = 0 .$$

By the quadratic formula, the roots of this equation may be found to be $\frac{1}{2}(-1 \pm \sqrt{7}i)$, each root counting twice, and since the real parts are negative stability again occurs. Nevertheless, the quadratic forms $A(u)$ and $B(u)$ (which are merely those of Example 7.2 interchanged) are neither symmetric nor negative definite. This shows that the conditions in Corollary 6.3 are not necessary for stability even when it is known that no roots of the characteristic equation (6.1) are real.

The stability conditions obtained in Section 6 thus only partially solve the problem of finding easily interpreted conditions equivalent to the basic condition that all roots of the characteristic equation have negative real parts. Those conditions can be interpreted, and are sufficient for stability, but they are not necessary for stability. There do exist necessary and sufficient conditions for stability involving certain test determinants associated with the names of the mathematicians Routh and Hurwitz,[6] and these test determinants can be calculated and applied in any concrete case, the problem of actually solving the characteristic equation being thus avoided. However, the Routh-Hurwitz test determinants for the present model depend upon the numbers A_{ij} and B_{ij} in such an intricate way that their *general* usefulness is slight and their economic significance almost nil. There are no known stability conditions which combine the scope of the Routh-Hurwitz conditions with the easy economic interpretability of those we have given in Section 6.

EXERCISES

7.1. It is known (Theorem 7.5, Chapter Eight) that if an equation (6.2) is to have only roots with negative real parts, then the coefficients of the various powers of λ must have the same sign—in this case, since the coefficient of λ^4 is always $+1$, they must all be positive. Expand the determinant (6.2) and express this *necessary* condition for stability by means of the four resulting inequalities. Then give interpretations of the separate inequalities as well as you can.

7.2. In physics, Newton's *Second Law of Motion* asserts that (for a given object and suitably chosen units) acceleration and force are equal: that the acceleration imparted to the object by a force acting on it is numerically equal to the force. Discuss the pseudo-physical interpretation this enables one to give to the terms on the right side of (7.2).

8. *Model VII: Final Observations.* If Model VII is suitably modified or subjected to certain additional assumptions, one obtains some of the simpler models which were discussed earlier in this chapter. For example, the limiting case in which the functions f_i of equations (5.3) do not depend on the excess stock demands X_i (this may be brought about by assuming that the investment coefficients k_i are zero or that the excess stock demands are identically zero) is the same as Model V. Indeed, it is clear that as the

---

[6] See A. Bronwell, *Advanced Mathematics in Physics and Engineering* (New York: McGraw-Hill Book Co., Inc., 1953), chap. xvi.

investment coefficients are made smaller, the behavior of a stock-flow model will be more nearly approximated by that of a pure flow model. In this connection, however, it is worthy of remark that in any concrete stock-flow situation it is reasonable to expect that the investment coefficients will not be very small.

The analogous case in which the functions f_i are independent of the excess *flow* demands (this may be brought about formally by setting the excess flow demand functions identically equal to zero) likewise leads to a pure stock model, as one might expect; for the economic meaning of the assumption $x_i \equiv 0$ is that the production and consumption of each commodity are always equal, irrespective of price movements. In particular, this will happen if the commodities are neither produced nor consumed. The equilibrium conditions (5.9) are automatically satisfied in this case, and the stability conditions derived in Section 6 may be restated in much simpler forms, since the numbers a_{ij} are all zero. But here again the direct approach as given in Section 1 is more effective.

A third special case of Model VII, something of a mixture of the corresponding pure flow and pure stock models, may be obtained by assuming that for each commodity either $k_i = 0$ or $x_i \equiv 0$, i.e., that market decisions regarding any individual commodity involve *either* its production and consumption *or* the holding of stocks, *but not both*. This leads to a *partial stock-flow model* and is a dynamical version of the models which underlie most recent writings in monetary theory in which stocks of money or bonds are treated as parameters but all ordinary commodities are regarded as flows.[7] From a formal standpoint, such a model is equivalent to Model V.

In view of the large amount of space that has been devoted to Model VII in the preceding pages, it is but just that we say something about its empirical significance, especially as compared with simple stock and flow models. As we have pointed out in Chapter One, the primary object of economic theory is to provide a general frame of reference to assist in organizing and deriving knowledge about the real world. It is therefore important that theories be formulated in such a way as to lend themselves to the interpretation of phenomena which arise in practice. In the domain of actual economic experience, nearly all commodities appear not merely as stock *or* as flows but simultaneously as stocks *and* flows. From the very outset, therefore, there is a presumption in favor of the use of stock-flow rather than stock or flow theories to describe the real world. However, whether or not this presumption is to be accepted as a controlling factor depends upon the extent to which flow or stock models—which, as we have seen, are considerably simpler than stock-flow models—are inadequate for

---

[7] For examples, see J. M. Keynes, *The General Theory of Employment, Interest, and Money* (New York: Harcourt, Brace & Co., 1935), chap. xviii; Lawrence R. Klein, *The Keynesian Revolution* (New York: Macmillan Co., 1947), pp. 192–96; Don Patinkin, "A Reconsideration of the General Equilibrium Theory of Money," *Review of Economic Studies*, Vol. XVIII, No. I, pp. 42–61.

the interpretation of observable phenomena; upon the extent to which stock-flow relationships can be ignored or else considered in an implicit way within stock or flow models. The preceding account sheds considerable light on this question. *If it were the case that stock-flow relationships could be safely ignored in any given situation, the previous discussion might have been expected to support this surmise by indicating the essential equivalence of, say, flow and stock-flow models.* But *our analysis leads to precisely the contrary conclusion.* In order to emphasize this point, we shall introduce one more example.

Example 8.1. We consider a stock-flow model for which $(\bar{p}_1, \bar{p}_2)$ is a pair of prices satisfying the equilibrium conditions $x_1 = x_2 = X_1 = X_2 = 0$ at a certain instant, and investigate the stability of this equilibrium point assuming that (in the notation previously used)

$$(8.1) \quad \alpha_1 = \alpha_2 = k_1 = k_2 = 1 \,,$$
$$(8.2) \quad a_{11} = a_{22} = -5 \,, \quad a_{12} = 1 \,, \quad a_{21} = 9 \,,$$
$$(8.3) \quad b_{11} = b_{22} = -5 \,, \quad b_{12} = 10 \,, \quad b_{21} = -7 \,,$$

at that point. Then the characteristic equation (6.2) becomes

$$\lambda^4 + 20\lambda^3 + 88\lambda^2 - \lambda + 16 = 0 \,.$$

As we have seen in Example 7.1, this equation must have at least one root with a positive real part; therefore the equilibrium is *unstable.*

Now let us see what would happen if one were to ignore either the flow or the stock aspect of this model and to regard it as a pure flow or pure stock model.

To treat it as a pure flow model, one might simply use $\alpha_1 = \alpha_2 = 1$ (or some other positive number) and (8.2); the other data would be irrelevant. According to Section 2, stability will occur in the resulting pure flow model (Model V) if the conditions (2.1) and (2.2) are satisfied; but it is a matter of simple arithmetic to verify that they *are* satisfied. Thus one would conclude that the equilibrium point is *stable.*

On the other hand, if one were to insist on regarding the system as a pure *stock* model with $x_1 \equiv 0$, one would retain (8.3) and (8.1). For this (stock) form of Model V the stability conditions (2.1) and (2.2) become

$$\alpha_1 k_1 b_{11} + \alpha_2 k_2 b_{22} < 0 \,,$$
$$\alpha_1 \alpha_2 k_1 k_2 (b_{11} b_{22} - b_{12} b_{21}) > 0 \,.$$

It is easy to see that these conditions are satisfied in this instance; again, therefore, one would infer that the given equilibrium state is *stable.*

We have thus constructed an example of a two-commodity system *with given demand and supply functions* in which a specified equilibrium state is stable under stock or flow hypotheses, but unstable under stock-flow hypotheses. Nothing could make more clear the limitations of arbitrarily postulating a flow or a stock theory of market price determination when stock *and* flow relationships may be pertinent; for it shows that the suppression of stock-flow relationships in favor of a stock or flow model may lead to *qualitatively* erroneous conclusions.

In fact, a flow theory may or may not ignore the *existence* of commodity stocks, but such a theory necessarily leaves unexplained the factors which govern the *holding* of such stocks. A stock theory errs in the contrary direction; it fails to describe the factors which govern the level of production and consumption flows. Moreover, there is no escape from these difficulties in the procedure of combining stock and flow models (using one to explain "flow" prices, the other to explain "stock" prices), for the result is simply a partial stock-flow theory which, as regards any single commodity, has precisely the same shortcomings as its constituents.

9. General n-Commodity Models. The models constructed and explored in this chapter have been restricted to the two-commodity case for reasons which were stated at the outset, and whose validity should now be fairly clear. These models can easily be extended to apply to n-commodity systems; the only effect will be to increase the number of variables of each kind, the number of equations (or inequalities) in each system, etc. In the n-commodity version of Model VII, for instance, there would be n prices $p_1, \ldots, p_n$; n excess flow demand functions $x_1, \ldots, x_n$; n differential equations in the basic system (5.3); $2n$ equations (2 for each commodity) in the system of equilibrium conditions (5.11); and so on. Once the corresponding changes were made throughout the discussion, one would obtain valid stability conditions corresponding closely to those in Section 6. The only difficulty would be the purely nonmathematical and noneconomic one of writing out longer expressions in place of the relatively short ones that suffice for the two-commodity case. Even this difficulty can be avoided by using a certain widely used mathematical notation, namely that of vectors and matrices, but this is neither necessary nor, in the short run, desirable.[8]

To be sure, things have been said in this chapter—notably in Section 2—which are rather severely limited to the two-commodity case, being difficult or impossible to extend to the more general system. More often than not, these special results have depended for their availability on the simplicity of the theory of quadratic equations as compared with those of higher degrees. It would be quixotic not to make some use of this algebraic windfall when possible. Nevertheless, we have dealt mainly with the generalizable aspects of the two-commodity models, for only those are likely to have any wide practicability.

SUGGESTIONS FOR FURTHER READING

Most of the subjects dealt with in this chapter have a short history, and a complete bibliography on them would require little space. Pure flow and stock theories are discussed *passim* in Part II of P. A. Samuelson's *Foundations of Economic*

---

[8] The reader who is concerned about the long run can learn about the vector and matrix notation in any one of a large number of books, e.g., R. A. Frazer, W. J. Duncan, and A. R. Collar, *Elementary Matrices* (Cambridge: The University Press, 1946), especially chaps. i, v, and vi.

Analysis (Cambridge: Harvard University Press, 1947); and are also treated extensively in O. Lange, *Price Flexibility and Employment*, Cowles Commission Monograph No. 8 (Bloomington: The Principia Press, Inc., 1944). Model VII made its debut, in a somewhat different form, in the authors' "Price Determination in a Stock-Flow Economy," *Econometrica*, Vol. XXII, No. 3 (July, 1954), pp. 328–43, where the n-commodity case is treated in detail. See also Karl Brunner, "Stock and Flow Analysis: Discussion," *Econometrica*, Vol. XVIII, No. 3 (July, 1950), pp. 247–51; L. R. Klein, "Stock and Flow Analysis in Economics," *Econometrica*, Vol. XVIII, No. 3 (July, 1950), pp. 236–41.

For the dynamics of aggregative models, see J. R. Hicks, *A Contribution to the Theory of the Trade Cycle* (Oxford: Clarendon Press, 1950); P. A. Samuelson, *Foundations of Economic Analysis* (Cambridge: Harvard University Press, 1947), pp. 276–83; W. J. Baumol, *Economic Dynamics* (New York: Macmillan Co., 1951); R. M. Goodwin, "The Nonlinear Accelerator and the Persistence of Business Cycles," *Econometrica*, Vol. XVIII, No. 3 (January, 1951), pp. 1–17.

Chapter Five

MICROECONOMICS I:

THE THEORY OF CONSUMER BEHAVIOR

BROADLY speaking, microeconomics is concerned, first, with specifying alternative possible decisions that an individual "economic unit" might make and, second, with describing the process by which decisions are selected from the admissable alternatives. It is impossible, however, to give a complete description of even the simplest concrete decision process; considerable idealization, abstraction from complicating factors, is essential from the outset. The immediate problem is to formulate models which, however narrowly conceived, are precise and not arrantly inconsistent with elementary facts of experience. The problem of interpreting and describing wider aspects of experience is best considered later; for the too hasty pursuit of "realism" may inhibit more than it furthers the acquisition of knowledge about actual decision processes.

Microeconomics may be studied either for its own sake or as a logical and factual background for analyzing macroeconomic phenomena. In either case, it is desirable to divide the problem into a set of separate problems, each concerned with a specific type of "economic unit," each amenable to appropriate methods of analysis.[1] We begin, therefore, by adopting the traditional division of microeconomics into a theory of consumer behavior and a theory of business behavior. We shall deal with the theory of consumer behavior in this chapter, with the theory of business behavior in the next. The economic decisions of governmental and other social groups also fall within the realm of microeconomics, but the study of these matters is a large subject in itself and will not be considered in this book.

---

[1] There have been attempts to make microeconomics a unified theory, the theory of the decision processes of "economic units" in general. These efforts are not without academic interest; but by reason of their technical complexity, lack of intuitive appeal, and questionable value as sources of greater generality or empirical plausibility, they cannot now be regarded as serious competitors against the familiar dichotomized version of the pure theory of economic behavior. The interested reader will find examples and references in J. DeV. Graaff's "Income Effects and the Theory of the Firm," *Review of Economic Studies*, Vol. XVIII(2), No. 46 (1950–1951), pp. 79–86; and R. W. Clower's "Mr. Graaff's Producer-Consumer Theory; a Restatement and Correction," *Review of Economic Studies*, Vol. XX(1), No. 51 (1952–1953), pp. 84–85. Cf. also J. R. Hicks, *A Revision of Demand Theory* (Oxford: Clarendon Press, 1956), chap. iii.

1. *Consumer Behavior: Basic Ideas.* The aim of the theory of consumer behavior is to describe how a theoretically "typical" household plans and carries out commodity management decisions. The subject is vast and full of complexities, and a comprehensive discussion is out of the question here. While we shall present a fairly systematic statement of the foundations of the theory, therefore, its implications will be explored only to a limited extent. For the sake of simplicity, moreover, we shall begin on the assumption that the consumer is concerned with purchasing quantities of two goods, both flow commodities. The argument will be extended to refer to more than two goods, and to include stock and stock-flow commodities, only after the two-commodity flow case has been developed in some detail.

Suppose, then, that the consumer receives a fixed quantity, say M, of money per unit of time (i.e., income) which may be spent to purchase quantities x_1 and x_2 of two commodities $(x_i \geqq 0)$, and write

$$(1.1) \quad p_1 x_1 + p_2 x_2 = M$$

for the *budget equation* of the consumer. The properties of equation (1.1) cannot be determined without making definite assumptions about the relation, if any, between the price variables p_i and the quantity variables x_i; and it is also desirable to establish, from the very outset, a link between the consumer and the markets in which he trades. In this connection, we shall adopt the simplest possible assumptions. We shall suppose (*i*) the consumer acts competitively (i.e., regards the prices of both commodities as given parameters over which he has no direct control), and (*ii*) that prices as seen by the consumer are identical with market prices.

On these assumptions, both of which are relatively plausible in reference to real-world consumer units, equation (1.1) constitutes a technical restriction on the consumer's freedom of choice among alternative quantity combinations. The properties of the equation are discussed most easily in geometrical terms. Thus, let us call a quantity combination (x_1,x_2) or, more shortly, x, a *budget*, and regard the totality of budgets x as points in a *budget plane*. We shall assume that each commodity is indefinitely divisible, so that *any* budget $x = (x_1,x_2)$ is meaningful, in the sense that x might conceivably be chosen by some consumer when x_1 and x_2 are any nonnegative real numbers whatever. Then for given prices p_1 and p_2 (determined in markets for the respective commodities) and for a given value of the consumer's income, M, equation (1.1) describes a definite downward sloping line in the budget plane. On and to the left of this line lie all budgets which the consumer might effectively choose; these budgets are represented by the shaded region in Figure 1.1. A budget on the line indicates that the consumer is spending all of his income on the two commodities (equation [1.1] is satisfied), while a point to the left of the line represents a budget which requires less than the whole of the consumer's income (the left side of equation [1.1] is smaller than the right); for given any such point, one can find, by drawing a horizontal line to the right and observing the point

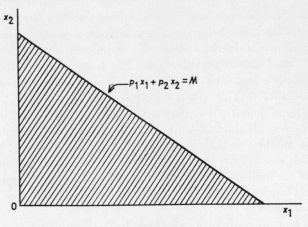

Fig. 1.1

at which the two lines intersect, a point at which x_1 is greater than in the given budget while x_2 is the same as in the given budget, so that at the given point the value of $p_1x_1 + p_2x_2$ is less than its value at the point of intersection, at which this value is simply M.

Which budget will be selected from the collection of budgets making up the shaded region might be decided in a variety of ways: by a conventional rule of thumb, by some outside authority, by reference to some moral code, at random, etc. These and other mainsprings of consumer decision are included in a general way, however, in the broad assumption that each individual consumer is a sovereign authority in matters affecting his own taste in consumer's goods: we need not enquire why the consumer's tastes are what they are, whether they arise from moral or political convictions, necessity, whim, or what have you. We may simply assume that the consumer will select that budget which best satisfies his "wants," however the latter are determined, given various restrictions (the budget equation in particular) on his freedom of choice. We shall soon see how this seemingly innocuous assumption can be elaborated into a theory of consumer behavior. But first we must explain how the "wants" of a consumer can be described in precise terms.

EXERCISES

1.1. What significance would it be natural to attach to negative values of x_1 and x_2 in the above discussion? How may the neglect of such values in consumer theory be justified?

1.2. The "wants" of a consumer may be expected to change from one income period to the next, if not more often. Does this fact threaten any weaknesses in the theory outlined above?

2. *The Indifference Map.* Our program in this section is to state some fundamental postulates about a consumer's preferences, and from these to arrive at the "indifference map" which is often taken as the starting point for theories of consumer behavior. The postulates required for this purpose are mainly simple statements about the manner in which a hypothetical consumer "rates" alternative budgets. For the most part they are intuitively plausible and agree in a general way with common sense; it is for these reasons that they provide a desirable point of departure.

As a matter of definition, we may write $x \dashv 3\ y$ to denote the fact that the consumer prefers the budget y to the budget x: given a completely free choice between the two budgets, he would definitely choose y. When this relation holds we shall say that x is *inferior* to y, and that y is *superior* to x. If neither of the budgets is superior to the other (if, in other words, the consumer wants y neither more nor less than x), we shall write $x \sim y$ and say that x is *indifferent* to y.

Turning now to postulates, we begin by asserting that the consumer knows his own mind in the matter of budget preferences.

Postulate I. *For any pair of budgets x and y, exactly one of the relations*

$$x \dashv 3\ y, \quad y \dashv 3\ x, \quad x \sim y$$

holds.

This postulate is sometimes called the "Axiom of Comparison" or the "Trichotomy Axiom."

Next, in order to elaborate some of the properties of the relations $\dashv 3$ and $\sim$, we introduce Postulate II.

Postulate II. *If x, y, and z are any budgets whatever,*

  a) $x \sim x$ (the indifference relation is reflexive);
  b) if $x \sim y$, then $y \sim x$ (the indifference relation is symmetrical);
  c) if $x \sim y$ and $y \sim z$, then $x \sim z$ (the indifference relation is transitive);
  d) if $x \dashv 3\ y$ and x' and y' are any budgets indifferent respectively to x and y, then $x' \dashv 3\ y'$ (preference is invariant under substitution of indifferents).

It is worth noting that Postulates I and II do not involve any specific interpretation of budgets as points in a budget plane, so they might be made to play a fundamental role in a theory of choice much more general than the one outlined below.

From parts (*a*), (*b*), and (*c*) of Postulate II it follows at once that the budget plane can be divided into mutually exclusive *indifference classes:* two budgets x and y belong to the same class if and only if $x \sim y$.

To demonstrate this, we begin by defining the *indifference class of a budget x*, denoted by $I(x)$, as the set of all budgets y satisfying the relation $x \sim y$. In the first place, it is clear that the indifference class of any budget x contains at least one budget, namely x itself (by part [*a*] of Postulate II). This means, in particular, that every budget belongs to at least one indifference class. Next, note that if $x \sim y$, then $I(x)$ and $I(y)$ are identical. For suppose that z is a budget in $I(x)$, so that $x \sim z$. Since $x \sim y$ by hypothesis, we know by part (*b*) of Postulate II that $y \sim x$; but $y \sim x$ and $x \sim z$ together imply, by (*c*), that $y \sim z$, i.e., that z is in $I(y)$. Thus every budget in $I(x)$ is also in $I(y)$. Likewise, one can show that every budget belonging to $I(y)$ belongs also to $I(x)$; and this means that $I(x)$ and $I(y)$ are identical.

A further consequence of Postulate II is that if any two indifference classes have a budget in common, they coincide. Suppose that a budget z is in both of the indifference classes $I(x)$ and $I(y)$: $x \sim z$, $y \sim z$. By symmetry and transitivity (parts [b] and [c] of Postulate II), these relations imply $x \sim y$, so that (as shown above) the indifference classes $I(x)$ and $I(y)$ must be identical.

Taken together, the preceding remarks show that the indifference relation $\sim$ separates the budget plane into nonoverlapping sets of points (the indifference classes) which may be characterized by the statement that two budgets x and y belong to the same class if and only if $x \sim y$. If the consumer is faced with an unrestricted choice between two budgets in the same indifference class, he favors neither; but if the choice is between budgets in different classes, he will certainly prefer one to the other.

The relation $\exists$ between budgets leads directly to the definition of a similar relation between indifference classes, viz., if x is a budget in the indifference class A, and y is a budget in the indifference class B, then $A \ \exists \ B$ if $x \ \exists \ y$. That this is a natural and sensible definition, in the sense that the relation between A and B does not depend on the particular pair of budgets chosen to represent them, follows at once from part (d) of Postulate II.

In order to provide more detailed information about the character of the indifference classes, introduce some assumptions about the manner in which the relations $\exists$ and $\sim$ are connected with the size of budget components. Our first such assumption, Postulate III below, expresses the fact that the consumer always prefers to get more of a commodity if he can do so without getting less of another. The postulate is expressed in terms of the concept of one budget being *larger* than another. In symbols, the budget $y = (y_1, y_2)$ is said to be larger than the budget $x = (x_1, x_2)$ if $x_1 \leqslant y_1$, $x_2 \leqslant y_2$, and there is inequality in at least one case. In words, the budget y is larger than the budget x if y involves at least as much of each commodity as does x, and definitely more of at least one commodity. This relation will be denoted by $x < y$. Geometrically, y is larger than x if it lies to the "Northeast" of x (see Fig. 2.1). Postulate III simply asserts that a larger budget is always preferred.

Postulate III. If $x < y$, then $x \ \exists \ y$.

This postulate has been called the "Axiom of Nonsatiety."

Finally, we assume that if x is a budget to which the budget y is inferior and the budget z is superior (see Fig. 2.2), then in moving continuously from y to z (along any path) in the budget plane, one encounters at least one budget indifferent to x. In the contrary case, there would necessarily be abrupt jumps from inferior to superior budgets (relative to x)—the consumer would be so very fastidious in his preferences that along the curve in question there would be no middle ground between inferiority and

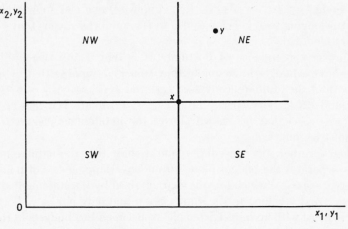

Fig. 2.1

superiority to x. While it is possible to imagine situations in which this phenomenon might occur, the simplifications in the theory resulting from their being ruled out more than compensate for the loss in generality.[2] In more formal terms, our assumption may be stated as follows:

Postulate IV. If $y \ni x \ni z$, then on any curve joining y and z in the budget plane there exists at least one budget x' such that $x' \sim x$ (cf. Fig. 2.2).

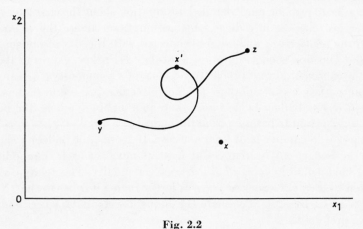

Fig. 2.2

It is now possible to prove the fundamental theorem about indifference classes:

Theorem 2.1. Indifference classes are continuous curves with the property that each line through the point $(0,0)$ into the budget plane intersects each such curve exactly once.

---

[2] W. M. Gorman of the University of Birmingham has developed a subtle and interesting version of consumer choice theory that concentrates on this phenomenon and its consequences. We are indebted to him for some of the ideas embodied in this section.

PROOF: Let us consider the indifference class made up of all budgets indifferent to a given budget x. In terms of Figure 2.3, Postulate III asserts that all budgets in the shaded region S are superior to x, while all budgets in the rectangle I are inferior to x. Let R be any line from 0 into the budget plane. It will necessarily intersect both I and S, so there are budgets y and z on the line which are respectively inferior and superior to x. Ac-

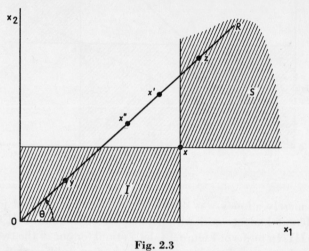

Fig. 2.3

cordingly, by Postulate IV, there is at least one budget x' on the line segment yz which is indifferent to x. But there can be only one such budget; for suppose there were another, say x'' (as marked in Fig. 2.3). Obviously, $x'' < x'$; therefore, by Postulate III, $x'' \dashv3 x'$; but since $x' \sim x$ and $x'' \sim x$, this implies, by part (d) of Postulate II, that $x \dashv3 x$. This, however, contradicts part (a) of the same postulate, in view of Postulate I.

This proves that every line R intersects the indifference class containing x at just one point. The indifference class can therefore be represented by a function $r = f(\theta)$, where θ is the angle that the line R forms with the horizontal, and r is the distance along the line from 0 to the point in the indifference class. The proof of the theorem will be complete once we have shown that the function $f(\theta)$ is continuous. To show this, suppose that $\bar{x}$ is the point (budget) corresponding to a certain angle $\bar{\theta}$ in the indifference class given by $r = f(\theta)$. If $\bar{\theta} + h$ is an angle near $\bar{\theta}$ (Fig. 2.4 shows h positive), then the point x corresponding to $\bar{\theta} + h$ in the indifference class must lie, by Postulate III, in the unshaded region, i.e. on the segment pq. Thus, as $h \to 0$, the distance from 0 to x [viz., $f(\bar{\theta} + h)$] must approach $f(\theta)$, the distance from 0 to $\bar{x}$. But this is exactly the condition for continuity.

Theorem 2.1 justifies our now calling the indifference classes *indifference curves,* and this we shall do. One property of indifference curves must be mentioned:

Theorem 2.2.   The line segment joining any two points on the same indifference curve is downward sloping.

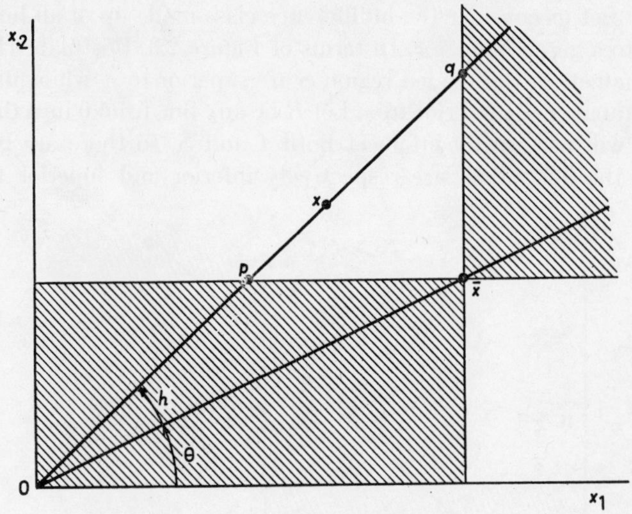

Fig. 2.4

This is merely a fancy way of saying that the line segment joining any two indifferent budgets is downward sloping. This follows at once from Postulate III. In terms of Figure 2.4, let $\bar{x}$ stand for one of the two budgets; then (as we have already pointed out) any budget indifferent to $\bar{x}$ must lie in the unshaded part of the budget plane. But the line segment joining any such point to $\bar{x}$ is certainly downward sloping.

If an indifference curve is smooth enough to have a slope at every point, Theorem 2.2 implies that its slope can never be positive, for the slope of a curve at any point is the limit of slopes of just such segments as are described in the theorem, and since the latter are always negative, the limit must be negative or at worst zero.

Theorems 2.1 and 2.2 together pin down the behavior of the indifference curves fairly well. In general, the budget plane is covered by the family of indifference curves, each of which is roughly downward sloping. Some of the indifference curves may terminate on one or both of the co-ordinate axes, others may not; but each one sweeps across the budget plane in the sense that it intersects any line through 0 into the budget plane. This configuration is called the *indifference map* for the consumer and commodities in question. Such a map is illustrated in Figure 2.5.

EXERCISES

2.1. Give an economic interpretation of each of the four parts of Postulate II. If any of them do not seem self-evident, or if any of them might reasonably fail for a real-world consumer, state and discuss your reasons for thinking so.

2.2. Prove that a preference relation $\dashv$ satisfying the postulates of this section is transitive; i.e., if $x \dashv y$ and $y \dashv z$, then $x \dashv z$.

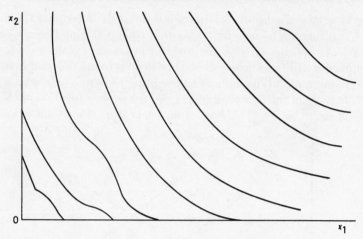

Fig. 2.5

2.3. In our proof of Theorem 2.1 we have not used Postulate IV in its full generality. Give a weaker version of Postulate IV that would have sufficed for our purposes.

2.4. Specifically, what is the geometrical significance of saying $A \dashv 3\ B$, where A and B are indifference curves?

2.5. What is the interpretation of an indifference curve's terminating on the x_1 axis? (Hint: What would be the character of the preference map if it were true that "Every man has his price"?)

3. Utility Indices. A function $U(x_1,x_2)$, or more simply $U(x)$, defined at every point of the budget plane, is called a *utility index* if it has the property

$$(3.1) \quad U(x) < U(y) \text{ if and only if } x \dashv 3\ y.$$

It follows at once from property (3.1) that $U(x) = U(y)$ if and only if $x \sim y$.

The existence of utility indices may be proved under the assumptions set forth in Section 2. To do this, let OA be any line entering the budget plane from the origin (Fig. 3.1), and let x be any budget. According to Theorem 2.1, there is just one budget x' lying on the line OA which is indifferent to x; and we define

$$(3.2) \quad U(x) = \text{the distance from the origin } 0 \text{ to } x'.$$

The function $U(x)$ defined in this way certainly has the property (3.1); for if $x \dashv 3\ y$, the same is true of the corresponding budgets x' and y' (this is an immediate consequence of part [d] of Postulate II): $x' \dashv 3\ y'$. But this in turn implies that the distance of y' from the origin is greater than that of x', so that $U(x) < U(y)$. Since this argument may be reversed, our statement is proved.

Of course, the condition (3.1) does not uniquely determine the utility index $U(x)$; this can be seen by noting that (unless the indifference curves happen to be quarter-circles) the above construction leads to infinitely many different utility indices—all one has to do is to use different lines OA. In fact, many more utility indices representing the same indifference map can be obtained in the following way: Let $F(u)$ be any function of the real variable u such that $F(u_1) < F(u_2)$ if and only if $u_1 < u_2$ (such a function

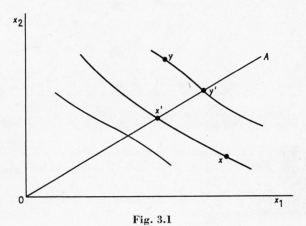

Fig. 3.1

is said to be a *strictly increasing* function of u). Then if $U(x)$ is a utility index, so is $F[U(x)]$. In fact, if $x \dashv 3\ y$, then $U(x) < U(y)$ by (3.1), and this in turn implies that $F[U(x)] < F[U(y)]$, since F is strictly increasing. Conversely, $F[U(x)] < F[U(y)]$ implies $x \dashv 3\ y$.

We have thus shown how a given indifference map leads to a whole class of utility indices. Conversely, any utility index in this class yields the indifference map, for the indifference curves are simply the graphs of equations

$$(3.3) \quad U(x) = \text{constant.}$$

A utility index measures, in a certain sense, the "satisfaction" that the consumer obtains from the budget x: the greater the value of $U(x)$, the greater his satisfaction. However, it is not sound to attach too much significance to any one utility index, for instance by saying that if for two budgets x and y, $Y(x) = 1.74307U(y)$, then the budget x yields 1.74307 times as much satisfaction as the budget y. (A utility index so interpreted is called a *cardinal* utility function.) The utility index should be taken merely as a way of representing the *order* in which the consumer places alternative budgets—in other words, as an alternative to the fundamental preference relation $\dashv 3$. (A utility index with this interpretation is called an *ordinal* utility function.) This interpretation prevents the existence of infinitely many distinct but equally valid utility indices from leading to any embarrassments or contradictions.

EXERCISES

3.1. Give a proof of the statement immediately following (3.1).

3.2. Give three distinct examples of strictly increasing functions $F(u)$ for which the domain, as well as the range, is the set of all nonnegative real numbers.

3.3. What is a simple way of characterizing *differentiable* strictly increasing functions?

3.4. Prove the following theorem: Two utility indices $U(x)$ and $V(x)$ represent the same indifference map if and only if the function F defined by

$$V(x) \equiv F[U(x)]$$

is strictly increasing. (Hint: Half of this theorem has been proved in the text.)

4. Equilibrium Budgets [Thirteen].   To return to the problem of consumer choice as formulated in Section 1, assume again that the consumer's selection among alternative budgets is limited by the budget constraint

$$(4.1) \quad p_1 x_1 + p_2 x_2 \leqslant M .$$

A budget satisfying this condition will be called a *permitted budget*. If, among all the permitted budgets, there is a budget with the property that it is superior or indifferent to all other permitted budgets (is inferior to no permitted budget), we shall say that it is a *maximal budget*.[3] Alternatively, let $U(x)$ be any utility index representing the given indifference map; then if a particular permitted budget x is superior or indifferent to every other permitted budget, $U(x) \geqslant U(y)$ (where y may be any permitted budget whatever), from which it follows that *a maximal budget is a permitted budget at which $U(x)$ attains an absolute maximum relative to the set of all permitted budgets.*

We now restate an earlier remark concerning the process of budget selection by introducing Postulate V.

Postulate V (Axiom of Selection).   The consumer always selects a maximal budget, if there is one.

This postulate is simply a restatement of the traditional assumption of "utility maximization." Its effect is to reduce the problem of consumer choice to a study of maximal budgets.

This accounts for the importance of Theorem 4.1.

Theorem 4.1.   There always exist maximal budgets, and all maximal budgets satisfy

$$(4.2) \quad p_1 x_1 + p_2 x_2 = M .$$

---

[3] In many accounts of the theory of consumption the word "equilibrium" is used in place of the word "maximal." Strictly speaking, this is an abuse of the former term, which is properly the name of a dynamical concept (cf. Chapter Three), for no dynamical considerations are involved here. However, since maximal budgets do represent equilibrium in certain dynamical extensions of the present theory, we shall defer to tradition and use the terms "maximal" and "equilibrium" interchangeably in what follows.

PROOF: The permitted budgets defined by (4.1) constitute the closed, bounded triangular region shown in Figure 1.1. Thus, by Theorem 4.1 of Chapter Thirteen, any continuous function attains an absolute maximum (relative to the region) at some point in the region. Corresponding to any indifference map defined in terms of Postulates I–IV, however, there exist continuous utility indices; in particular, it can be shown that the utility indices explicitly constructed in Section 3 have this property. Thus if the utility index referred to in the alternative definition of maximal budgets is taken to be continuous, it follows at once that it attains an absolute maximum on the set of permitted budgets; i.e., there exist maximal budgets.

The second part of the statement is a consequence of the Axiom of Nonsatiety (Postulate III); for if x is any budget satisfying (4.1) but not (4.2), that axiom asserts that there exist permitted budgets satisfying (4.1) superior to x, namely, those lying to the northeast of x within the triangle of permitted budgets. Thus x cannot be maximal.

The geometrical interpretation of Theorem 4.1 is that there is a highest indifference curve touching the budget line.[4] The point or points at which this highest indifference curve touches the budget line are exactly the maximal budgets. Moreover, the indifference curve in question—we may call it the *maximal* indifference curve—cannot *cross* the budget line; for if it did, then by moving from the point of intersection along the budget line one way or the other (depending on the direction in which the indifference curve crosses the budget line), one would reach higher indifference curves containing permitted budgets. In other words, the maximal indifference curve must be tangent to the budget line if it is smooth enough to have a tangent. However, tangency is not *sufficient* for maximality. In Figure 4.1 the indifference curve ab is tangent to the budget line but is obviously not the maximal indifference curve, which is cd. Any utility index, viewed as a function defined on the budget line, would have a *relative* maximum at x, but this would be less than the *absolute* maximum attained at y or y'.

We shall assume in what follows that the indifference curves are smooth, by which we mean that they should have no corners like y' in Figure 4.1. Indeed, we shall make the stronger assumption that the given indifference map has a utility index with continuous second derivatives. This somewhat raw assumption has as its sole justification the fact that it greatly simplifies the subsequent analysis.

On this assumption, the discussion above constitutes a proof of Theorem 4.2.

Theorem 4.2. The budget x can be a maximal budget only if the indifference curve through x is tangent to the budget line at x.

---

[4] One indifference curve is *higher* than another if the budgets on it are preferred to those on the other. If one draws a vertical line through the budget plane, it follows from the Axiom of Nonsatiety that higher indifference curves will interest the line (if at all) at higher points; hence the term.

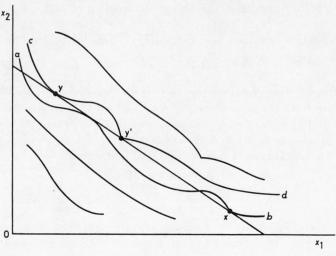

Fig. 4.1

Now let $U(x_1,x_2)$ be a fixed utility index for the given indifference map. Our problem is to find the maxima of this function subject to the condition

$$(4.3) \quad p_1x_1 + p_2x_2 - M = 0 .$$

The absolute maxima represent maximal budgets; but relative maxima, as indicated above, need not do so. They may represent only *relative* maximal budgets, i.e., budgets maximal as far as nearby permitted budgets are concerned, but possibly inferior to permitted budgets farther off. Since the available analytical methods deal directly only with relative maxima, we accordingly deal with relative maximal budgets; but the relevance of this inquiry to the more fundamental one of finding maximal budgets in the absolute sense is obvious.

According to the theory developed at the end of Chapter Thirteen, relative maximal budgets are found, if at all, among the solutions of the equation (4.3) which are also solutions of the equations

$$(4.4) \begin{cases} U_1(x_1,x_2) + \lambda p_1 = 0 , \\ U_2(x_1,x_2) + \lambda p_2 = 0 , \end{cases}$$

where $U_1 = \partial U/\partial x_1$, $U_2 = \partial U/\partial x_2$, and λ is a Lagrange multiplier. Moreover, any such solution will yield a maximum (will be a relative maximal budget) if the form

$$(4.5) \quad \Sigma_{ij} U_{ij} l_i l_j$$

is negative for all l_1, l_2 except 0, 0 satisfying

$$(4.6) \quad p_1 l_1 + p_2 l_2 = 0 .$$

Here U_{ij} is the value of $\partial^2 U/\partial x_i \partial x_j$ at the solution of (4.3)–(4.4) in question.[5]

The equation obtained by eliminating λ from (4.4) may be written

$$(4.7) \quad \frac{U_1}{p_1} = \frac{U_2}{p_2}.$$

Geometrically, this equation means that the indifference curve and the budget line have the same slope at (x_1,x_2) and are therefore tangent. Conversely, if (4.7) is satisfied it is possible to find a λ such that the equations (4.4) hold; all one needs to do is to put $\lambda = -U_1/p_1 (= -U_2/p_2)$. Thus necessary conditions for a relative maximal budget are

$$(4.8) \quad \begin{cases} p_1 x_1 + p_2 x_2 - M = 0, \\ \dfrac{U_1}{p_1} = \dfrac{U_2}{p_2}. \end{cases}$$

And these, together with the condition on (4.5) described above, are sufficient conditions. The conditions (4.8) alone are not sufficient; and the one on (4.5) is not necessary.

Looked at another way, the tangency condition is equivalent to the requirement that the *subjective* terms upon which the individual is willing to sacrifice marginal units of one good to obtain marginal units of the other must be the same as the *objective* terms upon which one good can in fact be exchanged for the other in the market. If the subjective and objective "exchange ratios" are different, the individual can obtain a subjective gain, without altering his expenditure, by refraining from the purchase of the good upon which the market places a valuation which is relatively greater than the individual's subjective valuation, spending his income instead upon the good which, from his viewpoint, the market undervalues.

Now since $U_1(x_1,x_2)$ and $U_2(x_1,x_2)$ are simply the marginal utilities of commodities 1 and 2 at a given budget (i.e., the rates at which utility increases per unit of increase in x_1 or x_2), U_i/p_i $(i = 1, 2)$ represents the rate at which utility increases per unit of money spent on commodity i. The ratio U_i/p_i may therefore be called the *marginal utility of expenditure on commodity i*. And so we have proved Theorem 4.3.

Theorem 4.3.   At a maximal budget, the marginal utilities of expenditure on the two commodities must be equal.

This common value of the two marginal utilities of expenditure (the "marginal utility of money") is just $-\lambda$, as shown above. This enables us to interpret the conditions (4.4) in the following simple way.

Theorem 4.4.   At a maximal budget, marginal utilities (in the usual sense) are proportional to the respective prices, the factor of proportionality being $-\lambda$, the marginal utility of money.

---

[5] This is sometimes referred to in the literature as a "stability" condition, but such terminology is both loose and misleading. Loose, because the concept of stability presupposes reference to a dynamical system, and the system discussed is strictly statical; misleading, because the careless reader may get the impression that this condition has some bearing on the problem of dynamical stability, which may or may not be the case.

The significance of the condition on (4.5) may be seen as follows: Let $\bar{x}$ be a maximal budget at which this condition is satisfied, and suppose that $U(\bar{x}) = c$. Then,

$$(4.9) \quad U(x_1,x_2) = c$$

is the equation of the indifference curve through $\bar{x}$, and may be thought of as defining x_2 as a function of x_1. Differentiating (4.9) with respect to x_1 gives

$$U_1 + U_2\frac{dx_2}{dx_1} = 0 ,$$

or

$$\frac{dx_2}{dx_1} = - \frac{U_1}{U_2}.$$

Differentiating this in turn gives (at $\bar{x}$)

$$(4.10) \quad \frac{d^2x_2}{dx_1^2} = -\left(\frac{U_{11}U_2^2 - U_{12}U_1U_2 - U_{21}U_1U_2 + U_{22}U_1^2}{U_2^3}\right).$$

Now if we take $t_1 = U_2$, $t_2 = -U_1$, (4.6) is satisfied, by (for instance) condition (4.7). Thus the quantity obtained by giving t_1 and t_2 these values in (4.5) must be negative, by assumption.[6] This quantity, however, is just the numerator in the parenthesis in (4.10). Thus, since $U_2 > 0$ by the Axiom of Nonsatiety, $d^2x_2/dx_1^2 > 0$ at $\bar{x}$. This means that the slope of the indifference curve at $\bar{x}$ is increasing, or, in more geometrical language, that the curve is *convex* at this point.[7]

Conversely, it is geometrically obvious that if *all* indifference curves are everywhere convex, any budget satisfying the tangency conditions (4.8) must be absolutely maximal.

EXERCISES

4.1. Make a chart showing how the assumptions and conclusions in this section are related. Use arrows to denote implication—two-way arrows to denote equivalence.

4.2. Find the maximal budget if $U(x_1,x_2) = 1 + x_1x_2^2$, $p_1 = 1$, $p_2 = 4$, $M = 20$.

4.3. Discuss some modifications that the theory developed in this section might require if some indifference curves terminate on one axis or the other.

4.4. Prove the statement immediately following equation (4.7).

4.5. The quantity $dx_j/dx_i = -U_i/U_j$ has been called the "marginal rate of substitution" of commodity i for commodity j. Give an alternative statement of Theorem 4.3 which makes use of this definition.

---

[6] $U_1 > 0$, $U_2 > 0$, by the Axiom of Nonsatiety.

[7] Strictly speaking a curve is convex if the line segment joining any two points on the curve lies above or on the curve. It can be shown that the positivity of the second derivative implies convexity.

4.6. The convexity condition imposed on (4.10) is sometimes "the principle of the diminishing marginal rate of substitution." In what sense may this rate— which is *increasing* in a numerical sense if the convexity condition holds—be considered to be *diminishing?*

5. The Comparative Statics of Consumer Demand. Suppose that a given indifference map is such that for any combination of prices p_1, p_2, and a fixed value of income M, there exists exactly one equilibrium budget. In this case it is possible to regard the components of the equilibrium budget as functions of those three variables:

$$(5.1)\begin{cases} \bar{x}_1 = \bar{x}_1(p_1, p_2, M)\,, \\ \bar{x}_2 = \bar{x}_2(p_1, p_2, M)\,. \end{cases}$$

These are the *demand functions* of the consumer. Since the equations (4.8) are *necessary* conditions for equilibrium budgets, the results obtained by substituting the functions (5.1) into the equations (4.8) are identities in the variables p_1, p_2, and M.

Our next task is to discover what can be concluded about the properties of the functions (5.1) on the basis of the various assumptions introduced up to this point.

First of all,

$$\bar{x}_i(kp_1, kp_2, kM) = \bar{x}_i(p_1, p_2, M) \quad (i = 1, 2)\,,$$

where k is any positive constant; i.e., *an equal proportionate change in both prices and in income does not affect the quantity demanded of each good.*[8] For such a change in prices and income does not alter the indifference map, and the equation $kp_1x_1 + kp_2x_2 = kM$ defines the same budget line as the equation $p_1x_1 + p_2x_2 = M$. Hence, if the quantities $\bar{x}_1$, $\bar{x}_2$ represent the equilibrium budget for the price-income state (p_1, p_2, M), the same values of x_1 and x_2 will give the equilibrium budget for the price-income state (kp_1, kp_2, kM). The empirical significance of this conclusion (and of corresponding conclusions obtained in later models) will be considered in Chapter Seven (Section 4).

Next, what effects upon the equilibrium values of x_1 and x_2 occur in response to independent variations in p_1, p_2, and M? From a formal standpoint, this question is the same as the comparative statics problem considered earlier (Chapter Two, Sections 9 and 10). The statical system which is relevant here is given by (5.1) or (what is equivalent, but more convenient for the present purpose) by the system of three equations

$$\begin{cases} p_1x_1 + p_2x_2 - M = 0\,, \\ U_1(x_1,x_2) + p_1\lambda(x_1,x_2) = 0\,, \\ U_2(x_1,x_2) + p_2\lambda(x_1,x_2) = 0\,, \end{cases}$$

---

[8] Mathematically, the demand functions are said to be homogeneous of degree zero in prices and income. See Chapter Eleven, Section 1.

i.e., the condition (4.3) together with the two conditions (4.4). For every set of equilibrium values $\bar{x}_1$, $\bar{x}_2$ of x_1 and x_2, this is an identical system in the variables p_1, p_2, and M, and may be written

$$(5.2) \begin{cases} p_1\bar{x}_1 + p_2\bar{x}_2 - M = 0 \,, \\ U_1(\bar{x}_1,\bar{x}_2) + p_1\lambda(\bar{x}_1,\bar{x}_2) = 0 \,, \\ U_2(\bar{x}_1,\bar{x}_2) + p_2\lambda(\bar{x}_1,\bar{x}_2) = 0 \,. \end{cases}$$

We shall use (5.2) to obtain explicit expressions for $\partial\bar{x}_i/\partial M$ and $\partial\bar{x}_i/\partial p_j$ ($i = 1, 2$).

(i) To find $\partial\bar{x}_i/\partial M$: Differentiate both sides of each identity in (5.2) partially with respect to M to obtain

$$(5.3) \begin{cases} p_1\dfrac{\partial\bar{x}_1}{\partial M} + p_2\dfrac{\partial\bar{x}_2}{\partial M} = 1 \,, \\ p_1\dfrac{\partial\lambda}{\partial M} + U_{11}\dfrac{\partial\bar{x}_1}{\partial M} + U_{12}\dfrac{\partial\bar{x}_2}{\partial M} = 0 \,, \\ p_2\dfrac{\partial\lambda}{\partial M} + U_{21}\dfrac{\partial\bar{x}_1}{\partial M} + U_{22}\dfrac{\partial\bar{x}_2}{\partial M} = 0 \,. \end{cases}$$

This system of three linear equations in the three unknowns $\partial\bar{x}_1/\partial M$, $\partial\bar{x}_2/\partial M$, $\partial\lambda/\partial M$ has for the determinant of its coefficients

$$\Delta \equiv \begin{vmatrix} 0 & p_1 & p_2 \\ p_1 & U_{11} & U_{21} \\ p_2 & U_{12} & U_{22} \end{vmatrix} \,.$$

Thus, writing Δ_{ij} for the cofactor of the element in the ith row and the jth column, it follows from Cramer's Rule (Theorem 6.1 of Chapter Eleven) that the solution of (5.3) for $\partial\bar{x}_i/\partial M$ ($i = 1, 2$) may be written in determinantal notation as $\partial\bar{x}_i/\partial M = \Delta_{1,i+1}/\Delta$.

Now

$$\Delta_{1,i+1} = p_1 U_{2.3-i} - p_2 U_{1.3-i} \,.$$

Here $3 - i$ is simply a tricky way of writing "2 if $i = 1$, 1 if $i = 2$." Thus, without knowing the properties of the indifference map (i.e., without knowing something about the signs and relative sizes of the terms U_{ij}) *nothing can be said about the expressions $\partial\bar{x}_i/\partial M$; they are restricted neither in sign nor in magnitude by our previous assumptions.* As a practical matter, on the other hand—and empirical research appears to bear this out—one would expect the equilibrium level of consumption of most commodities to increase with increases in "income," although for many commodities, particularly for technically inferior varieties of the same kind of good, this rule might often be reversed.

Both possibilities are illustrated in Figure 5.1. Corresponding to each different level of income (indicated by different parallel budget lines) there is one equilibrium budget (represented by the points P, Q, and R). The curve made up of all such equilibrium budgets (defined for given values of the two prices) is called an *income-consumption curve* since it shows how the equilibrium budget point varies with changes in income. The income-consumption curve in Figure 5.1 is such that the equilibrium level of consumption of both goods increases with increases in income up to a point (somewhere between Q and R); but beyond this point, the consumption of commodity 1 decreases with increases in income, while the consumption of commodity 2 continues to increase as before. This illustrates just one of many different possibilities, all of them consistent with our present assumptions. Indeed, the only restriction upon the income-consumption curve is that it must not intersect any one indifference curve at more than one point; a double intersection would contradict the requirement that the demand functions (5.1) are single valued.

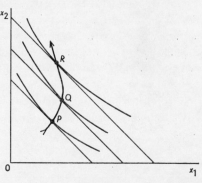

Fig. 5.1

(ii) *To find* $\partial \bar{x}_i / \partial p_j$: First differentiate both sides of each identity in (5.2) partially with respect to p_1 to obtain

$$(5.4) \begin{cases} p_1 \dfrac{\partial \bar{x}_1}{\partial p_1} + p_2 \dfrac{\partial \bar{x}_2}{\partial p_1} & = -\bar{x}_1, \\[2mm] p_1 \dfrac{\partial \lambda}{\partial p_1} + U_{11} \dfrac{\partial \bar{x}_1}{\partial p_1} + U_{12} \dfrac{\partial \bar{x}_2}{\partial p_1} = -\lambda, \\[2mm] p_2 \dfrac{\partial \lambda}{\partial p_2} + U_{21} \dfrac{\partial \bar{x}_1}{\partial p_1} + U_{22} \dfrac{\partial \bar{x}_2}{\partial p_1} = 0. \end{cases}$$

The determinant of this system is the same as for (5.3); accordingly, the solution of (5.4) for $\partial \bar{x}_i / \partial p_1$ is

$$\frac{\partial \bar{x}_i}{\partial p_1} = -\bar{x}_1 \frac{\Delta_{1,i+1}}{\Delta} - \lambda \frac{\Delta_{2,i+1}}{\Delta},$$

where Δ and Δ_{ij} are defined as in (i). By a similar argument,

$$\frac{\partial \bar{x}_i}{\partial p_2} = -\bar{x}_2 \frac{\Delta_{1,i+1}}{\Delta} - \lambda \frac{\Delta_{3,i+1}}{\Delta}.$$

But the first term in each of these expressions, viz., $-\bar{x}_j (\Delta_{1,i+1}/\Delta)$, is, by a result given in (i), simply $\partial \bar{x}_i / \partial M$ multiplied by the term $-\bar{x}_j$ ($i, j = 1, 2$). For the sake of brevity, we define

$$K_{ij} = -\lambda \frac{\Delta_{j+1,i+1}}{\Delta}.$$

Finally, therefore, we obtain

$$(5.5) \quad \frac{\partial \bar{x}_i}{\partial p_j} = -\bar{x}_j \frac{\partial \bar{x}_i}{\partial M} + K_{ij},$$

which gives the effect of a change in the price of commodity j upon the equilibrium consumption of commodity i, separated into two parts. What is the meaning of the two terms?

Clearly, a rise in the price of one good, money income and the price of the other good remaining fixed, is partially equivalent to a decrease in actual money income; and the consequent change in "real" income (the sacrifice of goods incurred because the given money income is now insufficient to purchase the original equilibrium budget) will obviously be greater the greater the initial consumption of the good whose price has changed. This provides a partial explanation of why a change in price is accompanied by a change in consumption; in particular, it provides a satisfactory economic interpretation of the first term on the right-hand side of equation (5.5).

A special calculation is needed to arrive at the interpretation of K_{ij}. Let $p_1{}^0$, $p_2{}^0$, M^0 be particular values of p_1, p_2, M. (The 0's are superscript indices, not exponents!) Suppose that p_1 is held fixed at the value $p_1{}^0$, while p_2 changes about $p_2{}^0$. Moreover, assume that M changes with p_2 in such a way that the budget $\bar{x}_1{}^0 = \bar{x}_1(p_1{}^0,p_2{}^0,M^0)$, $\bar{x}_2{}^0 = \bar{x}_2(p_1{}^0,p_2{}^0,M^0)$ stays on the budget line. This makes M a function of p_2; in fact,

$$M = M(p_2) = p_1{}^0\bar{x}_1{}^0 + p_2\bar{x}_2{}^0 .$$

From this, differentiation gives

$$(5.6) \quad \frac{dM}{dp_2} = \bar{x}_2{}^0 .$$

On these assumptions, $\bar{x}_i$ becomes a function of p_2 only: $\bar{x}_i = \bar{x}_i(p_1{}^0,p_2,M(p_2))$; and differentiation here gives

$$(5.7) \quad \frac{d\bar{x}_i}{dp_2} = \frac{\partial \bar{x}_i}{\partial p_2} + \frac{\partial \bar{x}_i}{\partial M}\frac{dM}{dp_2} .$$

If now (5.5) (with $j = 2$), (5.6), and (5.7) are combined, with everything evaluated at $(p_1{}^0,p_2{}^0,M^0)$, one obtains

$$\frac{d\bar{x}_i}{dp_2} = K_{i2} .$$

Thus K_{i2} measures the effect upon the equilibrium consumption of commodity i of a change in p_2, coupled with a simultaneous change in money income just large enough to enable the consumer to buy the original budget. The quantities K_{i1} may be interpreted analogously.

The preceding argument may be clarified by reference to Figure 5.2. Here the budget line before the change in price is L_1 and the equilibrium budget point is P; the budget line after a fall in the price of x_1 is L_2, and the new equilibrium budget is Q. However, if the fall in price was offset in such a way that no change in the consumer's "real" income occurred, that is to say, if (following the fall in p_1) the consumer was required to sacrifice actual money income up to the point at which he would just purchase the initial budget P, then the relevant budget line would be L_3 rather than I_2 and the equilibrium budget would be R—which lies to the right of P, to the left of Q. Thus, even if the change in "real" income were offset, a change in the equilibrium consumption of commodity 1 would occur nevertheless; because after the change in price the individual could obtain a subjective gain by substituting some of commodity 1 for commodity 2 in his equi-

librium budget. The change in question—represented in Figure 5.2 by the quantity $\bar{x}_1{}^R = \bar{x}_1{}^P$—is called the *substitution effect*[9] of the change in price. K_{11}, which represents the rate of the substitution effect in the present instance, is called the *substitution term* of the relation in (5.5) in which it occurs. The balance of the change in consumption of $x_1(\bar{x}_1{}^Q - \bar{x}_1{}^R$, in Fig. 5.2) is, for obvious reasons, called the *income effect* of the change in price, and the analytical expression for the rate of this effect $[-\bar{x}_1(\partial\bar{x}_1/\partial M)$ here] is called the *income term* of the relation in (5.5) in which it appears. Finally,

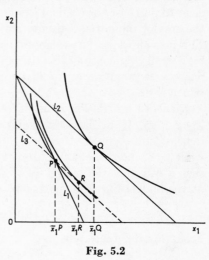

Fig. 5.2

the curve made up of points obtained by allowing one market price to assume various alternative values (P and Q in Fig. 5.2 are two such points) is called a *price-consumption curve*. Its properties depend, of course, upon the relative magnitude of the income and substitution effects; i.e., upon the sign and size of $\partial\bar{x}_i/\partial p_j$.

As for evaluating $\partial\bar{x}_i/\partial p_j$, since nothing can be said about the magnitude of the income terms in (5.5), the sign and size of $\partial\bar{x}_i/\partial p_j$ is also ambiguous. That is to say, our present assumptions do not lead to an unequivocal "law of demand" restricting the signs of these expressions. On the other hand, our assumptions do lead to "laws" about substitution effects. For

$$K_{ij} = -\lambda\frac{\Delta_{j+1, i+1}}{\Delta} = \lambda\frac{p_{3-i}p_{3-j}(-1)^{i+j}}{\Delta}$$

and the determinant Δ, when expanded, can be written as

$$-\{U_{11}p_2{}^2 - U_{12}p_2p_1 - U_{21}p_1p_2 + U_{22}p_1{}^2\} \ .$$

---

[9] It is also possible to regard the substitution effect as referring to substitution along the indifference curve containing P rather than to substitution along the budget line L_3. The effect defined in the former way is usually different from the effect as defined here. However, the difference between the two effects can be shown to be "of the second order of smalls." See J. Mosak, "The Fundamental Equation of Value Theory," *Studies in Mathematical Economics and Econometrics*, edited by Lange *et al.* (Chicago: University of Chicago Press, 1942) pp. 73–74.

By an argument like that used at the end of Section 4, it can be seen that this quantity is normally positive. Thus, since $\lambda < 0$ and prices are positive, the sign of K_{ij} will be that of $(-1)^{i+j+1}$:

$$\text{when } i = j, \ K_{ij} < 0 \ ; \quad \text{when } i \neq j, \ K_{ij} > 0 \ .$$

Ignoring income effects altogether, therefore, the equilibrium level of consumption of a good will rise with a fall in its own price, fall with a fall in the price of the other good. The first result turns out to be valid regardless of the number of commodities concerned. However, the conclusion $K_{ij} > 0$ for $i \neq j$ is generally valid only in the two-commodity case (see Section 6 which follows).

It should be noted that the conclusions reached here depend only upon the indifference map and its properties, not upon the particular utility index chosen to represent this map. More precisely, for given values of p_1, p_2, and M, all of the quantities $\bar{x}_i$, $\partial\bar{x}_i/\partial M$, K_{ij}, and therefore $\partial\bar{x}_i/\partial p_j$ $(i,j = 1, 2)$, are unaffected when the utility index U is replaced by the utility index $V = F(U)$, where F is a strictly increasing function with a continuous second derivative. This can be proved by using the identities

$$V_i = F'U_i$$
$$V_{ij} = F'U_{ij} + F''U_iU_j$$
$$-\lambda' = F'(-\lambda) \ ,$$

where $-\lambda'$ is the marginal utility of money in terms of the utility index V.

The values of x_1 and x_2 satisfying (5.1) are unchanged because the budget equation (1.1) is independent of U, and if $U_1/p_1 = U_2/p_2$, multiplication on both sides by F' gives $V_1/p_1 = V_2/p_2$; and the argument can be reversed. Thus, the conditions (4.8) defining (5.1) are unaltered by the substitution of V for U.

Furthermore, let

$$K'_{ij} = -\lambda' \frac{\Delta'_{j+1, \ i+1}}{\Delta'} ,$$

where
$$\Delta' = \begin{vmatrix} 0 & p_1 & p_2 \\ p_1 & V_{11} & V_{12} \\ p_2 & V_{21} & V_{22} \end{vmatrix}$$

and $\Delta'_{j+1, \ i+1}$ is the cofactor of the appropriate element in Δ'.

Then[10]

$$\Delta' \equiv \begin{vmatrix} 0 & p_1 & p_2 \\ p_1 & F'U_{11} + F''U_1^2 & F'U_{12} + F''U_1U_2 \\ p_2 & F'U_{21} + F''U_2U_1 & F'U_{22} + F''U_2^2 \end{vmatrix}$$

$$= F' \begin{vmatrix} 0 & p_1 & p_2 \\ p_1 & U_{11} & U_{12} \\ p_2 & U_{21} & U_{22} \end{vmatrix} + F'' \begin{vmatrix} 0 & p_1 & p_2 \\ p_1 & U_1^2 & U_1U_2 \\ p_2 & U_2U_1 & U_2^2 \end{vmatrix} .$$

---

[10] This statement is a consequence of general principles which do not appear in this book; but it can be verified by direct expansion.

But from (4.4), $p_i = U_i/(-\lambda)$, whence the second of the above determinants is

$$\frac{F''}{\lambda^2}\begin{vmatrix} 0 & U_1 & U_2 \\ U_1 & U_1{}^2 & U_1U_2 \\ U_2 & U_2U_1 & U_2{}^2 \end{vmatrix} \equiv \frac{U_1U_2F''}{\lambda^2}\begin{vmatrix} 0 & U_1 & U_2 \\ 1 & U_1 & U_2 \\ 1 & U_1 & U_2 \end{vmatrix} \equiv 0,$$

because two rows are identical. Therefore $\Delta' = F'\Delta$. Moreover, it is easily shown that $\Delta'_{ij} = F'\Delta_{ij}$ for $i,j = 2, 3$. Hence

$$K'_{ij} = -\lambda\frac{\Delta'_{j+1,\,i+1}}{\Delta'} = -\lambda\frac{F'\Delta_{j+1,\,i+1}}{F'\Delta} = -\lambda\frac{\Delta_{j+1,\,i+1}}{\Delta} = K_{ij}\ (i,j = 1, 2).$$

Finally, by a similar procedure, it can be proved that

$$\left(\frac{\partial \bar{x}_i}{\partial M}\right)' = \frac{\Delta'_{1,\,i+1}}{\Delta'} = \frac{F'\Delta_{1,\,i+1}}{F'\Delta} = \frac{\Delta_{1,\,i+1}}{\Delta} = \frac{\partial \bar{x}_i}{\partial M}\quad (i,j = 1, 2),$$

and it follows immediately that

$$\left(\frac{\partial \bar{x}_i}{\partial p_j}\right)' = -\bar{x}_j\left(\frac{\partial \bar{x}_i}{\partial M}\right)' + K'_{ij} = -\bar{x}_j\frac{\partial \bar{x}_i}{\partial M} + K_{ij} = \frac{\partial \bar{x}_i}{\partial p_j}.$$

Since the whole of the empirical content of the preceding analysis is expressed in terms of the quantities examined above and shown to be invariant against a substitution of $F(U)$ for U, we conclude that *the choice of a particular cardinal index of preference has no empirical implications whatever for consumer behavior.*

EXERCISES

5.1. Show that the "income effect" of a given change in price depends on relative prices as well as the properties of the indifference map.

5.2. Illustrate graphically that the intersection of a given indifference curve more than once by the same income-consumption curve implies that the demand functions of the consumer are not single valued.

5.3. It has been said that because consumers are in equilibrium some of the time, and because this would not be possible unless indifference curves were sometimes convex, therefore it is plausible to suppose that the latter requirement is frequently satisfied. Appraise this view.

5.4. The traditional law of "Diminishing Marginal Utility" states that $\partial^2 U/\partial x_i{}^2 < 0$ for all values of i. Show that even in the case of two goods, this "law" neither implies nor is implied by the "Law of Diminishing Demand" $(\partial \bar{x}_i/\partial p_i < 0)$.

6. Generalization to n Commodities. Once the two-commodity model of consumer behavior has been sketched, the transition to n commodities is relatively easy. One redefines a budget as a quantity combination $x = (x_1, x_2, \ldots, x_n)$ and rephrases the definitions, postulates, and proofs of Section 2 accordingly. This leads directly to the theorem that *through any given point $(x_1, \ldots, x_n)$ of the budget space there passes one and* *only one indifference "surface";* whence one is immediately enabled to generalize the utility index to apply to n-dimensional budgets, U now being defined as $U = U(x_1, \ldots, x_n)$. To facilitate analysis, this function is assumed to have continuous second derivatives $\partial^2 U/\partial x_i \partial x_j$ $(i, j = 1, \ldots, n)$.

Just as in the two-commodity model, the consumer's freedom of choice is restricted by the condition that the total value of purchases (at given prices) cannot exceed income; i.e.,

$$\sum_{i=1}^{n} p_i x_i \leqslant M,$$

or since the Axiom of Nonsatiety rules out budgets which do not lie in the budget "plane," by

$$(6.1) \quad \sum_{i=1}^{n} p_i x_i = M.$$

By the Axiom of Selection (Postulate V), the consumer is assumed to select that budget which is preferred to any other available budget, provided such a budget exists; so that the problem of consumer equilibrium reduces to that of finding a maximum for $U(x_1, \ldots, x_n)$ subject to the condition (6.1). A necessary condition for an equilibrium budget in the n-good case is therefore the existence of a number λ such that the equations

$$(6.2) \begin{cases} \sum_{i=1}^{n} p_i x_i - M = 0 \\ \\ U_i + \lambda p_i = 0 \quad (i = 1, . \quad , n) \end{cases}$$

are satisfied; while a sufficient condition for any budget satisfying this condition to be maximal is that the form

$$(6.3) \quad \Sigma_{ij} U_{ij} l_i l_j ,$$

where U_{ij} is the value of $\partial^2 U/\partial l_i \partial l_j$ at the budget in question, be negative definite relative to values of $l_1, \ldots, l_n$ satisfying

$$(6.4) \quad \sum_{i=1}^{n} p_i l_i = 0.$$

The budget restriction and the requirement that corresponding prices and marginal utilities be proportional are derived and interpreted precisely as before. The second-order condition (6.4) is again a "convexity" condition; but since convexity in n-dimensional spaces is a rather elusive concept, it may be better to express it by saying that a maximal indifference "surface" must lie entirely "outside" the budget "plane."[11]

---

[11] The case $n = 3$ suggests this terminology. Cf. J. R. Hicks, *Value and Capital* (2d ed.; London: Oxford University Press, 1946), pp. 24–25.

Now let (6.2) be determinate, so that the x's may be expressed in terms of the parameters $p_1, \ldots, p_n$ and M to obtain the *demand functions*

$$(6.5) \quad \bar{x}_i = \bar{x}_i(p_1, \ldots, p_n; M) \quad (i = 1, \ldots, n) .$$

This formulation also may be considered to include consumer *supply functions* by virtue of the fact that a quantity supplied may equally well be regarded as a quantity which is *negatively* demanded. Thus if $x_i > 0$, the relevant function of (6.5) is an ordinary demand function. If $x_i < 0$, it is a supply function and its properties will be precisely the same as the properties of an ordinary demand function *prefixed by a negative sign*. However, since it would only complicate the subsequent argument if we distinguished explicitly between supply and demand quantities, we shall leave it to the reader to remember that some of the x's may be negative and that conclusions for which the condition $x_i > 0$ is presupposed will be exactly reversed when $x_i < 0$.

Our next task is to examine the comparative statics properties of the functions (6.5), using information already at hand regarding (6.2). It is immediately apparent that the functions (6.5) are homogeneous of order zero in all price and income variables, just as in the two-commodity model; to proceed further, however, one must again have recourse to the methods of comparative statics which were outlined in Chapter Two.

With discussion now confined to equilibrium states of the variables $x_1, \ldots, x_n$, the conditions in (6.2) are identities in $\bar{x}_1, \ldots, \bar{x}_n$:

$$(6.6) \begin{cases} U_i(\bar{x}_1, \ldots, \bar{x}_n) + \lambda p_i = 0 , \\ \displaystyle\sum_{i=1}^{n} p_i \bar{x}_i - M = 0 . \end{cases}$$

Therefore each equation in (6.6) may be differentiated partially with respect to M on both sides, with the resulting equations

$$U_{11}\frac{\partial \bar{x}_1}{\partial M} + U_{12}\frac{\partial \bar{x}_2}{\partial M} + \ldots + U_{1n}\frac{\partial \bar{x}_n}{\partial M} + p_1\frac{\partial \lambda}{\partial M} = 0 ,$$

$$U_{21}\frac{\partial \bar{x}_1}{\partial M} + U_{22}\frac{\partial \bar{x}_2}{\partial M} + \ldots + U_{2n}\frac{\partial \bar{x}_n}{\partial M} + p_2\frac{\partial \lambda}{\partial M} = 0 ,$$

$$\cdots\cdots\cdots\cdots\cdots\cdots\cdots\cdots\cdots\cdots\cdots\cdots\cdots\cdots\cdots$$

$$p_1\frac{\partial \bar{x}_1}{\partial M} + p_2\frac{\partial \bar{x}_2}{\partial M} + \ldots + p_n\frac{\partial \bar{x}_n}{\partial M} = 1 .$$

In determinantal notation, the solution of this system of equations is

$$\frac{\partial \bar{x}_i}{\partial M} = \frac{\Delta_{n+1 \cdot i}}{\Delta} \quad (i = 1, \ldots, n) ,$$

where

$$\Delta = \begin{vmatrix} U_{11} & U_{12} \ldots U_{1n} & p_1 \\ U_{21} & U_{22} \ldots U_{2n} & p_2 \\ \cdots\cdots\cdots\cdots\cdots\cdots\cdots \\ U_{n1} & U_{n2} \ldots U_{nn} & p_n \\ p_1 & p_2 \quad \ldots p_n & 0 \end{vmatrix} ,$$

and Δ_{ij} is the cofactor in Δ of the element in row i and column j. Also, differentiating (6.6) partially with respect to p_j,

$$U_{11}\frac{\partial \bar{x}_1}{\partial p_j} + U_{12}\frac{\partial \bar{x}_2}{\partial p_j} + \ldots + p_1\frac{\partial \lambda}{\partial p_j} = 0$$

$$\ldots \ldots \ldots \ldots \ldots \ldots \ldots \ldots \ldots \ldots \ldots \ldots$$

$$U_{j1}\frac{\partial \bar{x}_1}{\partial p_j} + U_{j2}\frac{\partial \bar{x}_2}{\partial p_j} + \ldots + p_i\frac{\partial \lambda}{\partial p_j} = -\lambda$$

$$\ldots \ldots \ldots \ldots \ldots \ldots \ldots \ldots \ldots \ldots \ldots \ldots$$

$$p_1\frac{\partial \bar{x}_1}{\partial p_j} + p_2\frac{\partial \bar{x}_2}{\partial p_j} + . + p_n\frac{\partial \bar{x}_n}{\partial p_j} = -\bar{x}_j$$

the solution of which may be written

$$\frac{\partial \bar{x}_i}{\partial p_j} = -\bar{x}_j\frac{\Delta_{n+1,\,i}}{\Delta} - \lambda\frac{\Delta_{ji}}{\Delta} = -\bar{x}_j\frac{\partial \bar{x}_i}{\partial M} - \lambda\frac{\Delta_{ji}}{\Delta} ;$$

and, as a special case of this,

$$\frac{\partial \bar{x}_i}{\partial p_i} = -\bar{x}_i\frac{\partial \bar{x}_i}{\partial M} - \lambda\frac{\Delta_{ii}}{\Delta}.$$

Now the second-order condition is equivalent to the requirement that the determinants

$$\begin{vmatrix} U_{11} & U_{12} & p_1 \\ U_{12} & U_{22} & p_2 \\ p_1 & p_2 & 0 \end{vmatrix}, \begin{vmatrix} U_{11} & U_{12} & U_{13} & p_1 \\ U_{12} & U_{22} & U_{23} & p_2 \\ U_{13} & U_{23} & U_{33} & p_3 \\ p_1 & p_2 & p_3 & 0 \end{vmatrix}, \ldots, \begin{vmatrix} U_{11} & U_{12}\ldots\ldots\ldots U_{1n} & p_1 \\ U_{12} & U_{22}\ldots\ldots\ldots U_{2n} & p_2 \\ \ldots\ldots\ldots\ldots\ldots\ldots\ldots\ldots \\ \ldots\ldots\ldots\ldots\ldots\ldots\ldots\ldots \\ \ldots\ldots\ldots\ldots\ldots\ldots\ldots\ldots \\ \ldots\ldots\ldots\ldots\ldots\ldots\ldots\ldots \\ U_{1n} & U_{2n}\ldots\ldots\ldots U_{nn} & p_n \\ p_1 & p_2\ldots\ldots\ldots p_n & 0 \end{vmatrix} = \Delta$$

be alternately positive and negative,[12] so that in particular Δ has the sign of $(-1)^n$. Since the value of Δ is not altered by interchanging two columns or two rows, the condition also implies that all principal minors of Δ (i.e., all minors of diagonal elements) have the same sign, namely, that of $(-1)^n$. Therefore $\Delta_{ii}/\Delta < 0$, or

$$K_{ii} \equiv -\lambda\frac{\Delta_{ii}}{\Delta} < 0$$

for all values of i, just as in the two-commodity model. On the other hand,

$$K_{ij} \equiv -\lambda\frac{\Delta_{ji}}{\Delta}$$

is now ambiguous because for $n > 2$, the quantities Δ_{ji} $(i \neq j)$ are fairly complicated and their signs cannot be evaluated without additional information. Moreover, just as in the case $n = 2$, no restrictions can be placed upon the sign or magnitude of the terms $\partial \bar{x}_i/\partial M$, so that the expres-

---

[12] For a proof, see Hicks, *Value and Capital*, pp. 304–5.

sions $\partial \bar{x}_i / \partial p_j$ are also ambiguous in sign and magnitude whether or not $i = j$.

These findings do not detract so much from the usefulness of the n-commodity model as may appear to be the case at first sight. Simply as an instrument for the arrangement of ideas—to give one insight into the problem of consumer behavior—the model has considerable utility. The conclusion that "own-good" substitution effects are always negative is also of some interest, not because there are any *a priori* grounds for supposing that income effects will be swamped by substitution effects (for this is not so) but because there is good *empirical* evidence for believing that this will normally be the case—that the so-called "Law of Demand" will operate in nearly every instance. Furthermore, the ambiguity of "other-good" substitution effects (represented by the terms K_{ij} when $i \neq j$) is not too serious because goods which one would intuitively expect to be complements (e.g., gasoline and tires, bread and butter) are likely to be just that in practice, and similarly for goods which are intuitively expected to be substitutes[13] (e.g., butter and margarine, mutton and pork, etc.). Equally important, since prices for whole commodity groups frequently move up and down together in the real world, is the fact that our analysis can be used to shed some light upon probable changes in aggregate money demand for such commodity groups even when substitution and complementarity relationships are thoroughly confused within the group. This is accomplished[14] by showing that if the prices of a group of goods all change in the same proportion, the substitution effect on the group considered as a whole, the effect being measured in money terms, must be negative (cf. Exercise 6.3 which follows). (If there is an equal proportional and compensated change in *all* prices then, of course, the equilibrium values of $x_1, \ldots, x_n$ are not affected because of the homogeneity of the demand functions in prices and income.) That is to say, if the prices of a group of goods change all in the same proportion, the *money value* of that group of goods will behave in precisely the same way as if it were a single "commodity." Depending on the circumstances, therefore, one can apply to selected commodity groups much the same practical rules of thumb as apply to isolated commodities (remembering, always, that physical quantities may sometimes change in one direction while value sums involving these quantities change in the opposite direction!).

EXERCISES

6.1. If $K_{ij} > 0$, what can one say about the sign of $\partial x_i / \partial p_j$?

6.2. It has been suggested that an indifference map in which all indifference curves

---

[13] The jth good is said to be a *complement* to the ith good when $K_{ij} < 0$, a *substitute* for the ith good if $K_{ij} > 0$.

[14] The demonstration is too intricate and too specialized in content to be given here; however, the interested reader may consult Hicks, *Value and Capital*, pp. 50–51, 312–13; and P. A. Samuelson, *Foundations of Economic Analysis* (Cambridge: Harvard University Press, 1947), pp. 141–43, for the relevant mathematics and comments thereon.

are sharply "bent" ordinarily refers to goods which are complementary. Is this correct? Explain in detail.

6.3. Analyze the comparative statics of price changes in a three-commodity model on the assumption that the prices of two goods always change in the same proportion (i.e., suppose that, say, $p_2 \equiv kp_3$, where k is a fixed positive constant). In particular, what is implied by the second-order equilibrium conditions about the signs of the "double" substitution terms taken alone, and about the sign of their sum?

7. Generalization to Stock-Flow Commodities. The immediate consequence of supposing that the consumer may *hold* as well as *use* commodities is to double the number of variables that enter the utility index; so we write

$$U = U(x_1, \ldots, x_n; D_1, \ldots, D_n) ,$$

where the flow demand (or supply) variables $x_1, \ldots, x_n$ represent quantities of various commodities purchased for current consumption (or sold as current "output"), and the stock demand variables $D_1, \ldots, D_n$ represent corresponding quantities of the same commodities which the consumer wishes to hold for future disposal (through use or by sale). The D_i's may assume any real values, negative values indicating that D_i is a quantity of individual *debt* rather than assets.

While the decision to hold units of a given commodity is essentially independent of the decision to use (or "produce") units of the same or another commodity (this is implicit in the above definition of U), there will usually be links between the two decisions since commodities are not normally held for their own sake; and the properties of the utility index will reflect this fact (e.g., the demand to hold houses may be closely related to purchases of savings bonds, etc.). Furthermore, the decision to *alter* current asset holdings will usually have a direct influence upon current purchases generally since the consumer cannot acquire additional stocks of one good without either increasing sales from current output, diminishing current purchases for use, or disposing of units of other assets. As a matter of logic, however, changes in the demand for assets to hold cannot be related directly to commodity purchases because the former quantity is a stock while the latter is a flow. To define the budget equation of a consumer in a stock-flow economy, therefore, we must formulate a microeconomic counterpart to the investment function concept which was introduced in Chapter Two (Section 4).

To do this, we first denote by $S_i(i = 1, \ldots, n)$ the quantity of the ith commodity actually held by the consumer (this may or may not be equal to the corresponding quantity, D_i, that the consumer desires to hold). Then it is clearly plausible to suppose that the consumer will *wish* to increase, decrease, or leave unchanged his actual holdings of the ith commodity according as *desired excess stock demand* for the commodity, denoted by $X_i = D_i - S_i$, is positive, negative, or zero;[15] i.e.,

$$(7.1) \quad y_i \lessgtr 0 \text{ according as } X_i \lessgtr 0,$$

where y_i is the *desired* time rate of change of actual stock holdings of the ith commodity (a flow quantity).

But the mere desire to alter asset holdings may or may not be accompanied by action; the extent to which it *is* will depend upon a wide range of subjective, institutional, and technical considerations affecting the rate at which the consumer finds it desirable and feasible to match wishes with deeds. *Denoting actual purchases of the ith commodity to add to stocks by x_i'*, however, we may subsume these considerations in the form of a functional relationship between x_i' and X_i,

$$(7.2) \quad x_i' = x_i'(X_i) \quad (i = 1, \ldots, n).$$

If we then suppose that x_i' and y_i (i.e., *actual* and *desired* stock increases, respectively) are very nearly the same quantity—and this is a fairly sensible presumption under competitive hypotheses—we may state immediately, on the basis of (7.1), that the functions x_i' have the *statical* properties

$$(7.3) \quad \frac{dx_i'}{dX_i} > 0, \quad x_i' = 0 \text{ if and only if } X_i = 0.$$

The relations (7.2) and (7.3) may be regarded as the fundamental assumptions of stock-flow analysis.

The similarity of the above with the discussion in Section 4 of Chapter Two will be clear to the reader: the earlier discussion is, in fact, based upon the more detailed argument presented here. As in the former chapter, moreover, it is expedient to conduct analysis in terms of a simpler version of (7.2). Hence, we define

$$(7.4) \quad x_i' \equiv k_i X_i,$$

where k_i is a fixed positive number, to replace (7.2) in all subsequent discussion; i.e., we assume that the consumer's desired investment in stocks of the ith commodity is constantly proportional to his excess stock demand for that commodity.[16] It is worth remarking that (7.4) does *not* imply that

---

[15] We are suppressing subscripts which refer to particular economic units for the sake of notational convenience; but it is important not to confuse the quantities D_i, S_i, etc., in the present chapter with corresponding market quantities as defined earlier in the book. Written in full, the individual quantities to which we are now referring are denoted by D_{ij}, S_{ij}, etc., where the subscript j refers to some particular microeconomic unit.

[16] Unless the S_i's are defined as beginning of period stocks, and the D_i's are defined as end of period stocks, k_i must be considered to have a time dimension. In the exceptional case, however, one might assume that adjustments in S_i occur in a single period so that $k_i = 1$ (i.e., $x_i' \equiv D_i - S_i$); but this is merely one of an unlimited number of possibilities. The argument in the text is conducted throughout on the assumption that D_i and S_i are both defined with reference to the same point in time, implying that x_i' and X_i are not directly commensurable.

actual stock holdings, S_i, will be constant over time if $X_i = 0$; we assume only that changes in S_i will not occur *at the option of the consumer* unless $X_i \neq 0$ (but goods may still become obsolete, creditors may die, securities may be lost or stolen, houses may be burned or blown down, etc.).

The appropriateness of the term *investment function* to describe the functions defined by (7.4) (and [7.2]) is clear; for these functions give the individual consumer's current level of (desired) investment (disinvestment if x_i' is negative) in particular assets as a function of excess demand for that asset (the functions might also be regarded as *savings* functions). Under the purely competitive hypotheses prescribed earlier in the chapter, moreover, desired and actual investment (disinvestment) in any asset are always equal; so having introduced the investment functions (7.4), we may now proceed directly to define the *budget equation* of the consumer as

$$(7.5) \quad \sum_{i=1}^{n} p_i(x_i + k_i[D_i - S_i]) = M .$$

Total consumer purchases (sales) are now represented by $(x_i + x_i')$ instead of by x_i, since purchases may be for current use or to add to stocks and sales may be from current "output" or from stocks. The condition (7.5) states, in effect, that all demands must be *effective* (i.e., backed by purchasing power as well as desire); the total value of purchases for use or to add to stock $(\Sigma p_i[x_i + x_i']$ for positive values of the variables x_i and $x_i')$ must be equal to the total value of sales from current "output" and from stocks $(\Sigma p_i[x_i + x_i']$ for negative values of the variables) together with the value of income from other sources (M). (M may include negative elements representing contract interest payments on outstanding debts as well as positive elements representing contract interest receipts on outstanding loans, profits from business, etc.) If the kth commodity is money, moreover, then $p_k = 1$, and if the creation and destruction of money is a strictly governmental function, $x_k \equiv 0$; for the moment, however, we shall not destroy the symmetry of our notation by explicitly introducing assumptions of this kind into the argument.

In analogy with earlier discussion, we shall refer to a collection of flow quantities $(x_1, \ldots, x_n, x_1', \ldots, x_n')$ as a *budget*. Directly, of course, the consumer is concerned in the stock-flow case not with the selection of budgets but rather with the selection of a set of stock-flow quantities

$$(x_1, \ldots, x_n, D_1, \ldots, D_n).$$

Such a set will be called a *stock-flow plan*.

Now, supposing the consumer selects that stock-flow plan which is preferred to any other obtainable plan, we may proceed as before by maximizing U subject to the budget constraint (7.5) (regarding the S_i's, p_i's, and M as fixed), obtaining as necessary conditions for an *equilibrium stock-flow plan* (i.e., what might be called *plan equilibrium* as distinct from *budget* or *consumer equilibrium*)

$$(7.6) \begin{cases} U_r + \lambda k_r p_r = 0 \quad (r = 1, \ldots, 2n) \\ \displaystyle\sum_{r=1}^{n} p_r(x_r + k_{r+n}[D_r - S_r]) - M = 0 \,, \end{cases}$$

where

$$\begin{cases} k_r = 1 \quad \text{for } r = 1, \ldots, n \,, \\ U_r = \dfrac{\partial U}{\partial x_r} \text{ for } r = 1, \ldots, n \,, \\ U_r = \dfrac{\partial U}{\partial D_r} \text{ for } r = n + 1, \ldots, 2n \,, \\ p_r = p_{n+r} \text{ for all values of } r. \end{cases}$$

A sufficient condition for *plan equilibrium* is then that the form

$$(7.7) \quad \Sigma_{ij} U_{ij} t_i t_j$$

should be negative definite for values of the t's satisfying

$$\sum_{i=1}^{2n} k_i p_i t_i = 0 \,.$$

Here $U_{ij} = \partial^2 U / \partial u_i u_j$, where $u_i = x_i$ if $1 \leqslant i \leqslant n$, $= D_{i-n}$ if $n < i \leqslant 2n$. A budget defined by (7.6), (7.7) in conjunction with (7.4) is called an *equilibrium budget*. *Consumer equilibrium* is then defined by the further conditions

$$(7.8) \quad \bar{D}_i - S_i = 0 \quad (i = 1, \ldots, n) \,,$$

which implies and is implied by

$$\bar{x}'_i = 0 \quad (i = 1, \ldots, n) \,.$$

That is to say, *consumer equilibrium* occurs if the equilibrium plan (equilibrium budget) is such that desired and actual stock holdings are equal (desired investments are all zero). The consumer equilibrium requirements (7.8), which have no counterparts in earlier models, are essentially axioms of the statical stock-flow theory of consumer behavior. It may seem odd to distinguish between plan and consumer equilibrium in this way; but the procedure seems justified by the fact that (ignoring undesired destruction of assets) some asset holdings will be *changing* over time unless the conditions (7.8) are satisfied, which would contradict the common-sense notion of "equilibrium" as being a "state of rest."

Notice that the n-commodity flow model discussed in Section 6 is a special case of the present model obtained by assuming $S_i \equiv$ Constant (not necessarily zero), $X_i \equiv 0$, for all values of i, while an n-commodity *stock* model (involving only investment and disinvestment flows) is obtained by letting $x_i \equiv 0$ for all values of i. And a *partial stock-flow* model may be obtained by mixing these conditions, assuming that *either* $X_i \equiv 0$ (and $S_i \equiv C$) *or* that $x_i \equiv 0$ for each value of i. This gives the microeconomic background of the special macroeconomic models designated in the final section of Chapter Four.

Assuming that the system (7.6) is determinate, it may be solved to obtain the *flow demand* (*or supply*) and the *stock demand functions*

$$(7.9)\begin{cases} \bar{x}_i = \bar{x}_i(p_1, \ldots, p_n;\ S_1, \ldots, S_n;\ M) \\ \bar{D}_i = \bar{D}_i(p_1, \ldots, p_n;\ S_1, \ldots, S_n;\ M)\,. \end{cases} \qquad (i = 1, \ldots, n)$$

These functions, together with the investment functions (7.4), determine the functions

$$(7.10) \quad \bar{x}'_i = k_i(\bar{D}_i - S_i) \quad (i = 1, \ldots, n)\,.$$

The relations (7.9) and (7.10) provide the microeconomic foundations for the macroeconomic stock-flow models developed in earlier chapters. (The reader may notice that the present functions are more complicated in form than any discussed in the chapters on macroeconomics, by virtue of the inclusion of stock variables in the flow equations and stock demand equations (7.9). Thus the present formulation is not obviously consistent with the macroeconomic formulation given earlier; but we shall discuss this matter in Chapter Seven.)

The comparative statics properties of the functions (7.9) with respect to changes in market prices (or income, M) may be obtained by direct analogy with the n-commodity flow models outlined in Section 6, the only formal difference being that *a change in one price in the stock-flow model affects both stocks and flows of any given commodity*. Hence, the functions (7.9) are homogeneous of order zero in the p's and M. Moreover, (cf. Exercise 6.3), we may write (for the time being we work on the assumption that the values of the S_i's are fixed),

$$\frac{\partial \bar{x}_i}{\partial p_j} = -(\bar{x}_j + \bar{x}'_j)\frac{\partial \bar{x}_i}{\partial M} + K_{ij} + k_j K_{i,n+j}$$

$$\frac{\partial \bar{D}_i}{\partial p_j} = -(\bar{x}_j + \bar{x}'_j)\frac{\partial \bar{D}}{\partial M} + K_{n+i,j} + k_j K_{n+i,n+j}$$

and
$$\frac{\partial \bar{x}'_i}{\partial p_j} = k_i\frac{\partial \bar{D}_i}{\partial p_j},$$

where
$$K_{ij} = -\lambda\frac{\Delta_{ji}}{\Delta},$$

$$\Delta = \begin{vmatrix} U_{11} & U_{12} & \cdots & U_{1,n+1} & \cdots & U_{1,2n} & p_1 \\ U_{21} & U_{22} & \cdots & U_{2,n+1} & \cdots & U_{2,2n} & p_2 \\ \cdot & \cdot & & \cdot & & \cdot & \cdot \\ \cdot & \cdot & & \cdot & & \cdot & \cdot \\ \cdot & \cdot & & \cdot & & \cdot & \cdot \\ U_{n+1,1} & U_{n+1,2} & \cdots & U_{n+1,n+1} & \cdots & U_{n+1,2n} & k_1 p_1 \\ \cdot & \cdot & & \cdot & & \cdot & \cdot \\ \cdot & \cdot & & \cdot & & \cdot & \cdot \\ \cdot & \cdot & & \cdot & & \cdot & \cdot \\ U_{2n,1} & U_{2n,2} & \cdots & U_{2n,n+1} & \cdots & U_{2n,2n} & k_n p_n \\ p_1 & p_2 & \cdots & k_1 p_1 & \cdots & k_n p_n & 0 \end{vmatrix},$$

and Δ_{ij} is the usual cofactor. Since on our present assumptions currently desired stock holdings may differ from actual holdings, and since the former quantities are essentially nonobservable in this case, *empirical* demand behavior is described by the expressions for $\partial \bar{x}_i / \partial p_j$ and $\partial \bar{x}_i' / \partial p_j$ which refer to equilibrium budgets rather than to equilibrium stock-flow plans.[17]

The signs of off-diagonal elements of Δ are of course ambiguous in every case (in the absence of special assumptions); hence, the terms K_{ij} ($i \neq j$) may be zero or of either sign, so that the "own-good" stock-flow substitution terms $(K_{ii} + k_i K_{i,n+i})$ and $(K_{n+i,i} + k_i K_{n+i,n+i})$ might be zero or of either sign, just as in the case of "other-good" substitution terms for the pure flow model considered in Section 6. That is to say, purchases of a commodity for current consumption may be either a substitute for or a complement to purchases of the same commodity to add to stocks (and similarly for sales). On the other hand, the over-all substitution effect of a change in price upon total purchases (sales) of the good whose price has changed is given by

$$K_{ii} + 2k_i K_{n+i,i} + k_i^2 K_{n+i,n+i}$$

$(K_{n+i,i} = K_{i,n+i})$. The second-order condition implies that this expression has a negative sign (see Exercise 6.3, above). Thus, we obtain a "law" of demand (supply) restricting purchases (sales), although no such laws hold for consumption or investment purchases taken separately.

Finally, if we relax the assumption that the S_i's are fixed constants, it is evident that we have

$$\frac{\partial \bar{x}_i}{\partial S_j} = -p_j k_j \frac{\partial \bar{x}_i}{\partial M}$$

$$\frac{\partial \bar{x}_i'}{\partial S_j} = -p_j k_i k_j \frac{\partial \bar{D}_i}{\partial M} .$$

Then if we confine attention to equilibrium states for the consumer, $X_i = 0$ when $\bar{x}_i' = 0$ (i.e., $\partial \bar{x}_i' / \partial p_j = 0$). But since $\partial \bar{S}_i / \partial p_j = \partial \bar{D}_i / \partial p_j$, it can be shown that

$$\frac{\partial \bar{x}_i}{\partial p_j} = -\left[\bar{x}_j - \sum_{\substack{i=1 \\ i \neq j}}^{n} p_i k_i k_j \frac{\partial \bar{D}_i}{\partial M} \frac{\partial \bar{D}_j}{\partial p_j} \right] \frac{\partial \bar{x}_i}{\partial M} + K_{ij} + k_j K_{i,n+j} .$$

The substitution term in the last relation is ambiguous even if $i = j$; moreover, the income term in the expression, which indicates among other things the effect on $\bar{x}_i$ of changes in various asset holdings, and which is probably of more empirical significance than the substitution term, is always ambiguous in sign. This means that *a priori* considerations do not lead to any

---

[17] Actually, the expressions $\partial \bar{D}_i / \partial p_j$ may be of some empirical concern insofar as questionnaire and interview techniques may be applied to study consumer asset plans. In this connection the reader may be interested to read the National Bureau volume on *Short-Term Economic Forecasting*, Studies in Income and Wealth (Princeton, N.J.: Princeton University, 1955), Vol. XVII, pp. 7 ff.

conclusions regarding the effect of changes in prices upon consumer purchases if allowance is made for adjustments in asset holdings.

It will be seen that the stock-flow model is immeasurably richer than a flow model in actual and potential empirical implications, and that its conclusions are qualitatively very different in significant respects. The same observation may be extended to apply to various other special cases of the stock-flow model. Since, as a practical matter, it is difficult to conceive of a consumer who does not hold commodity stocks of one kind or another, this means that in dealing with empirical questions about consumer behavior it is essential that analysis be conducted (at least initially) in terms of a stock-flow model (either explicitly or implicitly). If consumer behavior were substantially the same under flow (or stock, or partial stock-flow) hypotheses one would be justified in dealing only with the simpler models; but, as indicated above, this is not the case.

EXERCISES

7.1. On the basis of everyday knowledge, would you expect stocks and flows of the same commodity to be complements or substitutes as a general rule? What are the formal implications of your conclusion?

7.2. What can be said about the sign and magnitude of $\partial \bar{x}_i'/\partial S_j$ and $\partial \bar{x}_i/\partial S_j$ on the basis of the argument in the text?

7.3. Justify the distinction between equilibrium plans (and budgets) and consumer equilibrium. Would the distinction make sense if the S_i's were defined as integrals over time of corresponding x_i''s? Explain.

7.4. In an empirical study of consumer demand, would it be legitimate to use consumption data alone to investigate the effects of price changes upon consumer purchases? Why or why not?

8. Dynamical and Other Generalizations. Aside from market aspects of the theory of consumer behavior (these will be considered in Chapter Seven), our argument is now substantially complete. It is fairly realistic to suppose that variables representing commodity quantities are the only ones over which individual consumers exercise direct control; and it is equally reasonable to assume that the parameters of primary importance in determining consumer choices are prices, incomes, and asset holdings. In these respects, the models presented in the preceding pages—particularly the stock-flow model—are reasonably accurate and comprehensive idealizations of everyday experience.

Nevertheless, the ideas outlined earlier might be extended in various directions, and so the theory might be improved as a logical background for the study of certain particular aspects of consumer behavior. It is no more than an exercise, for example, to generalize the utility function so that it deals with budgets involving prospective (future) commodity purchases. It is even easier to make theoretical provision for the fact that assets are normally held in part as a store of value as well as for their own sake—

this merely involves the introduction of price variables into the utility index. Similarly, one can deal with the social interdependence of consumers' preferences by putting into the utility index of one consumer variables representing budgets selected by other consumers. This brief list might be extended almost indefinitely.[18]

In nearly every case, however—and certainly in the ones just cited—the number of possible variations on any particular theme is so large as to limit very greatly the interest of abstract theorizing which is not motivated by the desire to clarify specific empirical problems. These and other generalizations which might be considered all involve the introduction of new variables and/or parameters into the elementary models described above, and for this procedure to be worth while, assumptions must also be introduced to characterize the roles which the new elements play. We do not wish to undertake the task of providing empirical justification for further assumptions, however, and we have no wish to manufacture models lacking a fairly clear basis in fact; so we shall not deal further with generalizations of the kind mentioned.

But apart from generalizations whose object is to broaden the class of factors embraced by a theory of consumer behavior, there is also the possibility of making *dynamical* extensions which yield a richer theory involving only those factors already considered. One may question whether the advantages accompanying dynamical extensions of the theory of consumption are sufficiently great to justify the effort involved; this is reflected in the fact that most of the literature on consumption theory is essentially statical in character. But unless one knows something about the character of consumer adjustment processes, it is hardly possible to pass judgment on this matter. Simply to assume that dynamical budget adjustments are strongly stable (as we require in order to ensure the empirical relevance of the analysis in preceding sections of this chapter) is to evade the issue entirely. We shall therefore consider a specimen dynamical model, which is merely one of several possible simple models that lead to conclusions consistent with the assumptions of the traditional statical theory of consumer behavior.

We shall deal with a flow system involving only three[19] commodity variables x_1, x_2, x_3 and a given utility index $U = U(x_1,x_2,x_3)$, where all budgets considered are required to satisfy the budget equation

---

[18] For examples of the generalizations suggested here, see Hicks, *Value and Capital*, chap. xvi; Don Patinkin, "A Reconsideration of the General Equilibrium Theory of Money," *Review of Economic Studies*, Vol. XVIII, No. I; J. S. Duesenberry, *Income, Saving and the Theory of Consumer Behavior* (Cambridge: Harvard University Press, 1949); and R. W. Clower, "Professor Duesenberry and Traditional Theory," *Review of Economic Studies*, Vol. XIX (3), 1952–1953, pp. 165–78.

[19] Here the consideration of only two commodities would lead to a model not sufficiently representative of the general n-commodity model, simply because along a budget *line* (as distinguished from its n-dimensional counterpart when $n > 2$) there are only two possible directions of motion, not infinitely many.

$$(8.1) \quad \sum_{i=1}^{3} p_i x_i = M ,$$

and where p_1, p_2, p_3, and M are all taken as given positive numbers. Thus, the variables x_i are the only functions of the time variable t within the model; and our immediate problem is to choose a hypothesis governing the manner in which the values of these variables tend to change over time. Time will be treated as a continuous variable.

Now if the consumer is purchasing a certain budget at a given instant but believes that by altering the budget in a certain direction within the budget plane defined by (8.1) he will thereby increase his satisfaction, it is natural to suppose that he will do so. Unless the current budget is maximal, however, it will normally happen that there are indefinitely many directions in which the budget might be altered with an associated increase in "satisfaction." To be more definite, therefore, we shall assume that *the consumer's budget is altered in that direction which involves the greatest rate of increase of the utility index U.* This assumption is suggested directly by statical consumption theory; out next problem is to reformulate it in mathematical terms.

As the point representing the consumer's actual budget moves smoothly through the budget plane, it traces out a curve with a tangent at each of its points. The tangent line at a certain point $(\bar{x}_1, \bar{x}_2, \bar{x}_3)$ on such a curve can be represented by equations

$$(8.2) \quad x_i = \bar{x}_i + \alpha_i \tau ,$$

where the numbers α_i have the property

$$(8.3) \quad \Sigma \alpha_i^2 = 1 ,$$

and the number τ is the distance (with a certain sign) from the point $(\bar{x}_1, \bar{x}_2, \bar{x}_3)$ to the point on the line given by (8.2). Moreover, since (8.2) represents the tangent to the given curve at the point in question, the budget component velocities along the curve, dx_i/dt, are proportional to the numbers α_i; i.e., there exists a positive number K such that

$$(8.4) \quad \frac{dx_i}{dt} = K\alpha_i ,$$

the derivatives being evaluated at $(\bar{x}_1, \bar{x}_2, \bar{x}_3)$. The value of K may vary from point to point, and will therefore be regarded in the applications of (8.4) as a function $K(x_1, x_2, x_3)$.

Now since the curve is constrained to lie in the plane (8.1), the same must be true of its tangents; thus any set of x_i's given by (8.2) must satisfy (8.1). This will occur if and only if[20]

---

[20] *Proof:* If the numbers x_i are given by (8.2) for some nonzero value of τ, then in order for them to satisfy (8.1) we must have
$$M = \Sigma_i p_i x_i = \Sigma_i p_i (\bar{x}_i + \alpha_i \tau) = \Sigma_i p_i \bar{x}_i + (\Sigma_i p_i \alpha_i)\tau = M + (\Sigma_i p_i \alpha_i)\tau ;$$
and subtracting M from the first and last expressions here gives the desired relation.

$$(8.5) \quad \Sigma_i p_i \alpha_i = 0 .$$

This is simply a condition on the numbers α_i, the satisfaction of which must be assumed throughout what follows. Another useful assumption, although it is neither necessary nor a real restriction of the generality of the model, is

$$(8.6) \quad \Sigma_i p_i^2 = 1 .$$

This can always be brought about by an appropriate choice of the money unit.

The dynamical assumption stated verbally above may now be brought into the argument. The instantaneous rate of change of utility *with respect to distance* along the budget "path" described above is the same as the rate of change of utility along the tangent at each point of the "path." Since τ represents distance along the tangent line, however, this rate is simply $dU/d\tau$, and the chain rule together with (8.2) gives

$$\frac{dU}{d\tau} = \Sigma_i U_i \frac{dx_i}{d\tau} = \Sigma_i U_i \alpha_i ,$$

where U_i is, as usual, the marginal utility of commodity i, $\partial U/\partial x_i$. Then to formulate our dynamical hypothesis, it is only necessary to know for what values of the numbers satisfying (8.3) and (8.5) $dU/d\tau$ attains its absolute maximum; and this information is given by the formulas

$$(8.7) \quad \alpha_i = \frac{A_i}{\sqrt{\Sigma_i A_i^2}} ,$$

where

$$(8.8) \quad A_i = U_i - p_i(\Sigma_j p_j U_j) .$$

This is proved in a Note at the end of the section. However, if the rate of change of U in every direction is zero, the information is gratuitous since in this case $\Sigma_i U_i \alpha_i = 0$ for all possible choices of the α_i's. In view of (8.5) this means that the U_i's must be proportional to the p_i's; i.e., there exists a constant λ such that

$$U_i + \lambda p_i = 0 \quad (i = 1, 2, 3) .$$

These are the familiar necessary conditions for an equilibrium budget in the usual three-commodity statical model; they are necessary and sufficient conditions for equilibrium (in the proper sense of the term) in the present model.

It follows from the above discussion, and in particular from (8.4), (8.7), and (8.8), that any budget path satisfying the dynamical assumptions of our model must also satisfy the equations

$$(8.9) \quad \frac{dx_i}{dt} = H(x_1,x_2,x_3) \cdot (U_i - p_i(\Sigma_j p_j U_j)) \quad (i = 1, 2, 3) ,$$

where $H(x_1,x_2,x_3)$ stands for the expression $K(x_1,x_2,x_3)/\sqrt{\Sigma_i A_i^2}$.

Hence, this system of three differential equations is the mathematical expression which was to be found.

Now let $(\bar{x}_1,\bar{x}_2,\bar{x}_3)$ be an equilibrium point, i.e. a point at which marginal utilities are proportional to the respective prices. The fundamental condition for stability is given by Theorem 8.1.

Theorem 8.1.   If the quadratic form

$$(8.10)\quad \Sigma_{ij}\bar{U}_{ij}t_it_j ,$$

where $\bar{U}_{ij}$ is the value of $\partial^2 U/\partial x_i\partial x_j$ at the equilibrium point $(\bar{x}_1,\bar{x}_2,\bar{x}_3)$, assumes only negative values when the variables t_i are not all zero and satisfy

$$(8.11)\quad \Sigma_i p_i t_i = 0 ,$$

then the equilibrium is stable.

Thus the stability condition for the present model is precisely the second-order condition encountered in earlier statical models; the same condition that guarantees that a budget satisfying the conditions (4.8) is a maximal budget now guarantees that an equilibrium budget is stable. Moreover, the conditions for an equilibrium budget are precisely the conditions (4.8), as we have seen.

The first step in the proof of this result is to linearize the differential equations (8.9). Near the equilibrium point, the marginal utility functions U_i are well approximated by their linear parts

$$\bar{U}_i + \Sigma_j\bar{U}_{ij}(x_j - \bar{x}_j) ,$$

where $\bar{U}_i = U_i(\bar{x}_1,\bar{x}_2,\bar{x}_3)$. Replacing each U_i by its linear part in (8.9), and replacing[21] $H(x_1,x_2,x_3)$ by $\bar{H} = H(\bar{x}_1,\bar{x}_2,\bar{x}_3)$, one obtains

$$(8.12)\quad \frac{dx_i}{dt} = \bar{H}\{\bar{U}_i + \Sigma_j\bar{U}_{ij}(x_j - \bar{x}_j) - p_i[\Sigma_j p_j(\bar{U}_j + \Sigma_k\bar{U}_{jk}(x_k - \bar{x}_k))]\} .$$

However, from the equilibrium conditions, $\bar{U}_i = -\lambda p_i$, where λ is a certain constant; using this fact and (8.6), we may write (8.12) in the form

$$(8.13)\quad \frac{dx_i}{dt} = \bar{H}\cdot[\Sigma_j\bar{U}_{ij}(x_j - \bar{x}_j) - p_i\Sigma_{jk}p_j\bar{U}_{jk}(x_k - \bar{x}_k)] .$$

Then if the indices in the second sum in (8.13) are reversed so that j becomes k and k becomes j, (8.13) reduces to

$$(8.14)\quad \frac{dx_i}{dt} = \bar{H}\cdot\Sigma_j(\bar{U}_i - p_i\Sigma_k\bar{U}_{kj}p_k)(x_j - \bar{x}_j) .$$

Now let $x_i = x_i(t)$ ($l = 1, 2, 3$) be any solution of (8.14) starting, and therefore remaining, in the budget plane (8.1). Our problem is to show that the function

$$\varphi(t) = \Sigma_i(x_i(t) - \bar{x}_i)^2 ,$$

---

[21] Strictly speaking, one should also replace H by its linear part; but the first-degree terms would immediately disappear from the linearized equations—by combining with others to form second-degree terms—so we omit them from the outset.

which gives the square of the distance from the moving point

$$(x_1(t),\ x_2(t),\ x_3(t)\ )$$

to the equilibrium point $(\bar{x}_1,\bar{x}_2,\bar{x}_3)$, has a negative derivative; for in this case, the moving point must always move closer and closer to the equilibrium point, and equilibrium will be stable. Using the chain rule and (8.14), we obtain

$$\frac{d\varphi}{dt} = 2\Sigma_i(x_i - \bar{x}_i)\frac{dx_i}{dt}$$

$$= 2\bar{H}\cdot\Sigma_{ij}(x_i - \bar{x}_i)(\bar{U}_{ij} - p_i\Sigma_k\bar{U}_{ki}p_k)(x_j - \bar{x}_j)\ .$$

Rearranging terms gives finally

$$(8.15) \quad \frac{d\varphi}{dt} = 2\bar{H}\cdot\Sigma_{ij}\bar{U}_{ij}(x_i - \bar{x}_i)(x_j - \bar{x}_j) - 2\bar{H}\cdot\Sigma_{ijk}\bar{U}_{ki}p_ip_k(x_i - \bar{x}_i)(x_j - \bar{x}_j)\ .$$

The second sum in the last expression is zero, for if one sums first with respect to i, one obtains, by (8.1),

$$(8.16) \quad \Sigma_i p_i(x_i - \bar{x}_i) = M - M = 0\ .$$

The formula (8.16) also shows that the quantities $t_i = x_i - \bar{x}_i$ satisfy (8.11). Thus, by assumption, the quadratic form in (8.15) must be negative. Since $\bar{H} > 0$ by an earlier assumption, (8.15) gives finally $d\varphi/dt < 0$, which is what had to be proved. As in earlier dynamical models, the stability thus proved for the linearized model implies local stability for the original model.

Thus the assumption that the consumer always tries to increase his satisfaction as rapidly as possible leads to a dynamical model whose conclusions are in evident accord with those of the statical theory. It is, however, a very narrow assumption, and institutional and technological limitations, the consumer's ignorance or whimsicality, and similar factors may prevent it from being fulfilled. Models allowing for these effects must begin with other, usually less specific assumptions, although it may always be supposed that the consumer (if he has any freedom of choice worth mentioning) will always attempt to increase his satisfaction, even if this increase is not as rapid as possible. Models of this kind are extremely complex, however, and stability conditions relevant to them are seldom in close rapport with the second-order equilibrium conditions of Section 4.

These remarks incidentally permit one to appreciate just how tenuous is the assumption, considered earlier, that consumer equilibrium budgets are normally strongly stable. But the stability assumption has an air of intuitive reasonableness about it, and because of its convenience we shall adopt it when we turn to the discussion of market aspects of consumer behavior in Chapter Seven.

NOTE

It has to be shown that the formulas (8.7) and (8.8) yield the maximum of the function

$$V(\alpha_1,\alpha_2,\alpha_3) = \Sigma_i U_i \alpha_i = \frac{dU}{d\tau} .$$

As noted in the text, in the case $V(\alpha_1,\alpha_2,\alpha_3) \equiv 0$, which occurs if and only if there is equilibrium, i.e., if marginal utilities are proportionate to prices, the problem is meaningless; we therefore exclude this case from consideration. First, we shall evaluate $\Sigma_i A_i{}^2$; it will be different from zero, so that the division indicated in (8.7) is meaningful. By (8.8),

$$\Sigma_i(A_i)^2 = \Sigma_i[U_i - p_i(\Sigma_j p_j U_j)]^2 = \Sigma_i(U_i)^2 - 2(\Sigma_i p_i U_i)^2 +$$
$$(\Sigma_i(p_i)^2)(\Sigma_i p_i U_i)^2 = \Sigma_i(U_i)^2 - (\Sigma_i U_i p_i)^2 ,$$

since the prices satisfy (8.6). However,[22]

$$(\Sigma_i U_i p_i)^2 < (\Sigma_i(U_i)^2)(\Sigma_i(p_i)^2) = \Sigma_i(U_i)^2 ,$$

unless the U_i's are proportional to the p_i's; and this is exactly the case we have excluded. Thus

$$(8.17) \quad \Sigma_i(A_i)^2 = \Sigma_i(U_i)^2 - (\Sigma_i U_i p_i)^2 > 0 ,$$

as claimed. Moreover, the numbers α_i defined by (8.7) and (8.8) are permissible values of the corresponding parameters, for one may easily verify that they satisfy (8.4) and (8.5). We shall denote these particular values of the α_i's by $\bar{\alpha}_1, \bar{\alpha}_2, \bar{\alpha}_3$. It only remains to show that $V(\bar{\alpha}_1,\bar{\alpha}_2,\bar{\alpha}_3) > V(\alpha_1,\alpha_2,\alpha_3)$ for any values of the α_i's other than $\bar{\alpha}_i$. By way of preparation, we shall show that

$$(8.18) \quad V(\bar{\alpha}_1,\bar{\alpha}_2,\bar{\alpha}_3) = \sqrt{\Sigma_i A_i{}^2} .$$

In fact,

$$V(\bar{\alpha}_1,\bar{\alpha}_2,\bar{\alpha}_3) = \Sigma_i \bar{\alpha}_i U_i$$
$$= \frac{\Sigma_i U_i(U_i - p_i(\Sigma_j p_j U_j))}{\sqrt{\Sigma_i A_i{}^2}}$$
$$= \frac{\Sigma_i U_i{}^2 - (\Sigma_i p_i U_i)^2}{\sqrt{\Sigma_i A_i{}^2}}$$
$$= \sqrt{\Sigma_i A_i{}^2} ,$$

by (8.17). This proves (8.18).

---

[22] Here we use the so-called Cauchy inequality, which asserts that if a_i and b_i are any real numbers $(i = 1, 2, \ldots, n)$, then

$$(\Sigma_i a_i b_i)^2 \leqslant (\Sigma_i(a_i)^2)(\Sigma_i(b_i)^2) ,$$

the equality holding if and only if the numbers a_i are proportional to the numbers b_i. This follows from the identity

$$(\Sigma_i a_i b_i)^2 = (\Sigma_i(a_i)^2)(\Sigma_i(b_i)^2) - \Sigma_{ij}(a_i b_j - a_j b_i)^2 ,$$

since the last sum is never negative and is zero if and only if the numbers a_i are proportional to the numbers b_i.

Next, we shall prove the equation

$$(8.19) \quad \frac{V(\alpha_1,\alpha_2,\alpha_3)}{V(\bar{\alpha}_1,\bar{\alpha}_2,\bar{\alpha}_3)} = \Sigma_i \alpha_i \bar{\alpha}_i \, .$$

In fact, the application of (8.7), (8.18), and (8.5) to the right side of (8.19) gives

$$\begin{aligned}
\Sigma_i \alpha_i \bar{\alpha}_i &= \frac{\Sigma_i \alpha_i (U_i - p_i \Sigma_j p_j U_j)}{V(\bar{\alpha}_1,\bar{\alpha}_2,\bar{\alpha}_3)} \\
&= \frac{\Sigma_i \alpha_i U_i - (\Sigma_i p_i \alpha_i)(\Sigma_i p_i U_i)}{V(\bar{\alpha}_1,\bar{\alpha}_2,\bar{\alpha}_3)} \\
&= \frac{\Sigma_i \alpha_i U_i}{V(\bar{\alpha}_1,\bar{\alpha}_2,\bar{\alpha}_3)} \\
&= \frac{V(\alpha_1,\alpha_2,\alpha_3)}{V(\bar{\alpha}_1,\bar{\alpha}_2,\bar{\alpha}_3)} \, ,
\end{aligned}$$

so that (8.19) is established.

However,

$$(8.20) \quad \Sigma_i \alpha_i \bar{\alpha}_i < 1 \, .$$

This may be proved using the Cauchy inequality once more:

$$(8.21) \quad (\Sigma_i \alpha_i \bar{\alpha}_i)^2 \leqslant (\Sigma_i (\alpha_i)^2)(\Sigma_i (\bar{\alpha}_i)^2) = 1 \, .$$

The equality can occur only if $\alpha_i = \lambda \bar{\alpha}_i$; and in view of (8.4) this can happen only if $\lambda = +1$ or -1. The case $\lambda = +1$ has been excluded already; and if $\lambda = -1$, we have

$$V(\alpha_1,\alpha_2,\alpha_3) = V(-\bar{\alpha}_1,-\bar{\alpha}_2,-\bar{\alpha}_3) = -V(\bar{\alpha}_1,\bar{\alpha}_2,\bar{\alpha}_3) < 0 \, ,$$

so that this set of values of the α_i's cannot compete with the $\bar{\alpha}_i$'s in maximizing V. Thus we may assume that the strict inequality holds in (8.21), and this of course implies (8.20).

Finally, combining (8.19) with (8.20) gives

$$V(\alpha_1,\alpha_2,\alpha_3) < V(\bar{\alpha}_1,\bar{\alpha}_2,\bar{\alpha}_3) \, ,$$

and this is precisely what had to be proved.

EXERCISES

8.1. Dynamical models of consumer behavior are extremely rare in the literature, largely because of the common assumption, usually tacit, that the consumer adjusts instantaneously to maximal budgets.

a) Is this assumption itself a dynamical hypothesis?

b) If it is, what can be said about stability in the resulting model?

c) Discuss the relative empirical merits of the "instantaneous" and "delayed" adjustment hypotheses.

8.2. Show that the structure of the model given in this section is unchanged if U is replaced by $F(U)$, where F is a strictly increasing and differentiable function.

SUGGESTIONS FOR FURTHER READING

The version of the theory of consumer behavior presented in this chapter is, in the strictest sense, only an introduction to the subject. The available literature not only contains many important details but also entire areas of analysis, which have been ignored here.

Among the best elementary treatments of the subject are J. R. Hicks, *Value and Capital* (2d ed.; London: Oxford University Press, 1946); and E. Schneider, *Pricing and Equilibrium* (New York: Macmillan Co., 1952), both of which were cited earlier in connection with the theory of price determination. The most instructive mathematical expositions of consumption theory are probably those of P. A. Samuelson, *Foundations of Economic Analysis* (Cambridge: Harvard University Press, 1947), chap. iv; and H. Wold and L. Jureen, *Demand Analysis* (New York, John Wiley & Sons, Inc., 1953). The latter work is particularly notable for its excellent summary of the history and literature of consumption theory up to 1950, and for its critical discussion of the foundations of the subject. On the last topic, see also P. K. Newman, "The Foundations of Revealed Preference Analysis," *Oxford Economic Papers*, 1955, pp. 151 ff.

The modern doctrine, as we have presented it, is the product of a long process of refinement and restatement which began almost a hundred years ago; yet several important problems have been solved only during the last decade, and empirical research in this area is still in its infancy. For information on these and related matters (largely ignored in our discussion), one may consult P. A. Samuelson, *op. cit.*, chap. v; G. J. Stigler, "The Development of Utility Theory," Parts I and II, *Journal of Political Economy*, August, 1950, pp. 307–27, and October, 1950, pp. 373–96; K. J. Arrow, *Social Choice and Individual Values*, Cowles Commission Monograph No. 12 (New York: John Wiley & Sons, Inc., 1951); J. R. Hicks, *A Revision of Demand Theory* (Oxford: Clarendon Press, 1956); R. H. Strotz, "Myopia and Inconsistency in Dynamic Utility Maximization," *Review of Economic Studies*, Vol. XXIII (No. 3), 1955–56, pp. 165–80.

Chapter Six

MICROECONOMICS II:

THE THEORY OF BUSINESS BEHAVIOR

WE come now to the second pillar of microeconomic analysis—the theory of business behavior. Broadly speaking, the distinction between the consumer portion of microeconomics and the business portion turns upon the use in the latter of a "profit-maximization" postulate as contrasted with the use in the former of the postulate of "utility-maximization." This choice of postulates is based upon compelling intuitive considerations, and it leads to different conclusions in the two theories; but the very fact that in both cases one is dealing with the maximization of certain quantities subject to appropriate constraints leads also to some very strong analogies, particularly since the quantities maximized are of the same general character. The exploitation of these analogies will enable us to simplify and abbreviate the development of the ideas in this chapter.

The distinction between consumer and business theories does not mean, however, that intuition dictates the adoption of a profit-maximization description of *actual* business behavior and a utility-maximization description of *actual* consumer behavior. On the contrary, there is no reason for excluding the possibility that in particular instances a theory of consumer behavior should be used to interpret business practices, and vice versa. The theoretical distinction between a "consumer" and a "business" is after all dependent upon the subjective motivation of individual economic units, not upon observable characteristics of behavior. In actual fact some people do conduct their consumption affairs in an unnaturally businesslike and miserly fashion, just as some people conduct their business affairs in an exceptionally unbusinesslike and Epicurean way. The desirability of distinguishing two (or more) branches of microeconomics arises not because the activities of certain economic units center exclusively about the "home," while those of others center exclusively about the "office," etc., but rather because any given person may conduct some of his affairs in one way, some in the other. The traditional separation of microeconomics into the two theories is thus not nearly so absolute as the differences in the postulational bases of the theories might lead one to believe.

1. Basic Assumptions and Ideas. We deal first with an elementary case in which the business decision unit, i.e., the *entrepreneur*, is concerned with three commodity flows only: an output flow and two input flows. This case serves as well as a more complicated one to express the substance of the theory of business behavior, and it is easily generalized later in order to elaborate various details of the theory. Thus let x $(x \geqslant 0)$ denote the output variable, let v_1 and v_2 $(v_1, v_2 \geqslant 0)$ denote the two input variables, and let q, p_1, and p_2 (all assumed to be positive) represent the respective prices of the three commodities. Assume, moreover, that each of the variables x, v_1, v_2, q, p_1, and p_2 is a well-defined and continuously variable quantity. Any combination of input quantities, $v = (v_1, v_2)$, will be called an *input*, and the aggregate of all possible inputs will be regarded as points in a (Cartesian) *input plane*. An input, v, such that one component is greater and the other component not smaller than the corresponding components of another input, v', is said to be *larger than v'* (and v' is said to be *smaller than v*). Finally, let entrepreneurial behavior be described by the following postulates:

Postulate I (Axiom of Entrepreneurial Decision).   The entrepreneur assigns a definite value of x for every input v, thus defining a function $x = x(v)$.

Postulate II (Axiom of Input Productivity).   For every v larger than v', $x(v) > x(v')$.

Postulate III (Axiom of Continuity). $x(v)$ is a continuous function of v.

Postulate IV (Axiom of Profit Maximization).   The entrepreneur chooses that input and output combination for which the quantity, π, defined by $\pi = qx - p_1v_1 - p_2v_2$, is greatest, provided such a combination exists.

The Axiom of Entrepreneurial Decision (Postulate I) states, in effect, that it is the entrepreneur rather than "the state of the industrial arts" which determines what alternative methods of operation are open to a business firm. The plausibility of this axiom may be queried on the ground that entrepreneurial management processes—decisions about the use of commodity inputs to produce commodity outputs, decisions about the holding of raw-material stocks, machines and equipment, financial assets, etc.—are essentially more impersonal than management processes directed towards the satisfaction of immediate consumer wants. But this is not really so. In fact, business decisions involve far more than the mechanical consideration of technically given alternatives and the selection of that alternative which offers the greatest money gain; for the determination of the field of alternatives is itself, to a large extent, a matter of personal choice. Just as a consumer may purchase noxious patent remedies which will sooner kill than cure him, so an entrepreneur may buy and use commodity inputs in such a way as to ruin rather than enrich himself. Just as a consumer may accept employment at an inferior wage in order to enjoy incidental benefits of a problematical character, so an entrepreneur may make concessions to his employees and rationalize his action by telling himself it is "good business"—although it may be very bad business from an objective point of view (if such a point of view were possible!). In principle, that is to say, the techniques of business are subject to the same variations from entrepreneur to entrepreneur as are the preferences of consumers from individual to individual—and for precisely similar reasons. Postulate I is designed to recognize this fact. However, the postulate does not deny the importance of existing technical knowledge in determining current business methods; it merely allows for the fact that some entrepreneurs are likely to be better informed than others, and also for the fact that the management of assets (money and securities in particular, but fixed assets and inventories as well) cannot be reduced to a "science" in the same way as can be the production of, say, wooden spoons.

The Axiom of Input Productivity (Postulate II) is less likely to be questioned. It imputes a fairly realistic rationality to entrepreneurial behavior by excluding from consideration inputs which represent sheer waste, that is, inputs which, if increased in quantity, would reduce output or leave output unchanged.

The Axiom of Continuity (Postulate III), like other "continuity" assumptions, is adopted because it is theoretically convenient. One could do without this postulate up to a point; but not without confronting mathematical complications which are out of place in the present context.

The Axiom of Profit Maximization (Postulate IV) is adopted because it is traditional and because it is intuitively plausible. Since some readers may question the validity of the latter ground, perhaps it should be emphasized that when business techniques are partly a matter of personal choice (Postulate I), Postulate IV does not require entrepreneurs to have a thorough-going "calculating machine" outlook on life; indeed, the profit-maximization postulate then acquires much the same status in the theory of business behavior, viz., that of a device for organizing ideas, as the utility-maximization postulate has in the theory of consumer behavior. In particular, there is no way in which Postulate IV might be refuted *directly* by empirical observation; its objective validity can be appraised only by comparing its *implications* with observed data.

2. The Production Function. Having examined briefly the rationale of Postulates I–IV, we may proceed to work out some of their implications. The function $x = x(v_1, v_2)$ defined by Postulate I is called a *production function*. It may be represented graphically by a surface in three-dimensional space; or, more conveniently, each point of the surface may be projected onto the input plane to obtain a "map" of the production surface in which each input point is associated with a particular level of output. Since Postulate I requires only that a definite level of output correspond to each point of the input plane, the map might be of almost any description.

Postulate II serves to orient the production map. It implies that all points which lie "northeast" of a given point v are associated with greater levels of output than v, and that all points which lie "southwest" of the point v are associated with smaller levels of output than v. From these considerations and the Axiom of Continuity it follows that all points representing input points associated with any given level of output form a curve which sweeps across the input "plane." In short, these curves (we shall call them *isoquants*) cover the input plane and form a configuration precisely like the indifference maps arrived at in Chapter Five. Postulate II of course implies that all isoquants are downward sloping throughout their length, in the sense that the chord joining two points on the same isoquant must have a negative slope.

An isoquant which lies above another is said to be *higher* than the second isoquant; all inputs on it yield a greater level of output than any inputs on the second isoquant.

In summary, Postulate I asserts the existence of production functions, and Postulates II and III then imply that entrepreneurial decisions involving these functions are restricted to input-output relationships of the kind depicted in the "map of production alternatives" in Figure 2.1. This map is composed of continuous and nonintersecting production isoquants which cross the whole quadrant (though they may or may not terminate on one or both axes) and are downward sloping throughout.

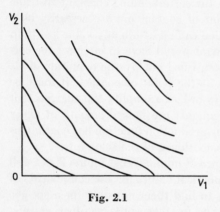

Fig. 2.1

The principal difference between a map of this kind and an indifference map in consumer theory is that the curves in the former are indexed in one specific natural way—there is a "cardinal production index," namely, output—while any utility index corresponding to a given indifference map should not be taken to be cardinal.

3. *Input Equilibrium and the Cost Function.* By the Axiom of Profit Maximization (Postulate IV), the entrepreneur selects an input-output plan which yields the greatest net revenue, provided such a plan exists. Such a plan may be called a *maximal* or *equilibrium plan*. Suppose that (v_1, v_2) is the input part of such a plan (the output is then immediately determined by Postulate I). Since moving along the isoquant containing this input cannot alter the gross revenue from the plan, which depends only on output, but may change the cost C of the input, it is clear that in order for (v_1, v_2) to maximize profit, it must minimize C along the isoquant concerned. In other words, *a necessary condition for an equilibrium plan is that at the corresponding point in the input plane the cost function $C = p_1 v_1 + p_2 v_2$ should attain an absolute minimum relative to the isoquant passing through that point.* An input with this property we shall call a *minimal cost input* for the given output. The condition is certainly not sufficient for an equilibrium *plan*, for by moving from one isoquant to another it may be possible to increase gross revenue, decrease minimum cost, or both.

Here, as in the preceding chapter, it is always assumed that all prices are taken as given and are, in fact, determined by "external" market conditions.[1] Under these circumstances, the necessary existence of minimal cost inputs on a given isoquant is easily demonstrated. Let us call the lines defined by the linear equations

$$(3.1) \quad C = p_1 v_1 + p_2 v_2$$

lines of constant cost. Since the prices are prescribed, all of these lines have the same slope; they differ only in their distance from the origin, which is governed by C. Now let a certain isoquant be given. If the isoquant contains the input point $(0,0)$, this is obviously a minimal cost input and there is nothing more to show. If the isoquant does not contain the origin (and this of course is the normal situation), one can imagine the line (3.1) moving outward from the origin, i.e., with values of C starting at 0 and increasing. Because of the nature of the isoquants as described in the last section, there will be a first value C_0 of C for which the corresponding constant cost line touches the given isoquant. Any point of contact must necessarily be a minimal cost input, for the cost function cannot attain any value less than C_0 on the isoquant; if it did, the isoquant would have to intersect the corresponding line (3.1), and this has been ruled out by the definition of C_0. Moreover, if the isoquant is smooth at the point of contact, it must be tangent to the line $C_0 = p_1 v_1 + p_2 v_2$. In order to simplify the analysis that follows, we shall assume that the isoquants are indeed smooth at every point; in fact, we shall assume that the production function has continuous second derivatives—this implies the smoothness of the isoquants.

The above argument for the existence of minimal cost inputs is not well adapted to the problem of finding numerical values for the components of those inputs, especially if one wishes to find them not only for a specific value of x but for arbitrary values of x or, in other words, as functions of x. This need is better met by a less geometrical approach.

Let x_0 be a certain value of output; then

$$(3.2) \quad x(v_1, v_2) = x_0$$

is the equation of the corresponding isoquant, and the problem of finding minimal cost inputs on this isoquant is merely that of finding the inputs (v_1, v_2) satisfying (3.2) at which the function (3.1) attains its absolute minimum. This is again a conditioned extremum problem of the kind discussed in Chapter Thirteen, and in view of the facts stated there one may say at once that any minimal cost input (v_1, v_2) on the isoquant (3.2) must satisfy not only (3.2) but also the condition that there exist a number μ such that

$$(3.3) \quad p_i - \mu x_i(v_1, v_2) = 0 \quad (i = 1, 2),$$

where $x_i = \partial x / \partial v_i$ (this is the so-called *marginal physical productivity* of the ith input component; it gives the rate of change of the output as the

---

[1] The more general case involving prices which depend upon output and other factors is considered later (Chapter Seven, Section 5).

size of v_i is changed). Elimination of μ from the two equations (3.3) leads to the equivalent condition

$$(3.4) \quad \frac{x_1}{p_1} = \frac{x_2}{p_2} .$$

Geometrically, this is the tangency condition. As a maxim of entrepreneurial behavior, the tangency condition is equivalent to the statement that for a given output the entrepreneur should not choose an input in which one component is cheaper than the other, "cheapness" in this case being measured by the rate of change in output with respect to expenditure on the component in question.

Any input satisfying the conditions (3.1) and (3.2), which are necessary for minimal cost inputs, will be a minimal cost input, relative at least to neighboring inputs on the given isoquant, if the isoquant is convex at the point of tangency. As we have seen in Chapter Five, this will occur if the quadratic form

$$(3.5) \quad \Sigma x_{ij} t_i t_j ,$$

where x_{ij} is the value of $\partial^2 x / \partial v_i \partial v_j$ at the point of tangency, is negative for all nonzero values of t_1 and t_2 satisfying

$$(3.6) \quad p_1 t_1 + p_2 t_2 = 0 .$$

We shall refer to this as the *second-order condition* for minimal cost inputs, even though it is not a second-order condition as the term is defined in Chapter Thirteen. As before, the second-order condition is merely a *sufficient* condition.

Now let us suppose that there is a unique minimal cost input on each isoquant; this will occur if the isoquants are all convex in the strict sense (i.e., without flat spots). The components of the minimal cost inputs $\bar{v}$ may then be regarded as functions of the parameters p_1, p_2, and x:

$$(3.7) \quad \bar{v}_i = \bar{v}_i(x, p_1, p_2) .$$

These functions, when substituted into the equation (3.4), yield identities. Moreover, the functions (3.7) may be used to define the minimal cost function, or simply the *cost function*

$$(3.8) \quad C = p_1 \bar{v}_1(x, p_1, p_2) + p_2 \bar{v}_2(x, p_1, p_2) .$$

This function gives the lowest cost at which the entrepreneur can produce the output x with prevailing input prices p_1 and p_2.

Postulate IV imposes on us the problem of finding the input-output plan for which

$$\pi = qx - p_1 v_1 - p_2 v_2$$

attains its maximum. In view of the above discussion, it will suffice to study the maxima of

$$(3.9) \quad \pi = qx - C ,$$

where C is given by (3.8); this is now a function of the single variable x, if p_1 and p_2 are taken to be fixed, and the investigation may accordingly be expected to be relatively simple. Before we undertake this investigation, however, we shall look into some of the comparative statics properties of the functions (3.7) and (3.8).

EXERCISES

3.1. Explain the sentence following equation (3.6) in the text. What *is* the second-order condition (in the usual sense of the term) for this situation? Is it of any value?

3.2. If $x = v_1 v_2$, find the functions (3.7) and (3.8). Use graphs to illustrate your results.

3.3. What policy recommendation would you make to an entrepreneur for whom the function (3.9) was strictly increasing? Strictly decreasing?

4. *Comparative Statics of the Two-Input One-Output Model.* We are to explore the manner in which the input demands (3.7) and total cost (3.8) vary in response to changes in p_1, p_2, and x. The functions (3.7) satisfy the identities

$$(4.1)\begin{cases} p_1 - \mu x_1(\bar{v}_1,\bar{v}_2) = 0 \,, \\ p_2 - \mu x_2(\bar{v}_1,\bar{v}_2) = 0 \,, \\ x(\bar{v}_1,\bar{v}_2) - x = 0 \,. \end{cases}$$

Differentiation throughout this system with respect to each of the variables x, p_1, p_2 in turn leads to three systems of linear equations in the "unknowns" $\partial\mu/\partial x$, $\partial\mu/\partial p_i$, $\partial\bar{v}_i/\partial x$, and $\partial\bar{v}_i/\partial p_j$. If these systems are solved by Cramer's Rule for the unknowns listed, the results are

$$(4.2) \quad \frac{\partial\mu}{\partial x} = \frac{\Delta_{33}}{\Delta}$$

$$(4.3) \quad \frac{\partial\mu}{\partial p_i} = \frac{\Delta_{i3}}{\mu\Delta} \quad (i = 1, 2)$$

$$(4.4) \quad \frac{\partial\bar{v}_i}{\partial x} = \frac{\Delta_{3i}}{\Delta} \quad (i = 1, 2)$$

$$(4.5) \quad \frac{\partial\bar{v}_i}{\partial p_j} = \frac{\Delta_{ij}}{\mu\Delta} \quad (i,j = 1, 2) \,,$$

where

$$\Delta = \begin{vmatrix} x_{11} & x_{12} & \dfrac{x_1}{\mu} \\ x_{21} & x_{22} & \dfrac{x_2}{\mu} \\ x_1 & x_2 & 0 \end{vmatrix}$$

and Δ_{ij} is the cofactor of the element in the ith row and jth column of Δ.

Now $\mu = \mu(\bar{v}_1,\bar{v}_2,x)$ is simply the value of *marginal cost* associated with minimal cost input at any given level of output, x; i.e., $\mu = \partial C/\partial x$. This may be seen as follows. Differentiate both sides of the cost identity (3.8) partially with respect to x to get

$$\frac{\partial C}{\partial x} = p_1 \frac{\partial \bar{v}_1}{\partial x} + p_2 \frac{\partial \bar{v}_2}{\partial x}$$

$$= p_1 \frac{\Delta_{31}}{\Delta} + p_2 \frac{\Delta_{32}}{\Delta} \quad \text{(by [4.4])}$$

$$= \frac{\mu}{\Delta} (x_1 \Delta_{31} + x_2 \Delta_{32}) \quad (\text{since } p_i = \mu x_i) \ .$$

Then if Δ is expanded by the elements in its last row, one has

$$\Delta = x_1 \Delta_{31} + x_2 \Delta_{32} \ ;$$

hence

$$\frac{\partial C}{\partial x} = \mu \frac{\Delta}{\Delta} = \mu \ ,$$

as claimed. This result together with (3.3) gives

$$p_i = \frac{\partial C}{\partial x} \cdot x_i \quad (i = 1, 2) \ ;$$

that is to say, regardless of revenue considerations, the presence of a minimal cost input requires that the price of each input component be proportional to its marginal physical productivity, marginal cost being the factor of proportionality. Since p_i and x_i are both positive by hypothesis, this implies that marginal cost is always positive. However, the behavior of marginal cost with respect to changes in output is characterized by (4.2); for

$$\frac{\partial^2 C}{\partial x_2} = \frac{\partial \mu}{\partial x} = \frac{\Delta_{33}}{\Delta} \ .$$

Thus marginal cost may be either increasing or decreasing with respect to increases in output, for the sign of Δ_{33}/Δ is ambiguous so far as the assumptions made thus far are concerned. The second-order conditions imply that $\Delta > 0$, but they imply nothing about the sign of

$$\Delta_{33} = \begin{vmatrix} x_{11} & x_{12} \\ x_{21} & x_{22} \end{vmatrix},$$

the so-called *Hessian* determinant of the production function.[2] This result

---

[2] The *Hessian* of a general function $f(u_1, \ldots, u_n)$ is the n by n determinant formed by taking all of the second partial derivatives of the function f and arranging them in the form

$$\begin{vmatrix} f_{11} & \cdots & f_{1n} \\ \cdots & \cdots & \cdots \\ \cdots & \cdots & \cdots \\ f_{n1} & \cdots & f_{nn} \end{vmatrix}$$

does not depend upon the denial of the usual laws of diminishing marginal productivity; i.e., whether x_{11} and x_{22} are negative (as often assumed) or positive, the Hessian of the production function may be negative—and so the marginal cost curve may be downward sloping—if the cross partial derivatives x_{ij} are sufficiently large.

Traditionally, of course, it has been usual to assume that the marginal cost curve rises at least for some ranges of output; and it is equally traditional to assume that the production function is homogeneous of order one in the v's (i.e., that $x(kv_1, kv_2) \equiv kx$, where k is some arbitrary positive constant). As a matter of fact, however, the homogeneity of the production function implies that the Hessian $\Delta_{33} \equiv 0$, which, in turn, implies that the marginal cost curve is *everywhere horizontal*.[3] It is therefore inconsistent to assume *both* that the marginal cost curve is somewhere upward sloping and that the production function is homogeneous of order one. We shall return to these matters and their implications in connection with the problem of determining equilibrium input-output plans. Meanwhile it may be noted that there is no basis for the second assumption, even in theory,[4] and that the first assumption has no clear basis in fact.

Proceeding now to other comparative statics aspects of the cost function (3.8), consider the expressions for

$$\frac{\partial \mu}{\partial p_i} \quad \text{and} \quad \frac{\partial \bar{v}_i}{\partial x}$$

given by equations (4.3) and (4.4). Our assumptions permit us to say nothing about the magnitude or sign of either quantity. However, from the fact that $\partial C / \partial x = \mu$, we have

$$\frac{\partial^2 C}{\partial x \partial p_i} = \frac{\partial \mu}{\partial p_i} = \frac{\Delta_{i3}}{\mu \Delta} \quad (i = 1, 2) .$$

Since the function x is assumed to be twice continuously differentiable, $x_{ij} = x_{ji}$, and so $\Delta_{i3} = \mu \Delta_{3i}$; accordingly,

$$\frac{\partial^2 C}{\partial x \partial p_i} = \frac{\Delta_{i3}}{\mu \Delta} = \frac{\Delta_{3i}}{\Delta} = \frac{\partial \bar{v}_i}{\partial x} .$$

That is, for minimal cost inputs, *the rate of change of marginal cost with re-*

---

[3] If x is differentiable and homogeneous of order one, then it may be written in the form

$$x \equiv v_1(\partial x / \partial v_1) + v_2(\partial x / \partial v_2)$$

(cf. Chapter Eleven, Exercise 1.4). Hence, partial differentiation on both sides of this identity, first with respect to v_1, then with respect to v_2, yields

$$v_1 x_{11} + v_2 x_{12} = 0 ,$$
$$v_1 x_{21} + v_2 x_{22} = 0 .$$

This is a homogeneous system of equations with the nonzero solution (v_1, v_2). Thus, by Theorem 6.2 of Chapter Eleven, the determinant of coefficients, which is precisely the Hessian Δ_{33}, must be zero.

[4] On this point, see P. A. Samuelson, *Foundations of Economic Analysis* (Cambridge: Harvard University Press, 1947), pp. 82–84.

spect to the price of any input component must be equal to the rate of change of that input component with respect to output.

Next consider (4.5). The expressions Δ_{11} $(= -x_2{}^2/\mu)$ and Δ_{22} $(= -x_1{}^2/\mu)$ are both negative in sign, whereas $\Delta_{12} = \Delta_{21}$ $(= x_1x_2/\mu)$ is positive; but since the second-order condition implies that Δ is positive, this means that

$$\frac{\partial \bar{v}_i}{\partial p_i} < 0 \quad (i = 1, 2)$$

$$\frac{\partial \bar{v}_i}{\partial p_j} > 0 \quad (i \neq j).$$

Thus, *a rise in the price of a given input component will reduce the amount demanded of that component and will increase the amount demanded of the other.* This theorem has a substitution-term analogue in the two-commodity model of consumer behavior (see Chapter Five, Section 4). In particular, the result $\partial \bar{v}_i/\partial p_i < 0$ holds in the general case of n input components, whereas the conclusion $\partial \bar{v}_i/\partial p_j > 0$, is valid only for two input components (i.e., two input components are necessarily *substitutes* in the production of a given output, but *complementarity* relationships are possible if the number of input components is more than two).

As noted above, $\Delta_{12} = \Delta_{21}$; hence we have the further theorem,

$$\frac{\partial \bar{v}_i}{\partial p_j} = \frac{\partial \bar{v}_j}{\partial p_i}.$$

That is, *at any given level of output, the rate of change of one input component with respect to the price of the other is equal to the rate of change of the other input component with respect to the price of the first.* This conclusion is valid for the general case of n input components.

Finally, from the equation (3.4) it appears that an equal proportionate change in p_1 and p_2 will not affect the minimal cost values of v_1 and v_2; for $\bar{v}_1$ and $\bar{v}_2$ will satisfy the equations

$$\frac{x_1}{kp_1} = \frac{x_2}{kp_2}$$
$$x(\bar{v}_1, \bar{v}_2) = x_0$$

if they satisfy the equations

$$\frac{x_1}{p_1} = \frac{x_2}{p_2}$$
$$x(\bar{v}_1, \bar{v}_2) = x_0.$$

On our assumptions, therefore, the demand functions $\bar{v}_i(x, p_1, p_2)$ are homogeneous of order zero in prices.

EXERCISES

4.1. The equations (4.2)–(4.5) are meaningless if $\Delta = 0$, and some of them are meaningless if $\mu = 0$. To what extent is it safe to assume that $\Delta \neq 0$? That $\mu \neq 0$?

4.2. What can you say about the shape of the cost curve $C = C(x)$ (prices being regarded as fixed) when the production function is homogeneous of order 1?

4.3. Give a geometrical proof of the result obtained in the last paragraph of this section. What does that result imply about the cost function as a function of prices?

5. Output Equilibrium. The preceding sections of this chapter have been devoted to a model specifically designed to emphasize the *input management* side of the entrepreneurial behavior. Having investigated that problem at some length, let us now look briefly at the situation from the other side, dealing now mainly with the *output management* side of entrepreneurial behavior. With this object in mind, assume that the entrepreneur deals with one input flow and two output flows. Let v denote the input variable, let x_1 and x_2 denote the output variables, and let the respective prices of v, x_1, and x_2 be given by p, q_1, and q_2. Any combination of output quantities, $x = (x_1, x_2)$ may be called an *output*, and the aggregate of all possible outputs may be regarded as points in an *output plane*, etc. Finally, interchange the letters "v" and "x" and the words "input" and "output" throughout Postulates I–III of Section 1, and define π by

$$\pi = q_1 x_1 + q_2 x_2 - pv$$

in Postulate IV. Then Postulate I defines an *input function*, $v = v(x_1, x_2)$, which is "oriented" (Postulate II), and "continuous" (Postulate III), and which may be represented graphically as an *output map* having precisely the same characteristics as the production map described in Section 2, above. An isoquant is now the curve made up of outputs obtainable with a given level of input rather than of inputs which yield a given level of output— but that is the only difference.

Postulate IV then implies as a necessary condition for *output equilibrium* that the entrepreneur selects that output which yields the largest *total* revenue for any given level of input (i.e., for any given level of total cost). Analytically, the problem is to maximize total revenue, $R = q_1 x_1 + q_2 x_2$, subject to the side restriction $v(x_1, x_2) = $ constant; that is to say, total revenue is to be maximized along some given isoquant. An output of this kind will be called a *maximal revenue output*. A necessary condition for this is the existence of a constant λ such that

$$(5.1) \begin{cases} q_1 - \lambda v_1 = 0, \\ q_2 - \lambda v_2 = 0, \\ v(x_1, x_2) - v = 0, \end{cases}$$

where $v_i = \partial v / \partial x_i$. The quantity v_i may be called the *marginal physical input requirement* of the ith output (the term "marginal physical inputivity" might recommend itself by analogy with previously introduced terms, were it not so barbarous!). The conditions (5.1), of which the first two have the expected equivalent

$$(5.2) \quad \frac{v_1}{q_1} = \frac{v_2}{q_2},$$

imply the tangency of the input isoquant in question with the appropriate *line of constant revenue* defined by

$$(5.3) \quad R = q_1 x_1 + q_2 x_2 \,,$$

with R, q_1, and q_2 regarded as parameters.

The second-order condition which is sufficient for a solution of (5.1) to represent a maximal revenue output, at least relative to neighboring points on the isoquant, is that the quadratic form $\Sigma_{ij} v_{ij} t_i t_j$ be *positive* for all values of t_1 and t_2, not both zero, which satisfy $q_1 t_1 + q_2 t_2 = 0$. Geometrically, this implies that the isoquant should be *concave*[5] at the point of tangency. If an isoquant is strictly concave throughout, the existence of a unique maximal revenue output on it can be shown by a simple geometrical argument. If this is true of each isoquant, we can represent the components of maximal revenue outputs by the functions

$$(5.4) \quad \bar{x}_1 = \bar{x}_1(v,q_1,q_2) \,, \quad \bar{x}_2 = \bar{x}_2(v,q_1,q_2) \,,$$

which are called the *output supply functions*. When x_1 and x_2 are replaced by these functions in (5.1) and (5.2), the latter become identities; and combining (5.3) and (5.4) gives the *revenue function*

$$(5.5) \quad R = q_1 \bar{x}_1(v,q_1,q_2) + q_2 \bar{x}_2(v,q_1,q_2) \,,$$

which gives the largest total revenue obtainable from the input v at output prices q_1 and q_2.

Following precisely the same procedure as in the preceding section (subsequent operations are left to the reader), it can be then shown that

$$\frac{\partial R}{\partial v} = \lambda \,;$$

i.e., that *marginal revenue with respect to input* is given by the Lagrange multiplier in (5.1) (notice that this *is not* the usual "marginal revenue" concept, for the latter is marginal revenue *with respect to output* rather than with respect to input). For a maximal revenue output, therefore, *the price of each output component must be proportional to the marginal physical input requirement of the corresponding component, where marginal revenue with respect to input is the factor of proportionality*. This result, like the analogous theorem for inputs, holds regardless of cost considerations. In further analogy with the cost function case, $\partial^2 R/\partial v^2$, the slope of the curve of "marginal revenue with respect to input" may be either negative or positive. This is simply the obverse of the corresponding conclusion regarding "marginal cost with respect to output."

Turning next to the properties of the supply functions for $\bar{x}_1$ and $\bar{x}_2$, one

---

[5] A curve is *concave* if the line segment joining any two points on the curve lies entirely on or below the curve. A concave curve is thus simply a convex curve turned upside down.

can easily show that normally (i.e., when the second-order condition is satisfied)

$$\frac{\partial \bar{x}_i}{\partial q_i} > 0 \quad (i = 1, 2)$$

$$\frac{\partial \bar{x}_i}{\partial q_j} < 0 \quad (i \neq j) \,.$$

Thus, *a rise in the price of one output component will increase the amount supplied of that component and will decrease the amount supplied of the other* (the last half of this theorem is valid, of course, only for the two-output case). Also,

$$\frac{\partial \bar{x}_i}{\partial q_j} = \frac{\partial \bar{x}_j}{\partial q_i} :$$

at a maximal revenue output, *the rate of change of one output component with respect to the price of the other is equal to the rate of change of the other output component with respect to the price of the first* (this theorem is valid for the general case of n output components). Finally, it can be shown that the supply functions $\bar{x}_1$, $\bar{x}_2$, like the demand functions $\bar{v}_1$, $\bar{v}_2$, are homogeneous of order zero in prices.

EXERCISES

5.1. Taking some values of q_1 and q_2 to be given, draw a typical output map, including isoquants on which there exist no maximal revenue outputs, and others on which there exist several points satisfying the tangency condition.

5.2. Derive, by methods analogous to those of Section 4, some of the results announced in the last part of this section.

6. *Profit Equilibrium and the Comparative Statics of Business Behavior.* The preceding section is in the nature of a digression, intended to demonstrate the essentially symmetrical nature of entrepreneurial problems involving the management of inputs and outputs, and to illustrate the theoretical flexibility of the "axiomatic" method of analysis. Turning now to the problem of determining equilibrium input-output plans, we revert again to Postulates I–IV as originally set forth in Section 1 of this chapter.

By Postulate IV, an equilibrium plan is defined as that input and output combination for which the quantity $\pi = qx - p_1v_1 - p_2v_2$ is greatest (provided such a combination exists), where possible alternative values of x, v_1, and v_2 are assumed to be related by the production function $x = x(v_1, v_2)$. Assuming given constant prices and the existence of unique minimal cost inputs, however, we may replace the expression $p_1v_1 + p_2v_2$ by the expression $p_1\bar{v}_1 + p_2\bar{v}_2 = C(x)$. Since this substitution presupposes the satisfaction of the condition $x = x(v_1, v_2)$, the problem of determining the equilibrium input-output plan may then be restated as that of determining a maximum for the function

$$\pi = qx - C(x) \; .$$

The assumption that inputs are minimal cost inputs merely fixes the input plan corresponding to each level of output. If, under these circumstances, one can find an "optimal" output, i.e., an output which, associated with the corresponding minimal cost input, minimizes the cost function, $C(x)$, then an equilibrium input-output plan has been found.

According to Chapter Thirteen, a necessary condition for an optimal output is

$$(6.1) \qquad \frac{\partial \pi}{\partial x} = q - \frac{\partial C}{\partial x} = 0 \; ;$$

and π will attain a (relative) maximum at a solution x of (6.1) if

$$(6.2) \qquad \frac{\partial^2 \pi}{\partial x^2} = - \frac{\partial^2 C}{\partial x^2} < 0 \; .$$

In other words, in equilibrium marginal revenue[6] $R_M (= q)$ must be equal to marginal cost $C_M (= \partial C / \partial x)$; and if C_M is increasing at an output satisfying this condition, the output is optimal, at least relative to neighboring outputs.[7] Such an output, say $\bar{x}$, together with the input components given by the input demand functions, $\bar{v}_1(\bar{x},p_1,p_2)$ and $\bar{v}_2(\bar{x},p_1,p_2)$, would give a (relatively) maximal input-output plan. Then there arises the usual problem of finding which, if any, of the relatively maximal input-output plans leads to an absolute maximum of π.

The comparative statics aspects of the input-output equilibrium problem are implicit in our earlier discussion (Sections 4 and 5). Instead of repeating earlier findings at this point, therefore, we shall next generalize the entire analysis, treating cost and revenue aspects of the profit equilibrium

---

[6] The change in notation from the traditional MR to R_M is prompted by the desire to avoid labels which have a geometrical, rather than an analytical, connotation. The notation used here has the further advantage that it distinguishes nouns from adjectives.

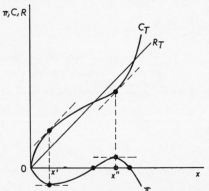

[7] In terms of total cost C_T, total revenue R_T, and net revenue π, this is illustrated in the accompanying figure, where output x is measured along the horizontal axis, and C_T, R_T, and π (all of which have the dimensions of money) are measured along the vertical axis. The condition $R_M = C_M$ (i.e., [6.1]) is satisfied at the two levels of output x' and x'', for the slopes of the R_T and C_T curves are equal for these values of x. Equivalently, the profit curve π has a horizontal tangent at each of these points. But of the two levels of output only x'' can be optimal, for C_M (the slope of the C_T curve) is increasing there, while it is decreasing at x'.

problem symmetrically in order to obtain comparative statics conclusions of a unified character.

EXERCISES

6.1. Find the equilibrium input-output plan if $x = v_1 v_2$, $q = 1$, $p_1 = 2$, $p_2 = 3$. (Cf. Exercise 3.2.)

6.2. In the model of Section 5, the input-output equilibrium problem would involve maximizing $\pi = R - pv$, where $R = q_1 \bar{x}_1 + q_2 \bar{x}_2$. Work out the analytical and graphical implications of this case.

7. The General Flow Model of Business Behavior. In order to bring symmetry into the theory of entrepreneurial behavior, we introduce a new concept which subsumes the concepts of input and output. Because of an entrepreneur's direct activity, the existing amounts of certain commodities are changed. The existing amounts of those commodities which the entrepreneur produces as an output are increased, while those that he consumes as inputs are decreased. If we express these changes as *rates*,[8] denoting by $-x_i$ the rate of change of the ith commodity (involved in the entrepreneur's activity) because of that activity, then $x_i < 0$ means that the ith commodity is a (net) output, while $x_i > 0$ means that it is a (net) input. The quantities x_i may be called *production flows*.

Assume now that the entrepreneur under consideration is concerned with commodities $1, 2, \ldots, n$ with the given prices, $p_1, p_2, \ldots, p_n$.

By analogy with Postulate I, furthermore, assume the existence of a function φ such that for given values of any $n-1$ of the variables $x_1, x_2, \ldots, x_n$, the entrepreneur assigns a definite value to the remaining variable in such a way that the condition

$$(7.1) \quad \varphi(x_1, x_2, \ldots, x_n) = 0$$

is satisfied. The function φ is called a *transformation function* since it characterizes alternative possible ways of "transforming" quantities of one commodity (input or output) into quantities of others. Moreover, replace Postulate II by the condition

$$(7.2) \quad \varphi_i \equiv \frac{\partial \varphi}{\partial x_i} > 0 .$$

This assumption corresponds to Postulate II. For suppose that all but two of the production flows, say x_i and x_j, are held fixed; then (7.1) may be thought of as defining x_j as a function of x_i, so that differentiation of (7.1) with respect to x_i gives

$$\varphi_i + \varphi_j \frac{\partial x_j}{\partial x_i} = 0 ,$$

---

[8] The rates are per-period changes if time is treated as a discrete variable, instantaneous if time is treated as a continuous variable.

or equivalently

$$(7.3) \quad \frac{\partial x_j}{\partial x_i} = - \frac{\varphi_i}{\varphi_j} < 0 .$$

If i is an input commodity, while j is an output, (7.3) means that an increase in the output of commodity j (i.e., a *decrease* in the corresponding production flow x_j) will result from an increase in the input x_i if all other inputs and outputs are held fixed. This is strictly analogous to Postulate II. Moreover, if commodities i and j are both outputs, (7.3) means that a reduction in the output $-x_j$ will result from an increase in $-x_i$, all inputs and other outputs being held fixed; and so on. The essential thing about the assumption (7.2) is that it asserts that all of the quantities φ_i have the same sign; one could replace the assumption (7.2) by the assumption $\varphi_i < 0$, and the subsequent theory would be entirely unaffected.

Next, in place of Postulate III, suppose that φ is continuous, and in fact that all of the derivatives $\varphi_{ij} = \partial^2 \varphi / \partial x_i \partial x_j$ exist and are continuous.

Finally, replace Postulate IV by the assumption that the entrepreneur selects values of the x_i's for which the function $\pi = - \sum_{i=1}^{n} p_i x_i$ (profit) attains an absolute maximum relative to the condition (7.1)—if such values exist. A set of values $\bar{x} = (\bar{x}_1, \bar{x}_2, \ldots, \bar{x}_n)$ with this property will be called a *maximal* or *equilibrium production plan*. An equilibrium production plan must satisfy not only (7.1) but also the condition that there should exist a (necessarily negative, by [7.2]) Lagrange multiplier μ such that

$$(7.4) \quad p_i + \mu \varphi_i = 0 .$$

A production plan $(x_1, x_2, \ldots, x_n)$ satisfying these conditions will be maximal if

$$(7.5) \quad \Sigma_{ij} \varphi_{ij} t_i t_j < 0$$

for all values of the t_i's, not all zero, satisfying

$$(7.6) \quad \Sigma_i p_i t_i = 0 .$$

The quantities φ_i and μ have no exact counterparts in earlier sections, but if μ is eliminated from (7.4) one obtains

$$\frac{\varphi_i}{\varphi_j} = \frac{p_i}{p_j} ,$$

which may be rewritten, because of (7.3), in the form

$$(7.7) \quad \frac{\partial x_j}{\partial x_i} = - \frac{p_i}{p_j} \quad (i,j = 1, 2, \ldots, n) .$$

These conditions have a ready economic interpretation (cf. Exercise 7.1).

The second-order condition (7.5) is an instance in which it is impossible to give a brief and correct translation from mathematics into English. Intuitive notions about the implications of "convexity" and "concavity," derived from the study of elementary models, are here a safer guide than any explicit statement in ordinary language (see, however, J. R. Hicks, *Value and Capital* [2d ed.; London: Oxford University Press, 1946], pp. 86–88).

If it is supposed that (7.4) may be solved to obtain the (net) supply (or demand) functions

$$(7.8) \quad \bar{x}_i = \bar{x}_i(p_1, \ldots, p_n) \quad (i = 1, \ldots, n),$$

the properties of these functions may be studied very much as in preceding microeconomic models. First replace the x_i's by $\bar{x}_i$'s throughout (7.1) and (7.4), thus obtaining identities in prices; then differentiate partially with respect to, say, p_j and solve the resulting system of linear equations to obtain

$$\frac{\partial \bar{x}_i}{\partial p_j} = -\frac{\Delta_{ji}}{\mu \Delta},$$

where

$$\Delta = \begin{vmatrix} \varphi_{11} & \varphi_{12} \cdots \varphi_{1n} & \dfrac{\varphi_1}{\mu} \\ \varphi_{21} & \varphi_{22} \cdots \varphi_{2n} & \dfrac{\varphi_2}{\mu} \\ \cdots\cdots\cdots\cdots\cdots\cdots \\ \varphi_{n1} & \varphi_{n2} \cdots \varphi_{nn} & \dfrac{\varphi_n}{\mu} \\ \varphi_1 & \varphi_2 \cdots \varphi_n & 0 \end{vmatrix}$$

and Δ_{ij} is defined, as usual, to be the cofactor of the (i,j)th element in Δ. Now substitute $-p_i/\mu$ for φ_i throughout Δ, using the conditions (7.4). Then $\Delta = D/\mu^3$, where

$$D = \begin{vmatrix} \varphi_{11} & \varphi_{12} \cdots \varphi_{1n} & p_1 \\ \varphi_{21} & \varphi_{22} \cdots \varphi_{2n} & p_2 \\ \cdots\cdots\cdots\cdots\cdots\cdots \\ \varphi_{n1} & \varphi_{n2} \cdots \varphi_{nn} & p_n \\ p_1 & p_2 \cdots p_n & 0 \end{vmatrix},$$

and $\Delta_{ij} = D_{ij}/\mu^3$, where D_{ij} is the cofactor of the (i,j)th element in Δ. Therefore

$$\frac{\partial \bar{x}_i}{\partial p_j} = -\frac{\Delta_{ji}}{\mu \Delta} = -\frac{D_{ji}}{\mu D}.$$

But when the quantities $D_{ji}/\mu D$ are compared with the quantities K_{ij} in the theory of consumer behavior (Chapter Five, Section 5), it is obvious that the properties of the two expressions will be very similar. Indeed, if we define

$$K'_{ij} = -\frac{D_{ji}}{\mu D},$$

then all comparative statics properties of (7.8) may be obtained by direct analogy with the theory of consumer behavior. In particular, $\partial \bar{x}_i / \partial p_i > 0$ if x_i is an output, $\partial \bar{x}_i / \partial p_i < 0$ if x_i is an input, and $\partial \bar{x}_i / \partial p_j$ is ambiguous in sign and size if $i \neq j$, etc.

The justification of the remark (in the introduction to this chapter) to the effect that the dichotomy between the theories of consumer and business behavior is not at all absolute, and that the empirical implications of income (revenue) and utility maximization are not remarkably dissimilar, will now be clear. The major difference between the two branches of microeconomics, from the standpoint of formal implications, is that "income effects" may occur in the theory of consumer behavior but not in the theory of business behavior. However, while this difference is easy to distinguish in the abstract theories, it would be quite another matter—in fact, an extremely intricate econometric undertaking—to decide, purely on this basis, whether a given economic unit in the real world were behaving like a consumer or like a business.

EXERCISES

7.1. Explain the economic significance of the equations (7.7) and discuss their intuitive plausibility as equilibrium conditions.

7.2. The transformation function φ for a given entrepreneur is not necessarily unique: for instance, if k is any positive constant, $k\varphi$ will do just as well as φ itself, leading to precisely the same equilibrium conditions, comparative statics conclusions, and so on. (a) Why should this be so? (b) Why did the analogous phenomenon not occur in our earlier models of business behavior?

8. A Stock-Flow Model of Business Behavior. Once an n-commodity model has been outlined, the transition to an n-commodity *stock-flow* model of business behavior is relatively easy. The rationale of this new step is also perfectly clear: viz., in a stock-flow economy, the typical business unit *holds* quantities of some commodities for future disposal and, at the same time, *uses* some flows and some existing stocks as inputs and *adds* to existing stocks or to flow supplies by producing new outputs. We use the variables x_i as in the last section, but now with a distinct emphasis on their being *flows*. An output flow can be described as an *excess flow supply*, an input flow as an *excess flow demand* of the firm in question.[9] We denote by D_i the stock of the ith commodity demanded to hold, and by S_i the stock of the ith commodity currently in the possession of the business unit. The quantities D_i and S_i may be of either sign, positive if they represent assets, negative if they represent liabilities (debts). Finally, on the basis of considerations precisely analogous to those considered in Section 7 of Chapter

---

[9] It may be noticed, in passing, that the money value of flow demand corresponds very closely to Keynes' "user cost." See the *General Theory of Employment, Interest, and Money*, chap. vi and Appendix to chap. vi.

Five, denote the business unit's *investment demand* for the ith commodity by x_i', and define the *investment demand functions*

$$(8.1) \quad x_i' \equiv k_i X_i \quad (i = 1, \ldots, n),$$

where k_i is some positive fixed constant (in general, different for each different commodity and for each different business unit), and where $X_i \equiv D_i - S_i$ is the *excess stock demand* of the business unit for the ith commodity.

Stock-flow complications are simply ignored, of course, in the familiar textbook theory of business behavior; for the usual procedure is the same as that adopted in earlier sections of this chapter. That is to say, alternative current plans of an entrepreneur are typically characterized by only two sets of functions: (*i*) a set of *output functions* relating current output flows to prices and to other parameters (e.g., anticipated future prices, quantities of capital goods held by the entrepreneur, etc.); (*ii*) a set of *input functions* relating current input flows to prices and to other (given) parameters. But this means that no explicit provision is made for the analysis of business "investment" decisions, decisions to alter business holdings of various assets. Instead, it is usual to suppose that the capital goods which are available to any entrepreneur are fixed quantities in the "short run," and to deal with investment in fixed plant, equipment, raw materials, and inventories either by fiat—as when one demonstrates the relation between short- and long-run "supply" curves—or by *ad hoc* description of "typical" (commonsense) business responses to profit opportunities. Or to put the matter another way, some of the "other parameters" in the input demand and output supply functions are assumed to represent quantities of capital goods held by the entrepreneur, and the latter parameters are simply juggled about at will.

Such a way of treating business investment may be criticized on various grounds. For example, the manipulation of capital-good parameters seems extremely arbitrary, despite the apparent accord among economists as to which kinds of juggling are realistic. Again, one may doubt whether it is logically consistent to postulate pure competition together with the fixity of plant and equipment in the short run. Although the total quantity of any capital good is fixed in the short run for the economy as a whole, in a competitive system any one entrepreneur may increase or decrease his individual holdings at will by buying from or selling to other entrepreneurs. Of course, this problem does not arise if the theory of the firm is built around decisions affecting a physical *plant at a given location*, and this procedure is almost universally adopted in the literature; but such an approach clearly leaves something to be desired. One is reminded here of the "Rime of the Ancient Mariner" and of the complex background circumstances outlined by Coleridge in order to make the unhappy union between the mariner and the albatross seem plausible. Even granting that the entrepreneur in the real world may have some difficulty in finding a willing purchaser for unwanted portions of his fixed plant and equipment, one can hardly accept as satisfactory an explanation which merely states that this is so because it *is* so. Finally, and this is the most serious and comprehensive objection to the traditional approach, it divorces the theory of business investment from the theory of price determination. For unless a microeconomic theory makes provision for investment *decisions*, it will be incompatible with a macroeconomic theory which does.

A theory which meets these points may be outlined briefly as follows. Suppose that entrepreneurial behavior in a stock-flow economy is described by the following postulates. First, for given admissable values of any $2n - 1$ of the $2n$ variables $x_1, \ldots, x_n, D_1, \ldots, D_n$, the entrepreneur assigns a definite value to the remaining variable such that

$$\varphi(x_1, x_2, \ldots, x_n; D_1, \ldots, D_n) \equiv 0 .$$

The function φ is appropriately called a *decision function*; for when allowance is made for the holding of assets (one of which may be money), the essentially subjective character of the function is apparent. Second, we require that all the second derivatives of φ exist and be continuous. Third, we assume that all first derivatives of φ be positive. Finally, the entrepreneur is assumed to want to hold a combination of assets, to use a combination of input flows, and to produce a combination of output flows such that the quantity

$$\pi = -\sum_{i=1}^{n} p_i(x_i + x_i') \equiv -\sum_{i=1}^{n} p_i[x_i + k_i(D_i - S_i)]$$

is a maximum, provided such a *stock-flow plan* exists. In symbols, therefore, *plan equilibrium* requires that $x_1, \ldots, x_n, D_1, \ldots, D_n$ assume values such that, for given stock quantities $S_1, \ldots, S_n$, the following conditions are satisfied simultaneously:

$$(8.2) \begin{cases} k_r p_r + u_r = 0 & (r = 1, \ldots, 2n; \quad p_{n+r} \equiv p_r; \quad k_r \equiv 1 \text{ for } r = 1, \ldots, n) \\ \varphi(x_1, \ldots, x_n; D_1, \ldots, D_n) = 0 , \end{cases}$$

with a corresponding second-order condition of the usual type. Then if the first-order conditions represent a determinate statical system, the equilibrium values of the variables $x_1, \ldots, x_n, D_1, \ldots, D_n$ may be expressed in terms of the parameters $p_1, \ldots, p_n$ to obtain the n business *excess demand (supply) functions*

$$\bar{x}_i = \bar{x}_i(p_1, \ldots, p_n) \quad (i = 1, \ldots, n)$$

and the n *stock demand functions*

$$\bar{D}_i = \bar{D}_i(p_1, \ldots, p_n) \quad (i = 1, \ldots, n) .$$

The latter functions, taken in conjunction with the functions (8.1) and the given values of $S_1, \ldots, S_n$, then determine corresponding equilibrium values for the investment demand variables x_i':

$$\bar{x}_i' = x_i'(\bar{D}_i - S_i) .$$

Finally, *business equilibrium* is defined, much like the concept of consumer equilibrium in Chapter Five, by the further requirements that

$$(8.3) \quad \bar{D}_i - S_i = 0 \quad (i = 1, \ldots, n),$$

which (by [8.1]) implies that $x_i' = 0$ for all values of i (i.e., business equilibrium requires that current rate of change of stocks be zero).

Now it is obvious that the functions giving $\bar{x}_i$, $\bar{D}_i$, and $\bar{x}_i'$ will be homogeneous of order zero in all prices, just like the demand and supply functions of other models considered earlier. This is an implausible result since it seems to imply that desired asset holdings do not depend upon the absolute level of prices, and this is unlikely to be true in practice. But the conclusion is a valid deduction from our assumptions, and we shall not stop to reconsider the matter here (see, however, Chapter Seven, Section 4).

Other comparative statics properties of the demand functions of the stock-flow model can be derived by analogy from the substitution terms in the stock-flow model of consumer behavior (Section 7 of Chapter Five), following a procedure similar to that outlined in the preceding section of this chapter.

9. Dynamical and Other Generalizations.   Market aspects of the behavior of individual business units will be considered in the next chapter. It is necessary at this point, however, to consider certain other gaps in the preceding analysis.

We may deal summarily indeed with the more obvious shortcomings of the models already considered. First, while it is clear that the decision function (transformation function, etc.) will, in practice, normally include prices (actual and anticipated) as explicit parameters, there is little point in taking this into account unless one is prepared to accompany the generalization with sensible restrictive hypotheses about the precise way in which prices enter the decision function. Similarly, as regards the interdependence of business units, it is hard to doubt that the form of the decision function for any one entrepreneur will depend upon his observation and knowledge of the actual behavior of other entrepreneurs. But while this interdependence is easily taken into account in a formal theory, the resulting model is unlikely to be instructive unless it is bolstered by special restrictions of a kind for which supporting empirical evidence is not currently available.

Dynamical aspects of the theory of business behavior require more detailed consideration. Let us begin by considering a situation in which the entrepreneur's inputs are always in equilibrium so that the only dynamical adjustments which occur involve changes in output. As a dynamical assumption, suppose that the entrepreneur alters output over time if and only if marginal *net* revenue is not zero. More specifically, suppose that total revenue is a function of output defined by $R(x)$, and that total cost is given by $C(x)$. ($C[x]$ is defined, of course, in terms of the assumption of continuous input equilibrium—instantaneous adjustment of inputs to "current equilibrium" values). Then a dynamical system is obtained of the form

$$(9.1) \quad \frac{dx}{dt} = \alpha[R'(x) - C'(x)],$$

where $R'(x) = dR/dx$ and $C'(x) = dC/dx$. Expressing (9.1) as a Taylor series at some output point $x = \bar{x}$,

$$\frac{dx}{dt} = \alpha\{R'(\bar{x}) + R''(\bar{x})(x - \bar{x}) + [\ldots] - C'(\bar{x}) - C''(\bar{x})(x - \bar{x}) - [\ldots]\},$$

where the expressions $[\ldots]$ represent terms of degree $\geqslant 2$, as usual. Then if $\bar{x}$ is an equilibrium output (i.e., if $R'(\bar{x}) - C'(\bar{x}) = 0$), and if the terms in $[\ldots]$ tend towards zero with $(x - \bar{x})$, the behavior of x in the neighborhood of the point $\bar{x}$ may be represented approximately by

$$(9.2) \quad \frac{dx}{dt} = \alpha[R''(\bar{x}) - C''(\bar{x})] \cdot (x - \bar{x}).$$

The differential equation (9.2) has the solution

$$x = Ae^{\lambda t} + \bar{x},$$

where λ is given by the equation

$$\lambda = \alpha[R''(\bar{x}) - C''(\bar{x})].$$

Hence, the equilibrium point $\bar{x}$ will be stable if and only if $\alpha[R'' - C''] < 0$. But the entrepreneur normally may be expected to increase output when marginal revenue exceeds marginal cost, and vice versa, so we may suppose $\alpha > 0$. Then since R'' is the slope of the marginal revenue curve, and C'' is the slope of the marginal cost curve, the condition $\lambda < 0$ will be satisfied if and only if the marginal cost curve intersects the marginal revenue curve from below at the equilibrium point. This is essentially the same as the statical second-order condition for profit equilibrium given by (6.2). Thus, if the business sells in a purely competitive market for which $R(x) = qx$ (q a constant), we have $R''(x) = 0$, and the stability condition is simply that marginal cost be rising at the equilibrium point.

Only the sign, not the size, of the adjustment coefficient, α, is relevant in connection with the stability of equilibrium; but the size of α does influence the time rate of change of output, and is of interest for this reason. As a matter of common sense, one may associate the size of α in the present model with a number of factors which are likely to be important in actual business experience: *technical* frictions affecting output changes, *institutional* factors governing ease of purchase and sale of output, and the *subjective* sensitivity of an entrepreneur to changes in market conditions. All of these (and possibly other) influences affecting the size of adjustment coefficients should be borne in mind, although the distinction between subjective, technical, and institutional factors is likely to be extremely vague in practice.

Little comment is required about the problem of expressing dynamically a statical theory more general than the one just considered. The problem is entirely analogous to that considered in Section 8 of Chapter Five, and the results equally so. The neatest plausible dynamical assumption is that the entrepreneur selects successive production plans in such a way that at any instant profit tends to increase as rapidly as possible; and on this assumption the second-order conditions imply that equilibrium is stable. The details of the analysis correspond, step by step, to those of the parallel dynamical model of consumer behavior. If the dynamical assumption is weakened to state merely that the entrepreneur selects successive production plans so that profit increases *somehow*, the stability conditions lose their statical significance because of the appearance of unequal adjustment coefficients associated with the several production flows.

EXERCISES

9.1. Suggest a means of characterizing Marshallian "market," "short-run," and "long-run" periods of analysis in terms of a dynamical model of business behavior. What are the disadvantages of the Marshallian procedure?

9.2. Empirical studies suggest that in many areas of manufacturing business, experience in producing a commodity leads directly to the gradual adoption of improved techniques such that labor and other "direct" costs can be reduced substantially for any given level of output. Outline in general terms a dynamical model in which provision is made for the existence of phenomena of this kind.

SUGGESTIONS FOR FURTHER READING

The literature on the theory of business behavior is, as a whole, one of the less edifying chapters in the book of modern economics. It is in large part the record of a constant conflict of ideas between writers interested primarily in theoretical and writers interested primarily in applied problems of business behavior, most of the contestants on both sides entering the lists well equipped with unconscious preconceptions. Two notable exceptions which deserve particular mention, the first theoretical, the second practical in orientation as well as theoretical, are: P. A. Samuelson, "A Comprehensive Restatement of the Theory of Cost and Production" (*Foundations of Economic Analysis* [Cambridge: Harvard University Press, 1947], chap. iv); and W. W. Cooper and A. Charnes, "Silhouette Functions of Short-Run Cost Behavior," *Quarterly Journal of Economics*, Vol. LXVIII, No. 1 (February, 1954), pp. 131–50. The first few chapters in Sune Carlson, *A Study of the Pure Theory of Production* Stockholm Economic Studies (London: P. S. King & Son, Ltd., 1939), may also be recommended very highly.

Like the theory of consumption, the analysis of business behavior has undergone many changes since its inception; but this has had the effect mainly of making the theory more elaborate, not more refined. And the advent of monopolistic competition theory in the 1930's, while it clarified some issues, appears to have muddied more water than it has settled. For references and mental stimulation, the reader may consult R. Triffin, *Monopolistic Competition and General Equilibrium Theory* (Cambridge: Harvard University Press, 1938); K. Rothchild, "Price Theory and Oligopoly," *Economic Journal*, Vol. XVII (1947), pp. 299–320; J. N. Wolfe, "The Problem of Oligopoly," *Review of Economic Studies*, Vol. XXI(3), No. 56 (1953–1954), pp. 181–92.

Chapter Seven

CONCLUDING GENERALIZATIONS
AND NOTES

OUR description of the main components of the theory of price determination is now complete. Several tasks remain to be accomplished, however, to round out the view of the economic system outlined in preceding chapters and to answer certain questions which the earlier analysis leaves open. First, the relation of microeconomics to macroeconomics has to be dealt with explicitly to establish the over-all consistency of our findings in the one area with those in the other. Second, we have to examine the implications for macroeconomics of certain microeconomic conclusions which were ignored in our discussion of market behavior in Chapters Two through Four. Third, the determination of equilibrium prices and quantities under other than purely competitive conditions has to be discussed in order to make a partial appraisal of certain shortcomings which are presumably associated with the use of competitive hypotheses in economic analysis. Finally, the relation of the analysis presented in this book to some of the broader problems of economic inquiry requires brief comment.

1. *From Microeconomics to Macroeconomics: Some Preliminaries.* For the time being we shall suppose that the economic system is composed of n distinct commodity markets and $r + s$ individual decision units—r "utility-maximizing" consumers and s "profit-maximizing" entrepreneurs. Price variables will be denoted, as before, by $p_1, \ldots, p_n$; and, unless otherwise specified, all "market" quantities will be distinguished by single subscripts (e.g., x_i will represent excess flow demand in the ith market, etc.). All "individual" quantities will be distinguished by double subscripts unless stated otherwise (e.g., x'_{ij} will represent investment demand for the ith commodity by the jth decision unit, etc.). To avoid unnecessary notational complexities, moreover, we shall use the following abbreviations:

$$P \equiv (p_1, \ldots, p_n)$$
$$S(j) \equiv (S_{1j}, \ldots, S_{nj})$$
$$S \equiv (S_{11}, \ldots, S_{n,r+s})$$

Now, simply as a matter of definition, market excess demands are obtained by summing appropriate excess flow and investment demands of individual decision units. The term "appropriate" means, among other things, that the values of the individual quantity variables which are to be summed must be associated either with statical equilibrium plans or with solutions of dynamical systems describing the behavior of decision units over time. Any other procedure might lead to market excess demand functions which were completely lacking in empirical content. However, the two alternatives are complementary rather than competitive. On the one hand, the statical interpretation is in some ways similar, and it can be linked explicitly with the argument in the two preceding chapters; on the other hand, the dynamical interpretation permits the relation of individual to market quantities to be expressed in an intuitively more satisfying way and can, in any case, be so stated that the statical interpretation follows as a special instance. We can have the best of both worlds, therefore, if we adopt the dynamical interpretation but formulate the problem in such a way as to base the argument squarely upon our earlier analysis of consumer and business behavior.

Let us proceed, therefore, by characterizing the situation of any given microeconomic unit at any instant of time by a *representative point* in some price-commodity (phase) space (cf. Chapter Three, Section 1), assuming from the outset:

(*i*) The position of each representative point in the relevant phase space is uniquely determined for every instant of time $t \geqslant t_0$ once the position of the representative point at some initial instant t_0 is given;

(*ii*) All equilibrium states of the representative point of a given decision unit coincide exactly with those states determined by the statical stock-flow consumer and business equilibrium conditions set out in the two preceding chapters.

The first of these assumptions permits us to express any microeconomic quantity variable as a well-defined function of the time variable, t, while the second assumption implies that the functions defined by (*i*) contain the same variables and parameters as appear in the relevant statical models.

By analogy with the stock-flow theory of consumer behavior, we may now write

$$(1.1) \begin{cases} x_{ij}(t) = x_{ij}(P, S(j), M_j) \\ D_{ij}(t) = D_{ij}(P, S(j), M_j) \\ x'_{ij}(t) = k_{ij}(D_{ij} - S_{ij}) , \end{cases} (i = 1, \ldots, n; \, j = 1, \ldots, r)$$

the variables P, $S(j)$, and M_j being regarded as functions of t along with the other quantities (other than the constants k_{ij}) in (1.1). M_j is of course the income of the jth consumer (see below). Similarly, on the basis of the stock-flow theory of business behavior, we may write

$$(1.2) \begin{cases} x_{ij}(t) = x_{ij}(P) \\ D_{ij}(t) = D_{ij}(P) \\ x'_{ij}(t) = k_{ij}(D_{ij} - S_{ij}) . \end{cases} (i = 1, \ldots, n; \, j = r + 1, \ldots, r + s)$$

The absence of the variables $S(j)$ from the excess flow demand and from the stock demand functions in (1.2) is a direct consequence of the lack of "income effects" in the theory of business behavior.

The quantities M_j in (1.1) and the quantities S_{ij} in (1.1) and (1.2) are both subject to further analysis. The variables M_j represent (positive or negative) elements of money income accruing to the jth consumer which are not associated explicitly with the other quantity variables or with the price variables in (1.1). However, these income elements include distributed entrepreneurial earnings, receipts of contract interest on asset holdings, and payments of contract interest on outstanding debts, all of which are implicitly dependent either on market prices or on various stock supply variables (e.g., contract interest earnings on a given class of bonds depend upon the number of such bonds held although not upon the current price of such bonds, etc.). For this reason, it is permissible, and certainly convenient, to ignore the quantities M_j altogether for the time being (i.e., to subsume them in the form of the functional relationships in which they appear). But we shall have reason to reintroduce them at a later stage in the discussion.

The quantities S_{ij} fall into a different category: we wish to make their definition more explicit rather than jettison them altogether. Thus, in general, S_{ij} represents an accumulation over time of the jth decision unit's investment demand (or supply) of the ith commodity, less such "autonomous" changes in stocks as may occur from time to time through accident, obsolescence, theft, etc. For our purposes, the latter considerations may be ignored, however, so that we may write

$$(1.3) \quad S_{ij}(t) = S_{ij}(0) + \int_0^t x'_{ij} dt ,$$

where $S_{ij}(0)$ represents the value of S_{ij} at some initial instant of time, $t = 0$.[1] This definition of S_{ij} requires that we regard all purchases for or sales from stocks as *market* purchases or sales, including those transactions in which the seller is himself the buyer or in which the buyer is himself the seller. This has awkward implications from a practical standpoint (e.g., the holder of a refrigerator will normally have to be regarded as disposing of a portion of his refrigerator stock in the market and purchasing refrigerator services in the market all the while his victuals are being preserved!); but that is part of the price which must be paid to avoid having to distinguish explicitly between, say, purchases for use which do, and purchases for use which do not, remain temporarily among the commodity holdings of the purchaser. The complexities attending distinctions of this kind prompt us to accept some sacrifice of realism.

---

[1] Alternatively, a discrete definition of $S_{ij}(t)$ is provided by writing

$$S_{ij}(n) = S_{ij}(0) + \sum_{t=0}^{n-1} x'_{ij}(t) .$$

Finally, so far as market behavior is concerned, we are not directly concerned with the quantities D_{ij} in (1.1) and (1.2); they, like the quantities S_{ij}, are of interest mainly because they influence the determination of the quantities x'_{ij}. Hence, suppressing the variables M_j in (1.1), and dropping the functions D_{ij} as separate entities, we may deal henceforth only with the functions

$$(1.4)\begin{cases} x_{ij}(t) = x_{ij}(P,S(j)\,) \\ x'_{ij}(t) = k_{ij}(D_{ij} - S_{ij}) \end{cases}\!\!\Big\}(j = 1, \ldots ,r)$$
$$\begin{cases} x_{ij}(t) = x_{ij}(P) \\ x'_{ij}(t) = k_{ij}(D_{ij} - S_{ij}) \end{cases}\!\!\Big\}(j = r+1, \ldots ,r+s)$$

bearing in mind that $dS_{ij}/dt = x'_{ij}$ (this follows by differentiating the identity [1.3]).

Given the functions (1.4), the market excess flow demand and market investment demand functions, hence also the market excess demand functions for all markets in the economy, are obtained immediately by defining

$$(1.5)\begin{cases} x_i(t) \equiv \displaystyle\sum_{j=1}^{r+s} x_{ij} = x_i(P,S(1), \ldots ,S(r)) \\[2mm] x'_i(t) \equiv \displaystyle\sum_{j=1}^{r+s} x'_{ij} = x'_i(P,S) \\[2mm] y_i(t) \equiv x_i(t) + x'_i(t) = y_i(P,S)\,. \end{cases}\!\!\!\Bigg\}(i = 1, \ldots ,n)$$

This provides the market functions upon which the remainder of our discussion will be based.

The preceding argument merely serves to illustrate the general method by which one may ascend from microeconomic to macroeconomic demand functions. The actual functions obtained will depend in any particular case upon the exact character of the underlying microdynamical system. For example, essentially different market functions (and, later on, essentially different macrodynamical models) are obtained if the relevant microdynamical functional relations contain time as a discrete rather than a continuous variable. So far as we are concerned, however, certain properties of the functions (1.5) are already specified implicitly by conditions imposed upon models considered in earlier chapters (these will be indicated below). For the sake of definiteness, moreover, we shall proceed subsequently on the assumption that time is a continuous rather than a discrete variable so that we may deal always with time derivatives rather than with time differences. But this assumption may be dropped without great difficulty at almost any stage in the argument.

EXERCISES

1.1. If the utility and profit maximization conditions applicable to consumers and firms, respectively, are assumed to be satisfied at every instant of time, then the market excess demand functions in a flow economy depend upon time only via prices. Discuss the shortcomings of this kind of approach to the study of empirical market behavior in comparison with alternative approaches in which consumer and business quantity variables are described by dynamical equations of one kind or another.

1.2. What kinds of dynamical lags are likely to exercise an important influence in practice upon the reaction of consumers and businesses to changes in market conditions? Suggest how some of these lags might be incorporated in a formal model of market behavior.

2. General Equilibrium. Except that individual stock supply variables, S_{ij}, occur in (1.5) instead of aggregate stock supply variables, S_i, we have now reached by an alternative route the point at which we began our discussion of multiple market dynamical systems in Chapter Four. Since the systems discussed there included as special cases all the systems considered in previous chapters, this might be regarded quite justifiably as the formal starting point for the whole of our earlier treatment of macroeconomics. However, the difference in the content of the functions defined in (1.5), as compared with the functions considered earlier, forces us to reconsider certain details of the previous argument. For the sake of brevity, we shall deal mainly with stock-flow models here, referring only incidentally to stock and flow models.

The phase space corresponding to a general stock-flow model obtained from (1.5) is (P,S), which means that the individual stock supply quantities S_{ij}, as well as market prices, $p_1, \ldots, p_n$, must be constant over time in order for equilibrium to occur in the economy as a whole. Thus, we are led to describe price behavior in terms of the system of differential equations

$$(2.1) \begin{cases} \dfrac{dp_i}{dt} = f_i(y_i(P,S)) & (i = 1, \ldots, n) \\[2mm] \dfrac{dS_{ij}}{dt} = x'_{ij} & (i = 1, \ldots, n; j = 1, \ldots, r + s), \end{cases}$$

rather than the simpler system

$$(2.2) \begin{cases} \dfrac{dp_i}{dt} = f_i(y_i(P,S_i)) \\[2mm] \dfrac{dS_i}{dt} = x_i \end{cases} \quad (\iota = 1, \ldots, n)$$

which underlies the discussion in Chapter Four.

For equilibrium in (2.1), we must have $dp_i/dt = 0$, $dS_{ij}/dt = 0$ for all i and j; this implies and is implied by

$$(2.3) \begin{cases} x_i = 0 & (i = 1, \ldots, n) \\ x'_i = 0 & (i = 1, \ldots, n) \\ x'_{ij} = 0 & (i = 1, \ldots, n; j = 1, \ldots, r + s). \end{cases}$$

This includes the relevant equilibrium conditions for (2.2) as a special case (i.e., equilibrium in [2.2] implies and is implied by $x_i = 0$, $x'_i = 0$).

In effect, our previous requirements for equilibrium are incomplete from the standpoint of the present analysis because they do not take into account the structure of aggregate stock supply quantities; that is to say, they ignore the influence of the distribution of stock supplies among individual decision units. This difference may or may not be significant from a practical point of view; that is an empirical rather than a theoretical question. But it is evident that the present view of price behavior in a stock-flow economy, since it is more complex, is less convenient as a basis for empirical research than the systems discussed earlier in the book.

In a pure flow economy, only the conditions $x_i = 0$ in (2.3) are relevant as equilibrium conditions, so in this case the present model is formally identical with the flow models discussed earlier; stock supplies being of no concern, their distribution among economic units is of no concern either.

In a pure stock economy, the conditions $x_i = 0$ in (2.3) are not relevant. Moreover, from the definition of x'_i (see [1.5], above) it is clear that the conditions $x'_{ij} = 0$ in (2.3) imply the conditions $x'_i = 0$. This may seem to leave fewer equations than are necessary to determine the unknowns P and S; however, since in a stock economy aggregate stock supplies are fixed in quantity by hypothesis, the stocks of any one economic unit are determined as soon as the stock holdings of other units are given; so our unknowns are actually n less in number than appears to be the case at first sight. This means that the system $x'_{ij} = 0$ $(i = 1, \ldots, n; j = 1, \ldots, r + s)$ is just determinate. It may be noticed in passing that equilibrium in a stock economy occurs if and only if there is a complete absence of current market transactions (cf. Section 3, Chapter Two). This result is offensive to common sense—as it should be, since stock economies are a thing which we do not see in the real world.

The conditions $x'_i = 0$ in (2.3) also follow from the conditions $x'_{ij} = 0$ under stock-flow hypotheses; but in this case aggregate stock supplies are variables rather than constants since aggregate stock supplies will be changing over time unless the conditions $x_i = 0$ are satisfied (this is the basis of the second requirement in the fundamental assumption of macrodynamics, Section 3, Chapter Three). Hence, in every case, necessary and sufficient conditions for equilibrium in (2.1) are provided by the equations

$$(2.4) \quad \begin{cases} x_i - 0 & (i = 1, \ldots, n) \\ x'_j = 0 & (i = 1, \ldots, n; j = 1, \ldots, r + s) \ ; \end{cases}$$

but the conditions $x_i = 0$ are not relevant in a pure stock economy while the conditions $x'_{ij} = 0$ are not relevant in a pure flow economy.

EXERCISES

2.1. On the basis of the system (2.1), show that equilibrium in a stock-flow economy implies, but is not implied by, $x_i = 0$ $(i = 1, \ldots, n)$, $X_i = 0$ $(i = 1, \ldots, n)$.

2.2. With reference to the system (2.1), discuss in a common-sense way the probable course of events in an economy, initially in equilibrium, supposing a new gold field were discovered, lasted for a year or two as a large source of supply, and then became exhausted. Pay particular attention to shifts in the distribution of assets over time and to the effect of this upon selected commodity prices, interest rates, and dividend policies.

3. General Equilibrium: Comparative Statics and Dynamics. Any statical system obtained from (2.1) will be of the general form suggested by (2.4); i.e.,

$$(3.1) \begin{cases} x_i(\bar{P},\bar{S},A_i) = 0 \\ x'_{ij}(\bar{P},\bar{S},B_{ij}) = 0 \, , \end{cases}$$

where all barred quantities represent equilibrium values of the corresponding variables, and A_i and B_{ij} represent *sets* of "autonomous" parameters of "taste," "technique," etc., affecting the market flow excess demand functions and the individual investment demand functions in (3.1). It is evident that the comparative statics properties of this system will differ from those of systems examined previously. Moreover, the task of analyzing the properties of (3.1) is more difficult, partly because the relevant equilibrium identities, if written out in full, are far more complicated than any which we have come across before, partly because the properties of the system (3.1) are known to depend upon the properties of individual excess demand functions (via [1.5]) so that in discussing (3.1) some reference has to be made to these underlying data. One's insight into these matters is best developed, however, by working through illustrative special cases of the kind suggested in the exercises at the end of this section (applying the methods outlined in Section 10 of Chapter Two). Hence, we shall confine our remarks to a few general comments on the microeconomic substructure of (3.1).

Since (ignoring the parameters A and B) all of the quantities in (3.1) are either microeconomic variables or sums of such variables, it is evident that definite restrictions could be placed upon all of the barred quantities appearing in (3.1), given sufficient information about the comparative statics of individual behavior. In fact, however, very little knowledge is provided by the formal theories of consumer and business behavior discussed in the two preceding chapters. Even if one deals with a pure *flow* economy, microeconomic analysis requires merely that $\partial x_{ij}/\partial p_i$ be negative for each business firm; the requirement holds for each consumer unit only if relevant substitution effects outweigh corresponding income effects in every instance. Since the behavior of businesses as a group and of consumers in part definitely tends to make the "own good" expression $\partial x_i/\partial p_i$ negative in a flow economy, however, one may be tempted to suggest that the net effect upon x_i of a rise in p_i will *normally* be to decrease market excess flow demand. But such a conclusion is warranted only by wishful thinking. From a theoretical standpoint it is clear merely that no conclusion is possible on *a priori* grounds. Even in a flow economy, moreover, the signs of "other good" expressions such as $\partial x_i/\partial p_j$ are entirely ambiguous, so one's knowledge would not be greatly advanced even if the direction of "own-good" substitution effects were given.

In the case of a stock-flow economy, the situation is even worse because the signs even of substitution terms, whether for consumers or for businesses, are theoretically ambiguous in every instance, and because the number of possible cross effects (via changes in the distribution of assets) is greatly increased. As regards inferring anything useful about the size or sign of macroeconomic equilibrium quantities on the basis of microeconomic analysis, therefore, ambiguity is the rule and definite conclusions the rare exception; and this is about all that can be said on the subject without making special assumptions of a kind for which we can provide no justification in this book.[2]

If we turn now to the problem of stability, it is clear that the system (2.1) and special versions of it are very similar to the dynamical models studied in earlier chapters—so similar, indeed, that an explicit analysis of the stability of equilibrium in the former models would involve little more than a retracing of ground already covered. The same observation applies to related models in which time is a discrete variable. Once the foundations of stability analysis are laid, the only remaining problem of any importance is that of formulating alternative dynamical models, either to investigate problems of a theoretical character or to provide a framework for empirical research into dynamical economic processes, or both. The theoretical derivation of stability conditions for various models is important mainly because it permits one to comprehend more adequately the manner in which the various elements of a dynamical model are related to one another and, in turn, to develop an intuitive feeling for concrete situations; but this is true only up to a point. Once the initial stages of the stability problem are left behind, further discussion leads rapidly to diminishing returns unless it is conducted with reference to special models for which definite empirical justification is being sought or for which such justification can be provided immediately. Accordingly, we shall leave the reader to conduct such further investigations into these problems as he thinks worthwhile. The exercises at the end of the section may serve as a guide in this connection. Attention is drawn, in particular, to the model outlined in Exercise 3.2 which involves the assumption that the market excess demand function depends directly upon *aggregate* commodity stocks, without regard to its distribution among individual economic units. This assumption, as compared with the more general assumption underlying (2.1), obviously simplifies the theoretical stability problem; but it is important primarily as a device for simplifying the study of empirical data. Confronted with the problem of interpreting actual market phenomena by reference to data drawn from individual economic units, one might well admit defeat from

---

[2] However, see Section 4 of this chapter, where a few of the implications of the homogeneity of individual excess demand and investment demand functions are examined.

the outset; but if one can make substantial use of aggregative data (and this seems justified in a remarkable number of instances), such researches may be undertaken with fair prospects of success.

EXERCISES

3.1. Given a model involving one stock commodity and two consumers (no firms), describe its general comparative statics properties.

3.2. Given a stock-flow model in which $x = x(p)$, $x' = k(D(p,S) - S)$, where S is defined as an integral over time of excess flow supply, analyze its dynamical stability.

4. *General Equilibrium and the Theory of Money.* If one of the commodities in (2.1) is regarded as money, the medium of exchange and unit of account, then one of the equations in the system (or in its statical counterpart [2.4]) follows from the rest by Walras' Law (see Section 8, Chapter Two); but the money price of money itself is identically unity, so one of the price variables is also redundant. This appears to leave the system (2.1) (or [2.4]) just determinate, which is in agreement with our earlier discussion of money in Chapter Two.

If one takes into account the implications of our discussion of consumer and business behavior, however, this conclusion is not correct. In fact, all individual excess flow demand and stock demand functions were shown earlier to be homogeneous of order zero in all prices and income, and this implies that an equal proportionate change in all market prices P and in all income variables M will leave the equilibrium values of all variables x_{ij} and x'_{ij} unaffected; and this being the case, it can be shown that the system (2.1) does not determine absolute money prices. This is accomplished as follows:

Since all market excess demand functions are defined by summing corresponding individual excess flow and investment demand functions, the homogeneity of the latter implies that of the former; i.e., the homogeneity requirement implies that

$$y_i(aP,aM,S) \equiv y_i(P,M,S) ,$$

for all values of i, where a is any positive constant. This conclusion is trivial if $a = 1$ (in which case prices and incomes are not affected by multiplication by a), so we shall suppose henceforth that $a \neq 1$. Then if the kth commodity is money, so that $p_k \equiv 1$, Walras' Law states that

$$-y_k(aP,aM,S) \equiv -y_k(P,M,S) \equiv \sum_{\substack{i=1 \\ i \neq k}}^{n} ap_i y_i(aP,aM,S) \equiv \sum_{\substack{i=1 \\ i \neq k}}^{n} p_i y_i(P,M,S) ,$$

from which we conclude that

$$(1 - a) \cdot \left[\sum_{\substack{i=1 \\ i \neq k}}^{n} p_i y_i(P,M,S) \right] \equiv 0 .$$

But $a \neq 1$ by hypothesis, so the first factor on the left-hand side of this equation is nonzero, and this implies that

$$\sum_{\substack{i=1 \\ i \neq k}}^{n} p_i y_i (P,M,S) \equiv 0 .$$

The last expression is simply *Say's Law* (cf. Section 8, Chapter Two); it asserts that the market excess demand for one commodity is determined as soon as the market excess demand for all other commodities (excluding money) is determined, and it asserts further (taken in conjunction with Walras' Law) that the demand for money is identically zero for every set of values of the price and income variables P and M. Thus, absolute prices are indeterminate in the systems (2.1) and (2.4); only *relative* prices can be specified in terms of these models. And there is no way in which the absolute price level can be determined as a function of the quantity of money, S_k, since the market excess demand equation for money is always satisfied identically. In effect, therefore, the homogeneity properties which follow from our analysis of consumer and business behavior lead to a macroeconomic model of a *barter* economy, not to a model of a money economy. Money does not influence the price determination process in any way whatever; Say's Law forbids it.

What this conclusion indicates is simply that our analysis in Chapters Five and Six of the factors governing the demand for assets in general, and the demand for money in particular, is inadequate (notice that Say's Law is simply a matter of common sense in a pure flow economy; it becomes implausible, and highly so, only under stock or stock-flow hypotheses). And a little reflection indicates where the inadequacy lies. Specifically, it is clearly an error in principle to suppose that the demand for money will not depend directly upon money prices in a money economy; for if there is, say, an increase in prices generally, the "purchasing power" of a given quantity of money holdings is decreased accordingly, and it would be curious indeed if individuals did not take this into account in deciding what quantity of money it is desirable to hold. Similarly, assets other than money may be held, in part, not for the sake of service or income yields but rather as a store of value, and in this event the demand to hold assets generally should also be made to depend directly upon the absolute level of money prices. If prices are introduced into the decision functions of businesses and into the utility functions of consumers in accordance with the above considerations, then as a formal matter the homogeneity properties used to prove Say's Law above are no longer valid. Hence, absolute money prices become determinate in macroeconomic models derived on this basis, and such models can be considered to describe a money economy in the strictest sense of the term.[3]

---

[3] For further discussion of this and related topics, together with a formulation of some specialized models in which the precise way in which prices enter microeconomic relations is specified, the reader may consult Don Patinkin, "A Reconsideration of the General Equilibrium Theory of Money," *Review of Economic Studies*, No. 45 (1949–1950).

5. Toward a Generalized Theory of Price Determination. It is taken for granted in Chapters Five and Six and in preceding sections of this chapter that economic units (consumers and businesses) act competitively in the sense that commodity prices are regarded as given parameters, and are in fact set equal to market prices so that any quantity can be acquired or disposed of at prevailing "market" rates. These assumptions permit important analytical simplifications; but it remains to be shown that the resulting gain in theoretical manageability is sufficient to offset the associated loss of realism. This question can be decided only by dealing explicitly with individual and market behavior under conditions less restrictive than those given above.

A partial answer to the question is provided in this and the following section; "partial," because we deal in detail only with the behavior of individual sellers each of whom is assumed to produce and offer for sale in a single market units of a homogeneous product, and because the total cost of each seller is regarded as a given function of output. The purpose of these restrictions is to reduce the task of exposition to manageable proportions. As it happens, nearly all of the conclusions reached can be generalized to apply to consumers as well as to businesses, to multiple commodity models, and to situations in which other than purely competitive behavior occurs on both sides of a given market; so despite certain limitations the discussion does not lack generality in any significant sense.

Let us begin by relaxing the "competitive" hypothesis that each seller can always dispose of any desired quantity of output at some going "market" price. As noticed earlier (Chapter Two, Section 6), this hypothesis is hardly ever satisfied in actual practice, even in supposedly competitive markets; i.e., in concrete situations, individual sellers (or their agents) normally act as independent price setters for their own offers of outputs, and they may easily miscalculate the true extent of demand for their product at prevailing prices, at least momentarily. The analytical import of this is simply to require that we deal with both output *and* sales variables together with *individual* prices, rather than confine attention solely to output variables and to a single "market" price.

To put matters another way, the state at any instant of the present model is described by specifying the values of the *output* quantities x_i ($i = 1, \ldots, n$, depending on the number of sellers), the *sales* quantities $x_i{}^*$, and the sale prices $p_i{}^*$; our immediate task is to impose appropriate restrictions on these variables to determine their behavior over time and, as a special instance of this, to provide equilibrium criteria for the market in question. Let us proceed by dealing in turn with each of four closely related matters: sales adjustment, price adjustment, sales estimation, and output adjustment.

Sales Adjustment. Define *effective price* to buyers by the identity

$$p^* \equiv \mathrm{Min}(p_1{}^*, \ldots, p_n{}^*) \; ;$$

i.e., suppose that prospective buyers wish to deal with the seller(s) offering the lowest price at any instant. Next, consolidate the planned purchases of buyers (this is a convenient, not a required simplification), denote the resulting aggregate *planned demand* variable by d and suppose that the value of d is determined at any instant by the value of p^* in accordance with a functional identity

$$d \equiv d(p^*) .$$

Now it is known as a matter of everyday observation that *actual* purchases by buyers in any market may differ from aggregate planned purchases, even over fairly long periods of time; but there is good reason to suppose that buyers try to adjust actual purchases over time in such a way as to lessen any existing difference between planned and actual purchases. If aggregate actual purchases at any instant are denoted by x^* ($\equiv \sum_{i=1}^{n} x_i^*$, since aggregate purchases are simply the obverse of aggregate sales), this may be expressed by the more precise assumption

$$\frac{dx^*}{dt} = A[d(p^*) - x^*] \quad (A > 0) ,$$

where A is a constant "adjustment" coefficient. However, this is of very limited value in describing the behavior of the *individual* sale variables, x_i^*; for while the latter may be expected to move in much the same way as aggregate sales *if the sale prices of all sellers are identical*, it is simply a matter of common sense to admit that the sales of any one seller may react in a very different fashion indeed if his current sale price differs appreciably from the sale prices of other sellers. Accordingly, let us recognize but idealize this aspect of experience by supposing that

$$(5.1) \quad \frac{dx_i^*}{dt} = A_i[d(p^*) - x^*] + B_{i1}(p_1^* - p_i^*) + \ldots + B_{in}(p_n^* - p_i^*)$$

$$(A_i, B_{ij} > 0) ,$$

where A_i and B_{ij} are constant "adjustment" coefficients. Then, among other things, the sales of the ith seller will increase if aggregate sales are increasing (with all prices identical), or will increase at the expense of other sellers if his own sale price is less than that of any other seller, etc.

From (5.1) it follows directly that the sales of the ith seller will be stationary *if* (i) planned demand is equal to aggregate sales and (ii) the sale prices of all sellers are equal; in symbols,

$$(5.2) \begin{cases} d(p^*) - x^* = 0 \\ p_1^* = p_2^* = \ldots = p_n^* . \end{cases}$$

Moreover, all sale variables will be stationary at the same time *only if* these conditions are satisfied. For suppose that all $dx_i^*/dt = 0$ even though (5.2) is not satisfied (this apparently might happen because for certain values of i, the terms on the right-hand side of [5.1] might be such that positive and negative items just offset each other). Then the terms with coefficients A_i will all have the same sign or will be zero. In the latter case, there will be at least one seller, say the kth, whose sale price is greater than that of any other seller; so all of the terms with coefficients B_{kj} will have a *negative* sign. But this contradicts the assumption that all $dx_k^*/dt = 0$, so we may confine attention to the case in which the terms in (5.1) with coefficients A_i are nonzero. Again, there will be at least one seller (the kth) whose sale price is greatest and also at least one seller (the lth) whose sale price is least; hence, all of the terms in (5.1) with coefficients B_{kj} will be *negative* while all terms with coefficients B_{lj} will be *positive*. But the terms with coefficients A_k and A_l are necessarily of the *same* sign, so if $dx_k^*/dt = 0$, then $dx_l^*/dt \neq 0$, and *vice versa*, which is again a contradiction. Therefore, $dx_i^*/dt = 0$ for all values of i *only if* all of the conditions (5.2) are satisfied simultaneously.

The economic sense of the price equality requirements in (5.2) is evident (the concept of a market is often "defined" by these conditions); as concerns the meaning of the first equation, however, a geometrical interpretation may be in order. Consider a hypothetical situation in which the actual sales of all sellers but the ith are fixed ($x_j^* = x_j^{*0}, j \neq i$); then for the sales of the ith seller to be stationary, it is necessary that the value of p_i^* be set such that

$$\left[d(p_i^*) - \sum_{j \neq i} x_j^{*0} \right] - x_i^* \equiv \delta(p_i^*) - x_i^* = 0 ,$$

where the expression in brackets, δ, represents the "statical" demand function for the product of the ith seller (i.e., planned market demand less the sales of all other sellers). Thus, measuring values of δ and x_i^* horizontally, values of p_i^* vertically, any point (x_i^*, p_i^*) in Figure 5.1 (e.g., $[x_i^{*0}, p_i^{*0}]$) represents a potentially *observable* quantity-price combination; but such a point is an admissable *equilibrium* combination only if it lies on the curve δ (as is true for the point $[x_i^{*1}, p_i^{*1}]$); otherwise not. A change in the value of any sales variable other than the ith will of course lead to a "shift," either to the right or to the left, in the position of the δ curve (e.g., from δ to δ' in Fig. 5.1); but the *form* of the curve δ is always exactly the same as that of the planned market demand curve so it is not affected by changes in the value of any sale variable.

Price Adjustment. Granted that current sales *may* differ from current output for a particular seller, it is a shade unrealistic to suppose that output is always equal to planned sales (current sale offerings); for if at any moment actual stock holdings differ from desired stock holdings (and this can hardly fail to happen if sales can differ from output), planned sales may be expected to differ from current output by a certain amount of planned investment or disinvestment in stocks. However, we shall not deal explicitly with this complication; indeed, we shall simply ignore the presence of stocks and of desired changes in them. At the same time, we shall assume that each seller attempts to avoid differences between sales and output with a view to maintaining constant whatever level of stocks he happens to hold at any instant.

Unwanted changes in stocks may be avoided in a wide variety of ways in any concrete situation: output may be adjusted directly to match sales; prospective buyers may be exhorted to purchase or not to purchase from a particular seller; sales by rival sellers may be influenced intentionally by

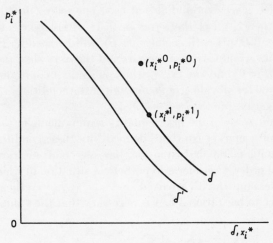

Fig. 5.1

political and other "nonmarket" activities of one or more other sellers; etc. Here, however, attention will be confined for the sake of simplicity to the balancing of output and sales via price adjustments; *nor is this at all unrealistic, for price adjustment is used to some extent in every actual market, including those in which other factors are perhaps more decisive.*

In analytical terms, we shall suppose that the behavior of the sale price of the ith seller is governed in every case by the condition

$$(5.3) \quad \frac{dp_i{}^*}{dt} = F_i(x_i{}^* - x_i) \quad (F_i > 0) ,$$

where F_i is a constant "adjustment" coefficient. This hypothesis is directly consistent with our earlier discussion of competitive price determination, and it does not contradict accepted views regarding price behavior in other than purely competitive markets. Moreover, it leads directly to the plausible equilibrium requirements

$$(5.4) \quad x_i{}^* - x_i = 0 \quad (i = 1, \ldots, n) ;$$

i.e., the ith sale price will be stationary if and only if sales are equal to output.

The Estimation of Current Sales Prospects. With the above restrictions on the behavior of the various sale and sale price variables in our model, it only remains to describe the behavior of the output variables, x_i. Now from our earlier discussion of sales adjustment, it is clear that the concept of "actual demand for the product of an individual seller" can be given no clear meaning in theory or in fact except when certain very special conditions are satisfied by the sale variables of other sellers. The practical implication of this is that current sales prospects are necessarily estimated by individual sellers; they cannot be known *ex ante*. In a moment, we shall wish to describe output adjustment as a function of estimated profit; since current profit prospects depend directly on estimates of current prices and sales, however, a brief digression is necessary at this point to discuss the general character of the current sales estimates of individual producers.

The main obstacle to be overcome in constructing a theory of sales estimation is to establish a definite and sensible link between estimates and observable facts; otherwise, the theory could have no operational significance, no empirical implications. To be sure, it can be stated immediately—as a formal matter—that the *highest price* at which the ith seller estimates that a given level of output can be sold at any instant will be a function of current and past values of all sale variables, of all sale price variables, and of the ith output variable (the current and past outputs of other sellers may or may not be known to the ith seller); i.e., *highest estimated price* (or simply *estimated price*), denoted by p_i, may be represented symbolically by

$$(5.5) \quad p_i(t) \equiv p_i[x_i; \overset{t}{\underset{-\infty}{x_1}}*, \ldots, \overset{t}{\underset{-\infty}{x_n}}*; \overset{t}{\underset{-\infty}{p_1}}*, \ldots, \overset{t}{\underset{-\infty}{p_n}}*; t].$$

Unfortunately, the definition (5.5) is too general to be of any immediate use; to make progress, some rather far-reaching restrictions must be imposed on (5.5) to obtain a simpler and more specific view of the data upon which estimated price depends and the nature of the dependence.

First, notice that the effect of (5.5) is to assert that estimated price depends on a learning process the *content* of which may change from instant to instant as the seller has new experiences; this is the implication of the inclusion of *past* together with *current* values of the various variables, and the implication is strengthened by the explicit presence in (5.5) of the time variable, t. Since little or nothing is known about such learning processes, however, and, more particularly, since one can only speculate about the factors which lead sellers to revise their over-all views of market conditions, it is just as well to subsume the entire content of the learning process in the form of the functions (5.5) rather than to attempt to state any general rules about the dependence of p_i on past experience. Analytically, this amounts to the substitution for (5.5) of the alternative function

$$(5.5') \quad p_i(t) \equiv p_i(x_i; x_1*, \ldots, x_n*; p_1*, \ldots, p_n*),$$

which involves only current values of the relevant variables. In other words, it is assumed that the ith seller takes currently observable information into account in estimating current sales prospects; but his general views on the nature of this dependence are already fixed by past experience and by subjective "hunches" about that experience and are not subject to change in the light of new data the implications of which are, in the nature of the case, somewhat ambiguous. This view is not at all plausible if it is considered to describe the behavior of a seller over a long interval of time; but it seems fairly realistic in reference to short time periods, and it may be accepted on a provisional basis accordingly.

Second, while knowledge about the behavior of other sellers (given by the values of the quantities x_j^*, p_j^* [$j \neq i$]) may be of some slight significance in estimating p_i, it cannot play a critical role unless the ith seller has definite information about over-all market demand conditions; and it is highly unrealistic to suppose that any seller knows very much about this! Hence, it is permissible to carry out a further specialization of (5.5), this time substituting for (5.5') the relation

$$(5.6) \quad p_i \equiv p_i(x_i, x_i^*, p_i^*) \, .$$

This function will serve as a basis for the whole of our subsequent discussion of sales estimation; for convenience, it will be assumed to be single valued, continuous, and to possess continuous first derivatives with respect to each of its variables.

It is not advisable to place any definite *quantitative* restrictions on the functions (5.6) at this stage; the views of individual sellers, since they depend upon subjective interpretations of possibly very different objective experiences, are likely to vary a great deal in practice, and it is as well to retain this aspect of the real world in our theoretical deliberations. However, there is one *qualitative* restriction which it does seem safe to impose on (5.6); viz., the requirement

$(5.7) \quad$ *For all values of x_i and x_i^* satisfying the condition $x_i = x_i^*$,*
$$p_i \equiv p_i^* \, .$$

The reason for defining p_i in terms of the requirement (5.7) is to ensure that the subjective sales estimates of the seller are never directly contradicted by current observation. That is to say, since any currently observed pair of values of x_i^* and p_i^* indicates unmistakably the quantity of output that can be sold at one particular estimated price at the moment of observation, it is natural to require that the estimated sales curve include the same point.

A statical illustration of the preceding comments is given in Figure 5.2, where quantities of output and sales are measured horizontally and values of price and estimated price are measured vertically. To the given observable point x_i^{*0}, p_i^{*0} there corresponds the estimated sales curve R_A^0, which indicates the highest level of price (average revenue) which the seller estimates will be associated with each alternative level of output (planned sales); one of the output-estimated price points thus specified coincides with the point (x^{*0}, p^{*0}) from which the curve R_A^0 is extrapolated. Since the given observable point is essentially arbitrary from a statical point of view, however, the function defining p_i must be represented geometrically by an entire family or *field* of such estimated sales curves, one curve for each possible sale-sale price point (no two curves in the field can intersect because the function [5.6] is single-valued). Thus, the estimate curve R_A^0 in Figure 5.2 is defined by the point (x_i^{*0}, p_i^{*0}), the estimate curve R_A' is defined by the point $(x_i^{*\prime}, p_i^{*\prime})$, and so forth. However, an unlimited number of different sale-sale price points may of course define the same estimated sales curve (e.g., the curve R_A' in Fig. 5.2 is defined by the point $[x_i^{*\prime\prime}, p_i^{*\prime\prime}]$ as well as by the point $[x_i^{*\prime}, p_i^{*\prime}]$). In particular, it is conceivable that in a single seller market where buyers adjust purchases instantaneously to

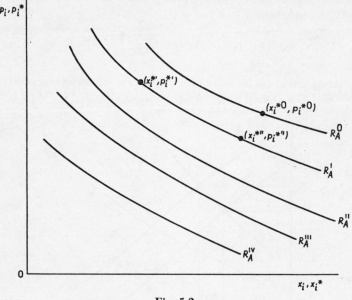

Fig. 5.2

planned demand, the seller might discover the "true" planned market demand curve for his product, in which event the sales field would degenerate to a single curve—the same curve being defined by *every* admissable observable point; this is, in fact, the assumption upon which traditional monopoly theory is founded.

Output Adjustment. Given the estimated sales function of the ith seller, we may proceed to deal with the behavior of output much as in Chapter Six (Section 11). First, denote the *total cost* of the ith seller by C_i and let the value of C_i be determined by the value of x_i at any instant in accordance with the identity

$$C_i \equiv C_i(x_i) .$$

Next, let *estimated net revenue* at any instant be defined by

$$R_i \equiv p_i(x_i, x_i^*, p_i^*)x_i - C_i(x_i) ,$$

so that *estimated marginal net revenue* is defined by

$$R_i' = p_i(x_i,x_i^*,p_i^*) + x_i\left(\frac{\partial p_i}{\partial x_i}\right) - C_i',$$

where $C_i' \equiv dC_i/dx_i$. Finally, assume that at any instant output varies directly with estimated marginal net revenue. In symbols,

$$(5.8) \quad \frac{dx_i}{dt} = H_i R_i' \quad (H_i > 0) .$$

As a further condition for market equilibrium, it is then necessary that, for arbitrary values of x_i^* and p_i^*, the value of the variable x_i be such as to satisfy the equation

$$(5.9) \quad p_i(x_i,x_i^*,p_i^*) + x_i\left(\frac{\partial p_i}{\partial x_i}\right) - C_i' = 0 ;$$

i.e., for the output of the ith seller to be stationary, estimated marginal revenue must be equal to marginal cost.[4]

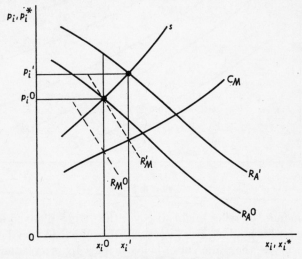

Fig. 5.3

This statical requirement is illustrated in Figure 5.3, with reference to a single seller where, as before, values of x_i and x_i^* are measured horizontally and values of p_i and p_i^* are measured vertically. To any given set of values of x_i^* and p_i^* there corresponds one and only one estimated sales curve and one and only one estimated marginal revenue curve (the latter curve is derived from the estimated sales curve and shown in dotted lines in Fig. 5.3). The intersection of any given estimated marginal revenue curve with the

---

[4] Here, and in all that follows, it is taken for granted that only those values of x_i for which net revenue is estimated to be nonnegative are admissable as equilibrium values of output.

marginal cost curve C_M then defines a particular level of equilibrium output which is associated, via the given estimated sales curve, with a particular level of estimated price. Thus, if the relevant marginal revenue curve is R_M^0 in Figure 5.3, the corresponding value of equilibrium output and the associated value of estimated price are x_i^0 and p_i^0, respectively; if the relevant marginal revenue curve is R_M', the corresponding equilibrium values of x_i and p_i are x_i' and p_i', etc. Allowing the variable parameters x_i^* and/or p_i^* to assume all possible values, therefore, and plotting corresponding values of equilibrium output against associated values of estimated price, a *supply curve* is obtained such as that illustrated by s in Figure 5.3. Any point is an admissable equilibrium output-estimated price combination if it lies on the supply curve s; otherwise not.

An interesting special case is that in which the estimated price function (5.6) takes the special form

$$(5.6') \quad p_i \equiv p_i^*,$$

so that the estimated sales field is composed entirely of horizontal straight lines as shown in Figure 5.4. In this instance, each estimated sales "curve"

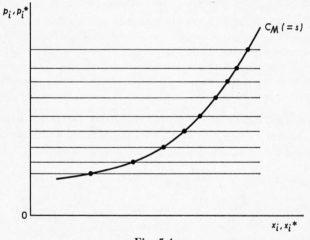

Fig. 5.4

is defined by a particular value of p_i^* independently of the value of x_i^* (i.e., the slope of the line is known to be zero relative to the quantity axis so the line as a whole is determined by its price intercept); hence, estimated marginal revenue is identically equal to estimated price regardless of the value of x_i; this means that the supply curve, s, coincides everywhere with the marginal cost curve, C_M (provided, of course, that the sales field is everywhere well defined).

The case described by the condition (5.6') may be characterized by saying that the sales estimates of the seller are *parametric* or, more conveniently in some instances, by saying that *pricing* is parametric. Otherwise, we may speak of *nonparametric sales estimates* or of *nonparametric pricing*. Of course, parametric pricing is associated only with selling under conditions of pure competition in the existing economic literature; but there is no *a priori* reason why such behavior cannot occur in a one-seller market since even in this case there may be fierce competition in a relevant sense among sellers in different but closely related markets. In any event, the preceding remarks are significant because they show that the theory of sales estimation asserted by (5.6) and (5.7) is already implicit in a special form in the accepted theory of purely competitive selling ([5.7] is satisfied vacuously when p_i is defined by [5.6']).

EXERCISE

5.1. If $p_i \neq p_i^*$ when $x_i = x_i^{*0}$ (where x_i^{*0} and p_i^{*0} are particular current values of x_i^* and p_i^*), would it be possible to test empirically any specific hypothesis about the dependence of p_i upon certain past and current values of x_i, x_i^*, and p_i^*?

5.2. If all estimated sales curves in the estimated sales field are downward sloping, where does the supply curve s lie in relation to the marginal cost curve? What is the situation if all the estimated sales curves are upward sloping?

5.3. As a general rule, sellers probably cannot be presumed to estimate sale prospects involving quantities or prices which differ greatly from those which they have actually experienced in the recent past. What would this imply about the domain of definition of estimated sales curves? What would it imply about the definition of the supply curve where sales estimates are parametric? (Hint: Would the supply curve still coincide *everywhere* with the marginal cost curve?)

6. *A Unified Theory of Price and Quantity Determination.* Combining the behavior equations (5.1), (5.3), and (5.8), we obtain a model of an n-seller market in which pricing is nonparametric; viz.,

$$(6.1) \begin{cases} \dfrac{dx_i^*}{dt} = A_i[d(p^*) - x^*] + B_{i1}(p_i^* - p_i^*) + \ldots + B_{in}(p_n^* - p_i^*) \\ \qquad\qquad (A_i, B_{ij} > 0, \quad i = 1, \ldots, n) \\ \dfrac{dp_i^*}{dt} = F_i(x_i^* - x_i) \quad (F_i > 0, \quad i = 1, \ldots, n) \\ \dfrac{dx_i}{dt} = H_i\left(p_i + x_i\dfrac{\partial p_i}{\partial x_i} - \dfrac{dC_i}{dx_i}\right) \quad (H_i > 0, \quad i = 1, \ldots, n), \end{cases}$$

where, as before, $p^* \equiv \text{Min}(p_1^*, \ldots, p_n^*)$, $x^* \equiv \sum_{i=1}^{n} x_i^*$, and the estimated price functions $p_i \equiv p_i(x_i, x_i^*, p_i^*)$ are defined to satisfy the condition (5.7). Now, since the model (6.1) comprises $3n$ independent differential equations in the $3n$ independent variables $x_1, \ldots, x_n, x_1^*, \ldots, x_n^*, p_1^*, \ldots, p_n^*$, it may without difficulty be regarded as a determinate system. To study its dynamical properties explicitly, however, would require a separate volume. Moreover, our object in the present analysis is merely to discover the extent to which competitive hypotheses (specifically, the assumption of parametric pricing) can serve to describe market situations in which pricing is *non-parametric*; and from this standpoint the dynamical model (6.1) has already served its purpose by providing a capacious grab bag out of which may be snatched a wide variety of *quantitatively* different statical models.

Let us proceed by considering first the special case of *monopoly*, defined by the condition $n = 1$. In this instance, $p_1{}^* = p^*$, and the system (6.1) takes the simple form

$$(6.2) \begin{cases} \dfrac{dx_1{}^*}{dt} = A_1[d(p_1{}^*) - x_1{}^*] \\[2mm] \dfrac{dp_1{}^*}{dt} = F_1(x_1{}^* - x_1) \\[2mm] \dfrac{dx_1}{dt} = H_1\left(p_1 + x_1\dfrac{\partial p_1}{\partial x_1} - \dfrac{dC_1}{dx_1}\right), \end{cases}$$

whence market equilibrium is defined by the conditions

$$(6.2') \begin{cases} d(p_1{}^*) - x_1{}^* = 0 \\ x_1{}^* - x_1 = 0 \\ p_1 + x_1\dfrac{\partial p_1}{\partial x_1} = \dfrac{dC_1}{dx_1}. \end{cases}$$

Expressed geometrically (Fig. 6.1), the sales of the monopolist will be stationary only if $p_1{}^*$ and $x_1{}^*$ are such that the point with these numbers as its co-ordinates lies on the planned demand curve $d(p_1{}^*)$, the output and estimated price of the monopolist will be stationary only if the point with corresponding co-ordinates lies on the monopoly supply curve s (defined as in the preceding section), and the sale price of the monopolist will be stationary only if these two points coincide, so that output and sales are equal. Moreover, sales, output, and price will all be stationary *if* all three of these conditions are satisfied simultaneously. Therefore, market equilibrium is defined by the intersection of the supply curve s with the demand curve d in Figure 6.1—a result which is remarkably similar to that which defines market equilibrium price in an isolated competitive market![5] Indeed, if we impose the special *quantitative* restriction on the estimated price function that $p_1 \equiv p_1{}^*$ (so that $\partial p_i/\partial x_i \equiv 0$), market equilibrium in (6.2) even im-

---

[5] A similar illustration holds for the case of traditional monopoly theory, except that in this model the sales "field" coincides with the planned market demand curve so that the monopoly supply "curve" degenerates to a single *point* which "intersects" (i.e., lies on) the planned market demand curve by hypothesis. Sale and price adjustment problems are essentially nonexistent in this instance. Analytically, the first requirement in (6.2') is gratuitous since it is assumed that $x_1{}^* \equiv d$ (instantaneous adjustment of purchases with changes in price); and while both of the remaining conditions might still be considered to be relevant, it is in fact usual to assume that $x_1 \equiv x_1{}^*$, which means that the dynamical restriction on $dp_1{}^*/dt$ in (6.2) has to be replaced by the essentially statical requirement $p_1{}^* \equiv f(x_i)$, where f is the function inverse to d. Thus, attention is ultimately focused on the problem of output adjustment alone.

plies equality of marginal cost and price, and the analogy already noted is strengthened further. To be sure, it is customary to regard competitive supply and demand schedules as relations which indicate the actual amount of a commodity that will be offered for sale or demanded to purchase at any given price; but this is valid only on the assumption that actual output and purchases adjust instantaneously to their equilibrium values at any instant. And even in this case, supply and demand functions can be legitimately regarded as "partial" equilibrium requirements, precisely as is done in the present analysis. It only remains to be seen, therefore, whether the analogy

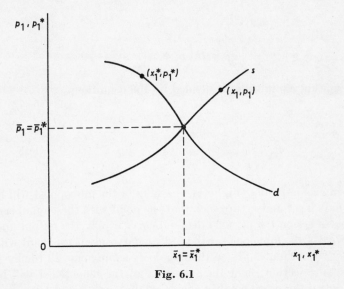

Fig. 6.1

between parametric and nonparametric pricing established in the case of monopoly can be established in more general instances.

If $n = 2$, the system (6.1) describes a general *duopoly* model, and may be written in full as

$$(6.3)\begin{cases} \dfrac{dx_1^*}{dt} = A_1[d(p^*) - x_1^* - x_2^*] + B_{12}(p_2^* - p_1^*) \\[2mm] \dfrac{dx_2^*}{dt} = A_2[d(p^*) - x_1^* - x_2^*] + B_{21}(p_1^* - p_2^*) \\[2mm] \dfrac{dp_1^*}{dt} = F_1[x_1^* - x_1] \\[2mm] \dfrac{dp_2^*}{dt} = F_2[x_2^* - x_2] \\[2mm] \dfrac{dx_1}{dt} = H_1\left(p_1 + x_1\dfrac{\partial p_1}{\partial x_1} - \dfrac{dC_1}{dx_1}\right) \\[2mm] \dfrac{dx_2}{dt} = H_2\left(p_2 + x_2\dfrac{\partial p_2}{\partial x_2} - \dfrac{dC_2}{dx_2}\right); \end{cases}$$

so market equilibrium is defined by the conditions

$$(6.3')\begin{cases} d(p^*) - x_1^* - x_2^* = 0 \\ p_2^* - p_1^* = 0 \\ x_1^* - x_1 = 0 \\ x_2^* - x_2 = 0 \\ p_1 + x_1\dfrac{\partial p_1}{\partial x_1} = \dfrac{dC_1}{dx_1} \\ p_2 + x_2\dfrac{\partial p_2}{\partial x_2} = \dfrac{dC_2}{dx_2} \cdot \end{cases}$$

Expressing these conditions geometrically but in an order the reverse of that in which they appear, we see first that the outputs of the two duopolists cannot be stationary unless the values of the output and estimated price variables of each duopolist are co-ordinates of points which lie on the respective supply curves s_1 and s_2 in Figure 6.2. Furthermore, since the

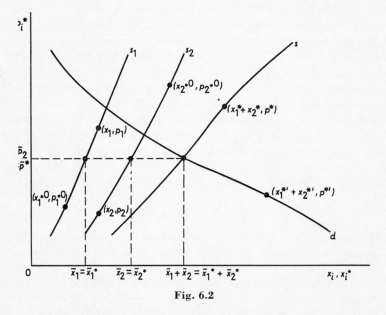

Fig. 6.2

price of each duopolist will vary over time unless his sales are equal to his output, and since the equality of output and sales implies the equality of sale price and estimated price (by [5.7]), it follows that for equilibrium to occur the sale price and sales of each duopolist must be such that the point with corresponding co-ordinates also lies on the appropriate supply curve. Next, since the sales of both duopolists will vary unless their respective sale prices are equal, equilibrium requires that aggregate sales together with the common value of the two sale prices be such that the point with corresponding co-ordinates lies on the *market supply curve s* in Figure 6.2, which is defined by simply adding the individual supply curves laterally.

Finally, aggregate purchases and the sale price of the duopolists must be such that the point with corresponding co-ordinates lies on the planned market demand curve, d. Hence, precisely as in the case of monopoly, market equilibrium is defined by the intersection of the market supply and demand curves s and d in Figure 6.2. As before, moreover, marginal cost will be equal to sale price for both duopolists in the case of parametric price estimates.

Now it should be evident that the above duopoly model is representative of the general case in every important respect. Regardless of the number of sellers in a given market, and regardless of their estimates of sale prospects, individual supply curves can always be defined and added laterally to obtain a market supply curve. The intersection of this curve with the planned market demand curve indicates the point at which aggregate equilibrium output is equal to aggregate sales at a common sale price, and individual equilibrium sales and output can then be read off from the individual supply curves which lie behind the market relation. And this is precisely the same procedure as one has to follow in dealing with the theoretical description of purely competitive selling. To be sure, it is usual in the latter case to suppose that sales and output are always identically equal for each seller so that some of the requirements which we have imposed as *equilibrium* conditions are there built into the basic structure of the model. What we have accomplished in the preceding analysis, therefore, is to outline a unified statical "supply and demand" theory of quantity and price determination which is valid *regardless of market structure considerations*. Different market models are obtained by imposing alternative *quantitative* restrictions, either on sales estimates or on the number of sellers involved in the market, but all of the models thus obtained are *qualitatively* identical.

EXERCISE

6.1. (Cournot's theory of duopoly.) Assume that two duopolists, each the proprietor of a mineral spring from which water can be obtained without cost, aim independently at maximizing their respective profits, given any (postulated) value of the other duopolist's sales, and given full knowledge of the planned market demand function for their (identical) products. More precisely, let the market demand function for the output of the two duopolists jointly be given by
$$x = x_1 + x_2 = -p + 6,$$
so that the sales curve for the product of the ith duopolist is
$$p = 6 - x_i - x_j^*$$
where x_j^* is a parameter representing the sales of the other duopolist. Given that the profit function of the ith duopolist is $R_i = x_i(6 - x_i - x_j^*)$, determine the supply curve of each duopolist analytically, represent your findings graphically, and show that market equilibrium is defined by the intersection of the consumer demand curve with the curve obtained by adding the quantity supplied by each duopolist at alternative levels of price. Compare and contrast your findings with those for a comparable competitive model.

7. *Monopoly and Competition: An Appraisal.* At this point it would be possible to deal at some length with questions which arise in connection with the statement of the model (6.1). For example, can the model be extended to deal with multiple market monopoly situations (monopolistic competition)? Is full allowance made for the presence of "conjectural interdependence" among sellers (i.e., for the fact that the actions of one seller may induce reactions by others)? Is it true, as suggested on numerous occasions in the preceding discussion, that "objective" market structure considerations do not play a controlling part in deciding whether sales estimates will be parametric or nonparametric? Will price behavior depend on such factors as the subjective cost of changing decisions, on institutional and legal restrictions, and similar things when sales estimates are parametric just as it does when sales estimates are nonparametric? Is the qualitative behavior of prices and quantities likely to be much the same from a dynamical point of view regardless of the character of sales estimates? And so forth, with virtually no limit. However, apart from noting that it would be possible to justify or to defend strongly an affirmative answer to each of the above queries, we shall turn immediately to the matter of using the analysis, as it now stands, to answer the original question raised at the beginning of Section 5.

In this connection, the preceding argument appears to support three general conclusions:

(*i*) The complexity of our unified model, which is itself greatly simplified in important respects, suggests that a comprehensive statement of the theory of nonparametric price and quantity behavior would be an extremely lengthy and difficult task, and would yield an unwieldy tool for applied analysis. Moreover, the complexity of a general dynamical theory of nonparametric pricing would probably have to be seen to be believed. Thus, in the absence of overwhelming arguments to the contrary, there seems to be every justification for the procedure adopted in the text by which nonparametric sales estimates are ignored. This is not to say that the formulation of a completely general theory would be pointless; such an undertaking would undoubtedly yield many interesting and useful results. But for reasons suggested below, the ultimate outcome of such an inquiry would probably be merely to increase the flexibility and to enrich the content of accepted competitive price theory, the latter being used for dealing with most practical problems, the general theory being used as a subsidiary frame of reference against which to check the appropriateness of applications involving the explicit use of "nearly" competitive models.

(*ii*) The fact that one can describe both "competitive" and "monopolistic" varieties of individual and market behavior in terms of a single model, allowance being made for quantitative differences, indicates that no compelling arguments can be advanced in favor of dealing, as a general rule, with "monopolistic" rather than with "competitive" models. Competitive hypotheses, since they are readily expressed to allow for the existence of alternative sets of demand estimates, are already considerably more general in this respect than the hypotheses underlying traditional monopoly theory (which involves only a single set of estimates; i.e., a single estimated demand curve); and the same observation applies to most "monopolistic" (nonparametric pricing) models which are considered in the economic literature. Moreover, the *methods of analysis* adopted in competitive price theory are immediately applicable to the analysis of any concrete situation (this remark is supported by the fact that, in every instance, whether competitive or not, one has to deal with much the same kind of equations, supply and demand functions, etc.). Thus, it is not difficult to show that duopoly is formally similar either to a competitive market in which there are only two sellers or to a system of two (related) competitive markets (depending on whether the commodities sold by the duopolists are or are not regarded as identical by buyers); and similarly for other oligopoly or oligopsony situations. In effect, therefore, competitive hypotheses, if appropriately elaborated, may always be regarded as workable approximations, suitable for most theoretical and for nearly all practical purposes.

(*iii*) Finally, our argument suggests that all differences between competitive and other formal theories of price determination are reducible in a logical sense to postulated differences in the subjective beliefs of the economic units which participate in any given market. This begs the question of the precise way in which the subjective beliefs of economic units (i.e., estimates of demand and supply conditions generally) are determined. Intuition suggests that "objective" market circumstances have much to do with this; but the problem of linking "beliefs" with "facts" cannot be attacked properly using armchair methods. To make any progress in this area, explicit models must be formulated and tested in the light of behavior observed in actual markets. At bottom, however, the problem of describing the formation of current demand estimates under other than competitive hypotheses is similar to that of describing the formation of future price anticipations under competitive hypotheses. Regarded as subjects of empirical research, problems of a particularly difficult and intricate character are involved in both instances. In any event, the problems in question fall within the scope of theoretical economics only to a very limited extent; they belong essentially to the realm of applied economics.

To the question, "Does the loss of realism associated with the adoption of competitive hypotheses more than offset the resulting gains in theoretical manageability?", the above considerations appear to support a negative reply. In fact, there appears to be no appreciable loss of realism associated with the adoption of competitive hypotheses; hence, there are no very substantial disadvantages to be set off against the admitted advantages of competitive assumptions. In short, the general presumption that competitive hypotheses are inadequate to describe other types of market situations is only a presumption; its validity cannot be demonstrated because the presumption does not appear to be correct. What is true is that accepted statements of competitive price theory are themselves inadequate in certain important respects; but that is altogether a different matter.

8. Conclusion. The view of an economic system which emerges from the discussion in this and preceding chapters is analogous to a scale drawing of an intricate piece of machinery accompanied by blueprints which describe the working of various internal gears and pulleys. Such a picture represents an obvious oversimplification of economic activity as we experience it in everyday life, where fitfully human things overlie and modify profoundly the mechanistic elements which have been the main concern of this study. While our analysis may be useful for studying and interpreting many important aspects of behavior in the real world, therefore, this can be true only to a limited degree.

Perhaps the most obvious and important nonmechanical elements to be taken into account (among those to which it is possible to attach a label at all) are governmental and political activity, activities leading to the creation and destruction of units of economic decision, and activities involving the development of new consumer tastes and new business techniques. In principle it is of course possible to study the economic effects of these activities in terms of the comparative statics of a general equilibrium system, or, more generally, in terms of the *comparative dynamics* of a general dynamical system (describing changes in the motion or behavior over time of an economic *system* resulting from various "once-over" changes in initial conditions or in the functional structure of a model—cf. P. A. Samuelson, *Foundations of Economic Analysis* [Cambridge: Harvard University Press, 1947], pp. 351–53). As a practical matter, however, it is clear that the activities in question are to some extent related to happenings in the strictly economic sector of the economy; i.e., the effects in question work in two or more directions, not in one direction only. This is particularly clear as concerns the creation and destruction of economic units and the development and introduction of new techniques, although even here the connection is extremely complicated. If a change in taste has the effect of making the expenditures of a consumer consistently exceed his income, the consumer may die; but he may also beg, borrow, or steal additional funds or, more likely yet, curtail his fancies to suit his purse. Similarly, a change in technique which increases the profits of certain firms and threatens other firms with bankruptcy may easily encourage further changes in technique among the threatened firms. The difficulty in these and in other cases of the kind, however, is to discover a way in which to relate "economic" to "legal," "political," "institutional," "psychological," and "biological" factors. These considerations naturally lead to the study of questions which are far wider in scope than any considered in this book—to what one writer has called ". . . the majestic problems of economic development." The general principles underlying study of this kind may be clarified, however, by reference to the same principles which guide one in analyzing market behavior.

To investigate the properties of an isolated market, one formulates a model involving, say, a single variable u_1 together with any number of parameters which are held constant by the assumption of *ceteris paribus*. The model may be expressed, under appropriate circumstances, as a functional equation of some kind (perhaps a statical, perhaps a dynamical equation) having the general (symbolic) form

$$f_1(u_1;a_1, \ldots ,a_m) = 0 \, ,$$

in terms of which most of the actual analysis is to be conducted. Having pursued the examination of such a model as far as seems worth while, however, one is immediately prompted to ask what effects will follow if one or more of the parameters, $a_1, \ldots ,a_m$, previously held constant, are permitted to vary. This leads directly to questions in comparative statics or comparative dynamics, and, in turn, to the statement of more general models described by systems of equations in which *quantities previously regarded as parameters are treated as explicit variables*. That is to say, one is led to consider systems of functional equations having some such symbolic expression as

$$(8.1) \quad f_i(u_1, \ldots ,u_n; a_n, \ldots ,a_m) = 0 \quad (i = 1, \ldots ,n) \, ,$$

where $u_i = a_{i+1}$ in terms of the simple one-variable model mentioned above. To be sure, if one continues to proceed in this fashion indefinitely, he will eventually convert into variables all parameters which are clearly "economic" in character, without, as a rule, having satisfied himself that his knowledge of economic phenomena is at all complete even in a theoretical sense. Eventually, therefore, it will seem desirable to treat various governmental and institutional quantities, etc., *as explicit variables*, $v_1, \ldots ,v_q$, within the framework of more general models represented symbolically in the form

$$f_i(u_1, \ldots ,u_n;v_1, \ldots ,v_q;a_{n+q}, \ldots ,a_m) = 0 \, ,$$

where $v_i = a_{n+i-1}$ in terms of the original one-variable model. In this way, provided that one is sufficiently ingenious in quantifying "noneconomic" parameters and expressing them as explicit variables in various functional equations, the range of subjects upon which precise methods of analysis can be brought to bear might be extended almost indefinitely.

PART II

The Mathematics

Chapter Eight

FUNCTIONS, GRAPHS, AND EQUATIONS

THIS book has been written on the assumption that the reader comes to it equipped with at least a moderate knowledge of elementary algebra and that he can solve a quadratic equation, graph simple equations, and perform other feats at approximately the same level. In the present chapter and those following we begin at this level and develop, in a more or less logical order, certain mathematical topics which are of particular importance for the economist and are used extensively in Part I.

The present chapter is therefore that most likely to overlap the field of the reader's previous knowledge of mathematics, and we have accordingly been sparing of details, putting the emphasis on terminology and on certain aspects of the subjects discussed which are not normally emphasized in mathematics texts and courses but are exceptionally significant in economics.

The key concepts of the chapter are those named in the title, and since these terms should be familiar to the reader already, we proceed at once to the discussion without further words of introduction.

1. *Variables and Functions.* What distinguishes algebra from elementary arithmetic is the practice of using letters in place of numbers; by this device one can use a formula $a + b = b + a$ in place of the infinite list of formulas which includes $2 + 1 = 1 + 2$, $3 + 5 = 5 + 3$, $8.2 + (-11.73) = (-11.73) + 8.2$, etc. The gain in simplicity, in directness, and, most important, in generality obtained by this device is inexpressibly great. We shall consistently use letters (Roman and Greek) in this way. Letters so used are called *variables*. A specific number for which a given variable may stand is called a *value* of the variable, and the set of all possible values of the variable is sometimes called the *range* of the variable. A variable which is supposed to stand for a fixed (even if unspecified) number throughout a particular discussion, in other words a variable whose range consists of a single number, is called a *constant*.

A valuable simplifying device used in labeling variables is that of introducing *indices*. If one wishes to deal with several variables at the same time, all of them representing similar quantities (e.g., the prices of various commodities in an economic system), one must of course use a distinct symbol for each variable; but to call these variables a, b, c, . . . , quite apart from the fact that one might soon exhaust whatever alphabets were at his disposal, would do nothing to emphasize their kinship. In such a case it is customary, and clearly better, to indicate the ith price (if one is speaking of prices) by, say, p_i; if there are n prices, the list of variables becomes $p_1, p_2, \ldots, p_n$. Numbers i used in this way are called *indices* or (indicial) *subscripts;* they have no mathematical significance but are merely aids in labeling. Instead of writing out the whole list, one may write simply p_i, the range of possible values of i being either understood from the context or explicitly expressed by a parenthesis ($i = 1, 2, \ldots, n$). This system not only unifies and clarifies the notation but also enables one to proceed without saying exactly how many variables there are.

A virtue of this system which is especially valuable, although it may not appear at first sight, is the ease with which it enables one to write sums of many terms of the same type. Thus instead of writing

$$a_1 + a_2 + a_3 + a_4 + a_5 + a_6 + a_7 ,$$

we may refer to the "sum of the a_k's as k ranges from 1 to 7," or something similar. This approach lends itself to an even more abbreviated symbolism, and one writes

$$\sum_{k=1}^{7} a_k$$

for the same sum, where the symbol Σ (the Greek capital letter *sigma*) can be regarded as meaning "the sum of," a_k denotes the typical term of the sum, and the symbols above and below the Σ (which may be omitted if the context makes them unnecessary) indicate the range of the index k. This notation can be extended and modified in various ways which are almost self-explanatory and need not be enumerated here; examples will be encountered in Part I.

From our point of view, the most important characteristic of variables is that they may appear as *functions* of one another. The variable y is said to be a function of the variable x if, for any given value of x, there corresponds either exactly one value of y, or none. A function may therefore be thought of as a correspondence; the rule by means of which the correspondence is expressed may for instance be given as an explicit formula, as an explicit verbal rule of some kind, or it may not be given explicitly at all but merely assumed to exist. The simplest functions are those expressible by means of formulas; e.g.,

$$(1.1) \quad y = 2x + 1;$$

here the value of y corresponding to any particular value of x can be immediately calculated. In general, one may write

$$(1.2) \quad y = f(x)$$

as an abbreviation for the statement "y is a certain function (which shall be denoted by f) of x." The particular function involved may be left unspecified, or the letter f may be understood to represent a particular function; for instance, (1.2) might be taken as an abbreviation for (1.1) in some discussion. Since it is often necessary to mention several different functions in a single context, it is important to be able to distinguish between the functions by means of a suitable notation; and this is again accomplished by using different letters for different functions, or by using subscripts. For instance,

$$y = f(x), \quad z = g(x)$$

could be used to express the fact that y and z are two (generally different) functions of x; or

$$y_i = f_i(x_i) \quad (i = 1, 2, \ldots, n)$$

could be used to express n distinct functional relationships: y_1 is a certain function (denoted by f_1) of x_1, y_2 is a certain function (denoted by f_2) of x_2, etc.

If a functional correspondence between x and y is given by (1.2), the symbol $f(0)$ is used to denote the value of y (if it exists) corresponding to the value of 0 of x; $f(-3)$ denotes the value of y (if it exists) corresponding to the value of -3 of x; and so on.

There is a certain amount of traditional terminology associated with the idea of a function. If the variables x and y are related by the equation (1.2), for example, then x (as far as this relation is concerned) is the *independent variable* and y is the *dependent variable*.[1] The set of values of x for which corresponding values of y are defined is the *domain* of the function, and the set of values of y so obtained is the *range* of the function.

The notion of a function as defined above may be broadened in two important ways. First, since the assumption that variables represent numbers is in no way essential for the meaningfulness of the function concept, this assumption may be dropped. The variables related by a functional correspondence may stand for objects of any kind, even of kinds which do not seem to be of a mathematical nature at all. Second, one may have functions of several variables; i.e., the value of the dependent variable y may depend on the values of all the variables $x_1, x_2, \ldots, x_n$. In a case of this kind one writes

$$(1.3) \quad y = f(x_1, x_2, \ldots, x_n) .$$

The preceding remarks about a function of a single variable also apply, with appropriate qualifications, to a function of several variables. Perhaps it should be mentioned explicitly that the domain of a function of several variables is the set of all "n-tuples" $(a_1, a_2, \ldots, a_n)$ of values of the independent variables $x_1, x_2, \ldots, x_n$ for which a corresponding value of y is defined; and that it may not be possible to describe this domain by imposing restrictions on the variables x_i separately. Almost all of the functions oc-

---

[1] Of course, a variable which occurs as the dependent variable relative to one function may at the same time be the independent variable relative to another.

curring in this book are functions of several variables; and the range of the variables is almost always a set of real numbers.

EXERCISES

1.1. Allowing the variables involved to stand for real numbers only, describe the domain of each of the functions defined by the following formulas and verbal rules.

a) $y = x^3$

b) $y = \dfrac{x}{1 + x}$

c) $y = \dfrac{1}{1 - \sqrt{x}}$

d) $y = \sqrt{1 - (x_1)^2 - (x_2)^2}$

e) y is the largest whole number smaller than the positive fourth root of x.

1.2. If $f(x) = 1 - x^2$, find:

$$(a)\ f(0)\,,\quad (b)\ f(-1)\,,\quad (c)\ f\!\left(\frac{1}{x}\right),\quad (d)\ f(u^2)\,.$$

1.3. It is sometimes convenient to use a double set of indices in labeling a set of variables. For instance, in an economy where m commodities are offered for sale by n firms, p_{ij} might be used to denote the price at which the ith commodity is offered by the jth firm $(i = 1, \ldots, m; j = 1, \ldots, n)$. However, the symbol p_{123} would then be ambiguous; it might stand for the price at which the first commodity is offered by the twenty-third firm, or the price at which the twelfth commodity is offered by the third firm. How might the notation be modified so as to avoid this ambiguity? List several possibilities and discuss their relative merits.

2. *Equations and Their Solutions.* Equations and their general significance are to some extent matters of common knowledge, but in order to be able to use them properly one should be aware of certain facts of a more technical character.

In the first place, three kinds of equations may be distinguished. Examples of the first kind are:

$$2 = 1 + 1\,,$$
$$x = (x + 1) - 1\,,$$
$$(x + y)^2 = x^2 + 2xy + y^2\,.$$

The first equation is certainly true for the particular constants appearing in it; and the other two equations are true for any values of the variables whatever. Equations of this kind are called *identities*, for they express the fact that two expressions have identical values either as they stand (as in the first example above) or for whatever values may be assigned to the variables involved. In general, an identity is an equation which is true for all values of the variables for which both sides of the equation are defined.[2]

In order to emphasize that a certain equation is an identity, one frequently uses the sign "$\equiv$" (read: "is identically equal to") in place of the ordinary sign of equality, but this identity sign is not mandatory, and its absence should not be interpreted to mean that a given equation may not be an identity.

On the other hand, the equations

$$1 = 7 + 2 ,$$
$$2^x = 0 ,$$

are certainly not identities; the first is false as it stands, and the second fails to be true for any value of x. Equations of this type, which are true for *no* choice of values of whatever variables are involved, may be called *inconsistent equations.*

Intermediate between these two extremes is the vast class of equations which are true for certain values of the variables and false for others; for example,

$$x^2 = x ,$$
$$x - y = 2.73 ,$$
$$xyz = \frac{1}{xyz} .$$

Equations of this kind are called *conditional equations.*

If, when each of the variables in a conditional equation is replaced by a certain one of its values, both sides of the equation reduce to the same number, this set of values of the variables is said to *satisfy* the equations and is said to constitute a *solution* of the equation.[3] For example, either of the values 0, 1 of x satisfies the equation $x^2 = x$, so each of these numbers is a solution (these are, in fact, the only solutions) of that equation. The values 3.85 and 1.12 of x and y, respectively, satisfy the equation $x - y = 2.73$; this pair of numbers is therefore a solution of the equation, although it is by no means the only solution. The number of solutions of a given conditional equation need not be finite; the second and third conditional equations listed above are examples of equations having infinitely many solutions without being identities.

To *solve* a conditional equation is to find all of its solutions. If there are only finitely many solutions (say three) of a particular equation, then one merely needs to find and list these solutions to have solved it; but if there are infinitely many solutions, as in the example $x - y = 2.73$ mentioned above, then it is necessary to give the solution in some other way, usually

---

[2] The qualification at the end of this definition is made in order to allow for cases like that represented by the equation $x + 1 = (x^2 - 1)/(x - 1)$. If $x = 1$, the right side of this equation is undefined, for both terms of the fraction become 0, and the fraction $0/0$ is meaningless. For any other value of x, however, both sides of the equation are defined and are equal; therefore this equation is an identity according to the definition.

[3] If the equation involves just one variable, a solution is frequently called a *root* of the equation.

by means of one or more formulas. For the example just mentioned, any solution may be obtained from the formulas

$$x = u + 2.73 ,$$
$$y = u ,$$

by giving u a suitable value (the previously mentioned solution $x = 3.85$, $y = 1.12$ is obtained by choosing u to be 1.12); and any pair of values of x and y obtainable in this way constitutes a solution.

It may happen that one is able to say that a certain equation has solutions even though he is unable to determine precisely what even one of those solutions is. For instance, consider the equation

$$(2.1) \quad x^5 + 2x^4 + 2x^3 + 2x^2 + 2x - 2 = 0 .$$

There is no algebraic formula giving solutions of an equation of this kind, so that anyone faced with the problem of finding even one solution is in a rather difficult position; but it is nevertheless easy to see that there *exists* at least one solution. Indeed, when $x = 0$ the value of the left side of (2.1) is negative (namely, -2), but when $x = 1$ the value of the left side of (2.1) is positive (namely, $+7$). Thus, since the value of the left side changes continuously as x changes continuously, there must be some value of x between 0 and 1 at which the value of the left side of (2.1) is 0; and this value of x will be a real solution of the equation.

This situation, although it occurs frequently in mathematical work, does not totally impede progress: first, because for most theoretical purposes it is enough to be sure of the existence of solutions, and perhaps to know some of their properties (whether or not they are real, whether or not they are positive, etc.)—their precise values are often not important; second, because there exist methods for systematically finding *approximations* to the solutions of the more important kinds of equations, these approximations being as close to the true solutions as may be required and therefore adequate for any practical purpose.

The point to remember is that there *is* a difference between knowing that a certain equation has solutions and being able to solve it explicitly. This is especially important in this book, since we frequently speak of the solutions of certain equations without even pretending to be able to say precisely what those solutions are.

A given equation may always be put in a form in which the right side is zero. For example, the equation

$$(2.2) \quad g(x,y) = h(x,y) ,$$

where g and h represent two functions of the variables x and y, may be written in the form

$$(2.3) \quad g(x,y) - h(x,y) = 0 ,$$

irrespective of the nature of the functions g and h. Of course (2.2) and (2.3) are different equations; what we mean by saying that the first may be written in the form of the second is that *the two equations have the same solutions.* This follows from the basic arithmetical fact that if $A = B$, then $A + C = B + C$, where A, B, and C are arbitrary numbers.[4] Thus whenever we are interested in an equation for the sake of its solutions, we may assume that it is in the form

$$(2.4) \quad f(x,y, \ldots) = 0 .$$

The character of the solutions will of course depend entirely on the character of the function f.

EXERCISES

2.1. Determine whether each of the following equations is an identity, an inconsistent equation, or a conditional equation, and for each conditional equation find at least one solution.

a) $(x + 1)^2 - 2x = x^2 + 1$

b) $(x + 1)^2 = (x + 2)^2$

c) $x + 1 = x + 2$

d) $\dfrac{u^2}{u^3} = \dfrac{u}{u^2}$

e) $x + y + z = 2$

f) $(x + y)^2 - (x - y)^2 = 2xy$

2.2. By a line of reasoning analogous to that applied to the equation (2.1) in the text, show that the equation

$$\left(\frac{x - 1}{x + 1}\right)^4 = \frac{1}{2}$$

has at least one solution.

2.3. Write each of the equations (a), (c), (e), (f) of Exercise 2.1 in the form (2.4), simplifying as much as possible.

3. Graphs. When f stands for a function of just one variable, say x, the graph of the function gives insight into the nature of the solutions of the equation (2.4) and, in particular, enables one to find approximate values for the real solutions of the equation. In order to obtain the graph of such a function, one proceeds as follows:[5] one first constructs a *co-ordinate system* consisting of two perpendicular axes with an appropriately chosen unit of length on each, and then assigns to each point in the plane a pair of numbers (its *co-ordinates*) which express the position of the point relative to the

---

[4] *Proof:* Suppose that the pair of numbers a,b constitute a solution of (2.2); then $g(a,b) = h(a,b)$ is a true equation between numbers. Utilizing the principle stated in the text, we add the number $-h(a,b)$ to both sides of this equation, thus obtaining the true equation $g(a,b) - h(a,b) = 0$. This equation means, however, that a,b is a solution of (2.3). In a similar way, one can easily prove that every solution of (2.3) is also a solution of (2.2); and this statement, combined with the last, means that the equations (2.2) and (2.3) have exactly the same solutions, as claimed. It should be clear that this proof does not depend on the number of variables involved.

[5] Since graphical techniques are very familiar to economists, our treatment of this subject is intentionally brief and incomplete.

axes. If the first co-ordinate is denoted by x and the second by y, one can identify these co-ordinates with the similarly labeled variables in the functional relation $y = f(x)$, where f denotes the given function. The set of points whose co-ordinates (x,y) satisfy this equation constitutes a certain figure in the plane, which in the simplest and most frequently occurring cases will be made up of one or more smooth, continuous curves. This figure is the *graph* of the function; and by observing various aspects of its shape and position one may immediately grasp certain important properties of the function itself. The graph may be drawn by the method of *plotting points*, which consists in assigning various convenient values to one of the variables, calculating the corresponding values of the other variable, marking the points so determined on the plane, and connecting these by what one judges to be the appropriate curve or curves. The more points one first determines, the better the idea one should expect to have of the shape of the graph; but one must always be aware of the possibility that certain possibly interesting properties of the graph (small wiggles, gaps, etc.) may not be revealed in this way. In drawing a graph, the practiced graph-plotter uses all the information he can extract from the given functional equation.

The way in which the graph of the function f may be used to find approximate values for the real solutions of (2.4) in the one-variable case may now be illustrated by means of an example. We take as our example the equation (2.1). The function of x represented by the left side of (2.1) is taken as f, so that the basic functional relation is

$$y = x^5 + 2x^4 + 2x^3 + 2x^2 + 2x - 2 .$$

This function, if graphed, becomes the curve in Figure 3.1. The graph is a smooth and continuous curve which extends infinitely far to both left and right; hence it is possible to sketch only a part of it. However, the figure shows the interesting part; outside the part of the plane which is shown the curve merely goes steeply upward to the right and steeply downward to the left. Notice, in particular, that the curve crosses the x-axis at the point P. Because $y = 0$ at this point (the x-axis being the set of all points with this property), the value of x at P must be a solution of the original equation (2.1). Therefore, since the value of x at P seems to be about 0.55, one may conclude that 0.55 is approximately a solution of (2.1); moreover, this must be the only real solution of (2.1), for the curve in Figure 3.1 crosses the x-axis at P only.

This method makes it possible to find approximate values for all of the *real* solutions of a given equation involving one variable. *Complex* solutions never appear, for complex values of x have no graphical meaning. If the scale is made large enough, and if enough care is taken in plotting the graph, the approximate solutions can be made as close to the true solutions as one wishes. Needless to say, however, this method is not only inherently inexact but is usually laborious—extremely so if a high degree of accuracy is required. Whenever there is available a relatively simple algebraic procedure for solving an equation, therefore, it is to be preferred to the graphical procedure. For the equation (2.1), however, and for many other equations, there is no such procedure and the graphical method is a welcome expedient. There do exist algebraic methods for finding approximate solutions of equations like (2.1), and in the long run these are better than the graphi-

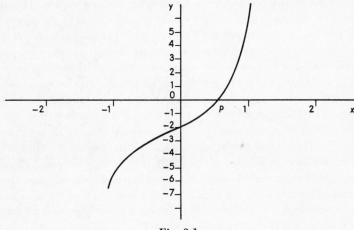

Fig. 3.1

cal method; but a discussion of even the simplest of these methods would be out of place here.

We shall discuss the significance of other aspects of the graph of a function subsequently.

EXERCISES

By the graphical method described in the text, find the real solutions (if any) of each of the following equations. Check by solving by nongraphical methods when possible.

3.1. $3x + 2 = 0$.

3.2. $x^2 - 3x + 2 = 0$.

3.3. $x^2 + 2x + 2 = 0$.

3.4. $\left(\dfrac{x-1}{x+1}\right)^4 - \dfrac{1}{2} = 0$ (cf. Exercise 2.2.).

4. Polynomials. In almost all of the explicit equations of the form (2.4) with which we deal, the function f is a *polynomial*. We shall therefore now recall the definition of this term and enumerate some of the most important properties of equation (2.4) when f is a polynomial.

A *monomial*, first of all, is any expression obtained by multiplying together a set of variables, each raised to some positive integral power, and multiplying this product by some number other than zero. Thus the typical monomial is

$$ax^m y^n \ldots w^p,$$

where x, y, ..., w are variables, m, n, ..., p are positive whole numbers, and a is some nonzero number (called the *coefficient*). The sum of the exponents m, n, ..., p is called the *degree* of the monomial. By a special convention, a number by itself is called a monomial of degree zero.[6]

A polynomial is simply an expression formed by adding together a finite number of monomials. A polynomial in which all the coefficients are real numbers may be called a *real* polynomial. The *degree* of a polynomial is the largest number occurring as the degree of one of the monomials whose sum is the polynomial.

Polynomials whose degree is *one* are of special interest. They are called *linear polynomials*. The most general linear polynomial involving the three variables x, y, and z is

$$ax + by + cz + d,$$

where a, b, c, and d stand for constants and at least one of the constants a, b, c, is not zero. By this we mean that any such polynomial can (after some algebraic simplifications, perhaps) be written in the form indicated. The most significant fact about equations of the form

$$(2.4) \quad f(x,y, \ldots) = 0$$

is probably the theorem: *If* $f(x,y, \ldots)$ *is a polynomial of positive degree, the equation (2.4) has at least one solution.* The importance of this theorem is indicated by the fact that it is frequently called the *fundamental theorem of algebra*. The theorem may be proved in a variety of ways, but every proof involves the use of methods outside the domain of algebra; we shall therefore ask that the theorem be accepted without our proving it.

Using the fundamental theorem, one can prove the following more informative results:

If (2.4) satisfies the conditions of the fundamental theorem, and moreover involves only one variable, then the number of solutions of (2.4) is equal to the degree of the polynomial f. Some of the solutions may be equal, but in any case one may say that the number of distinct solutions of (2.4) in this case lies between 1 and d, where d is the degree of the polynomial f.

If (2.4) satisfies the conditions of the fundamental theorem, and moreover involves at least two variables, the number of solutions of (2.4) is infinite.

The proof of this statement is simple. To be specific, we shall suppose that (2.4) involves the three variables x, y, z. Then if one assigns a value z_0 to the variable z in such a way that the degree of the resulting equation involving x and y is not zero, then according to the fundamental theorem this equation has at least one solution (x_0,y_0). The three numbers x_0, y_0, z_0 thus constitute a solution of the given equation; and since there are infinitely many possible values of z_0, there must be infinitely many solutions of the given equation. (The statement that there are infinitely many values of z

---

[6] Some writers insist that the number 0 itself should be regarded as a monomial whose degree is undefined.

for which the corresponding x, y equation has a positive degree requires a bit of proving, but its proof will not be given here.)

It should be noted that we have nowhere stated that any of the solutions whose existence is asserted by these theorems must be *real;* it may well happen that all solutions are complex (i.e., not real) even if the polynomial f is a real polynomial.

EXERCISES

4.1. Find the degree of each polynomial:

   a) $x^2 + 3x - 5$

   b) $x^3 + y^3 + 3x^2y^2 - 5xy$

   c) $(x - y + 1)^3$

4.2. To which of the equations in Exercises 2.1 and 2.2 does each of the theorems in this section apply?

5. Systems of Equations. In this section we shall deal with *systems* of equations. The typical system can be conveniently written in the form

$$(5.1)\begin{cases} f_1(x_1,x_2,\ldots,x_m) = 0, \\ f_2(x_1,x_2,\ldots,x_m) = 0, \\ \ldots\ldots\ldots\ldots\ldots \\ f_n(x_1,x_2,\ldots,x_m) = 0. \end{cases}$$

Here the f_i ($i = 1, 2, \ldots, n$) are functions of the m variables x_j ($j = 1, 2, \ldots, m$); m and n may or may not be equal. Some of the functions f_i may not actually depend explicitly on certain of the x_j's. For instance, f_1 may depend on x_1 only, even if $m > 1$; but it is still possible to regard f_1 as a function of all the x_j's, as reference to our definition of such functions (Section 1) will show.

Each of the equations in the system (5.1), viewed separately, is subject to the discussion in Section 2; in particular, each equation is either an identity, an inconsistent equation, or a conditional equation. The whole system (5.1) may be regarded in a similar light. In order to do this, one must first decide what is to be meant by a solution of the *system.* This decision is made by means of the following definition: A set of numbers $(a_1,a_2,\ldots,a_m)$ is said to be a solution of the system (5.1) if it is a solution of each of the equations in the system. In other words, a solution of the system (5.1) is merely a solution which all the equations of the system have in common. By analogy with the definitions given in Section 2, one may say that the system is an *identical system* if *any* set of numbers $(a_1,a_2,\ldots,a_m)$ is a solution of the system, an *inconsistent system* if the system has no solution, and a *conditional system* in any intermediate case. These terms (except for *inconsistent system*) are seldom used, but the analogy is worth observing. It is also worth while to note the following facts, which are immediate consequences of the definitions: (*a*) The system is identical if and only if each of the equations in the system is an identity; (*b*) the system is inconsistent if (but not only if) any one of the equations in the system is inconsistent. The absence of the phrase "and only if" from (b) is significant. Indeed, a system may be inconsistent even though no equation in the system is itself inconsistent. This fact is easy to establish by means of examples, for instance by the example

$$x - 1 = 0 ,$$
$$x + 2 = 0 .$$

Here $m = 1$ (the subscript on x_1 is therefore omitted) and $n = 2$, with $f_1(x) = x - 1$, $f_2(x) = x + 2$. Clearly, neither of the equations involved is inconsistent, but the system as a whole is inconsistent. This is a trivial example, but one can construct examples of this kind which are as complicated as one wishes.

Deciding whether or not a given system (5.1) is inconsistent, and if it is consistent (i.e., conditional or identical), finding information about the properties of the solutions (at best, finding the solutions themselves) can be problems of unlimited difficulty. We shall have little of a general nature to say about the matter in this book. When all of the equations are linear, however, the situation is relatively simple; this case will be treated at length in Chapter Eleven.

EXERCISES

5.1. Determine whether each system is identical, conditional, or inconsistent:

    a) $x_1{}^2 - x_2{}^2 = 0$
          $x_1{}^2 + x_2{}^2 = 2$

    b) $(x_1 - x_2)^2 - x_1{}^2 - x_2{}^2 + 2x_1x_2 = 0$
          $(x_1 - x_2)^0 = 1$

    c) $x_1 - 2x_2 = 1$
          $\frac{1}{2}x_1 - x_2 = 2$

    d) $x_1 - 3 = 0$
          $x_2 + 3 = 0$

5.2. Write out a proof for the statement that a system is identical if and only if each of the equations in the system is an identity.

6. *Counting Equations and Unknowns.* We shall complement Section 5 with a note of warning. In the economic literature one often encounters the assumption, made either tacitly or explicitly, that if $m = n$ for a system (5.1) (if, that is, the number of equations equals the number of variables or "unknowns"), the system has exactly one solution which, in turn, is sometimes supposed to have even further desirable properties, for instance that of consisting of positive numbers. Similarly, it is often assumed that if $m < n$ (there are more equations than unknowns), the system must be inconsistent, while if $m > n$ (there are fewer equations than unknowns), the system must have more than one solution. These assumptions are not mathematical theorems; if $m = n$ the system may nevertheless be inconsistent or have more than one solution, while a system may have exactly one solution irrespective of the relative sizes of m and n for that system. This is not to say that the assumptions cannot be made; but if they are made their extra-mathematical character should be frankly recognized, or they should be derived from more specific assumptions about the equations involved in the system under consideration.[7]

Some readers, especially those who have done some reading in the Walrasian theory of exchange, may doubt the truth of some of the assertions in the last paragraph simply because they have seen the contrary assertions repeated so often. Some specific examples may carry conviction.

Example 6.1 ($m = n$, *no solutions*). The system consisting of the equations

$$x + y - 5 = 0,$$
$$x + y - 6 = 0,$$

clearly has no solutions (real or not), for the same two numbers cannot add up to 5 and 6 simultaneously. Here, of course, $m = n = 2$.

Example 6.2 ($m = n$, *infinitely many solutions*) The system of equations

$$x - 2y + 3z - 2 = 0,$$
$$x + 4y - z - 4 = 0,$$
$$x + y + z - 3 = 0,$$

for which $m = n = 3$, has infinitely many different solutions. This may be seen in the following way. Let x be an arbitrary number, and solve the first two equations for y and z. The solution so obtained will also satisfy the third equation, as substitution will show. In general, a solution of this system may be obtained by giving any value whatever to t in the formulas

$$x = t,$$
$$y = \frac{7 - 2t}{5},$$
$$z = \frac{8 - 3t}{5},$$

as may be verified by substitution.

Example 6.3 ($m < n$, *exactly one solution*). The system

$$2x + 3y - 9 = 0,$$
$$3x - 4y - 5 = 0,$$
$$4x - 11y - 1 = 0,$$

for which $m = 2$, $n = 3$, has precisely one solution, namely, $x = 3$, $y = 1$. One can verify that this is a solution by substitution; and one can see that it is the only possible solution by solving any two of the equations (this will lead to the given solution), thus verifying that no other pair of numbers can satisfy those *two* equations simultaneously, much less all three.

---

[7] One can convince himself of the difficulty of this second course by looking at the paper by A. Wald, "On Some Systems of Equations of Mathematical Economics," *Econometrica*, Vol. XIX, No. 4 (October, 1951), pp. 368–403.

In the fourth example we must restrict ourselves to *real* solutions; since this is customary in economics, the example loses none of its relevance because of this restriction.

Example 6.4 (m > n, exactly one solution). The "system"

$$(x - 1)^2 + (y + 2)^2 = 0,$$

for which $m = 2, n = 1$, has the sole solution $x = 1, y = -2$. This may be seen to be a solution by substitution; and that it is the only solution follows from the fact that for any other pair of values one at least of the nonnegative quantities $(x - 1)^2$ and $(y + 2)^2$ must be positive, so that their sum certainly cannot be zero.

It is easy to construct examples illustrating the other possible cases (e.g., $m < n$, and no solution); but the cases illustrated in Examples 6.1–6.4 are the ones which are sometimes thought to be impossible.

7. Roots with Negative Real Parts.   Elsewhere in this volume we are much concerned with the problem of deciding when a polynomial equation with *real* coefficients, say

$$(7.1) \quad a_0 x^n + a_1 x^{n-1} + \ldots + a_n = 0, \quad (a_0 \neq 0),$$

has the property that all of its roots have negative real parts, i.e. that every real root is negative and in every complex root $a + bi$ (a and b being real) the value of a is negative. This question is scarcely at the same fundamental level as the other subjects in this chapter, but we shall assemble some of the facts about it in this section for future reference.

We first consider the case $n = 2$, for which (7.1) becomes the familiar quadratic equation which we shall write in the customary form

$$(7.2) \quad ax^2 + bx + c = 0, \quad (a \neq 0).$$

We may assume that a is positive; for if it were not, we could obtain an equivalent equation for which it is by multiplying both sides by -1. The two roots of (7.2) are given by the "quadratic formula"

$$(7.3) \quad x = \frac{-b \pm \sqrt{b^2 - 4ac}}{2a}.$$

From this formula it follows that the *product* of the two roots of (7.2) is equal to c/a, and their *sum* is equal to $-b/a$. If the two roots of (7.2) are negative, therefore, c/a and thus c itself must be positive; and $-b/a$, being the sum of the two roots, must be negative, so b is also positive.

If the two roots of (7.2) are complex, they are of the form $s \pm ti$, where s and t are real. Suppose that s is negative; then the sum of the roots, which is equal to both $2s$ and $-b/a$, is negative, and it follows that b must be positive. By considering the product of the two roots, one arrives at the equation

$$s^2 + t^2 = \frac{c}{a},$$

so c must be positive—in fact, whether or not s is negative.

We have now proved the theorem:

Theorem 7.1. If the roots of (7.2) (with $a > 0$) have negative real parts, then both b and c must be positive.

Moreover, the converse is also true.

Theorem 7.2. If the coefficients a, b, and c in (7.2) are all positive, the roots of this equation have negative real parts.

PROOF: If the roots are complex, formula (7.3) shows that the real parts of both roots is $-b/2a$, and since b and a are both positive, this must be negative.

If the roots are real, then $b^2 - 4ac > 0$, but since a and c are both positive, $4ac$ is positive and $b^2 - 4ac < b^2$. Therefore $\sqrt{b^2 - 4ac} < b$, and the numerator in (7.3) is negative whichever sign is used; thus both roots are negative. This completes the proof.

By applying Theorems 7.1 and 7.2 to the equation (7.2) with both sides multiplied by -1, it is easy to see that corresponding statements referring to negative coefficients are valid. In summary, then, we may assert Theorem 7.3.

Theorem 7.3. Both roots of equation (7.2) have negative real parts if and only if the coefficients a, b, and c are all positive or all negative.

The corresponding statement for the general equation (7.1) when $n > 2$ is not true; Theorem 7.5 below is the analogue to Theorem 7.1 for this case, but the proposition analogous to Theorem 7.2 is false, as the following example shows.

Example 7.1. Although all of its coefficients are positive, the equation

$$x^3 + x^2 + 4x + 30 = 0$$

has the roots -3, $1 + 3i$, $1 - 3i$, as one may verify by substitution, and two of these roots do *not* have negative real parts. This shows that the analogue of Theorem 7.2 for (7.1) with $n = 3$ is false.

A *partial* analogue to Theorem 7.2 is Theorem 7.4.

Theorem 7.4. If all of the coefficients a_k ($k = 0, 1, \ldots, n$) in equation (7.1) have the same sign, every real root of the equation is negative.

PROOF: Clearly, 0 is not a root of (7.1) under these circumstances, for if it were it would be necessary that $a_n = 0$, and this would contradict the assumption. It will therefore suffice to show that such an equation can have no positive real root. But if x is replaced by any positive number in (7.1), all of the terms on the left side will have the same sign, so their sum must be negative or positive (depending on the common sign of the coefficients) but cannot be zero, and the equation consequently is not satisfied.

It should be noted that this theorem is consistent with Example 7.1, where the trouble is caused by complex roots.

Theorem 7.5. If all roots of the equation (7.1) have negative real parts, the coefficients a_k must all have the same sign.

The proof uses two basic algebraic theorems which we shall merely state here and ask the reader to accept without proof:

Theorem 7.6.   If $r_1, r_2, \ldots, r_n$ are the n roots of equation (7.1) (cf. Section 4), then

$$(7.4) \quad a_0 x^n + a_1 x^{n-1} + \ldots + a^n = a_0(x - r_1)(x - r_2) \ldots (x - r_n) .$$

Theorem 7.7.   If $s + ti$ is a root of (7.1), where s and t are real and $t \neq 0$, then $s - ti$ is another root of (7.1).

Proof of Theorem 7.5.   We assume that all roots of (7.1) have negative real parts. In the right side of (7.4), therefore, the real roots of (7.1) contribute factors $(x - r_k)$ with positive coefficients, since $r_k < 0$. Now let $s + ti$ be a complex root of (7.1); then by Theorem 7.7, $s - ti$ is also a root of (7.1), and the two corresponding factors in (7.4) are $(x - (s + ti))$ and $(x - (s - ti))$. The product of these two factors is $(x^2 - 2sx + s^2 + t^2)$ which, since $s < 0$ by assumption, has all coefficients positive. If all complex roots of (7.1) are paired off in this way, one sees that the product

$$(x - r_1)(x - r_2) \ldots (x - r_n)$$

may be regarded as a product of real factors some of which are linear, some of which are quadratic, but all of which have only positive real coefficients. When the multiplication is carried out, therefore, one obtains a polynomial with all coefficients positive; and the right side of (7.4) has the same property unless $a_0 < 0$, in which case all of its coefficients will be negative. By (7.4), the same will thus be true of the left side of (7.1), and the theorem is proved.

SUGGESTIONS FOR FURTHER READING

There are countless textbooks dealing with the notions introduced in this chapter. The function concept and related matters are discussed to some extent in nearly all mathematics textbooks intended for college students, but they receive particularly careful attention in chaps. i and v of Alfred Tarski's *Introduction to Logic* (2d ed.; New York: Oxford University Press, 1946), a book which can be recommended unreservedly to all serious students of mathematical economics. The study of equations, systems of equations, and their solutions, especially when the functions involved are polynomials, is the basic task of classical algebra, and any recent textbook with the title *College Algebra* (e.g., that by Moses Richardson [New York: Prentice-Hall, Inc., 1947]) may be consulted for basic facts, examples, and exercises. A standard, though in many ways outdated treatise is *The Theory of Equations* by W. S. Burnside and A. W. Panton (5th ed.; Dublin: Hodges, Figgis, & Co., 1904).

Chapter Nine

ELEMENTS OF THE DIFFERENTIAL
CALCULUS

EVER since the great resurgence of mathematics in the seventeenth century, the notion of the *derivative* has been a cornerstone of mathematics, and more particularly of applied mathematics. The importance of this concept rests on the fact that it is the mathematical expression of the ubiquitous idea of a rate of change. This chapter begins with an investigation of the meaning of this idea, and this investigation leads quite naturally to a definition of the derivative. The rest of the chapter provides an account of the fundamental part of the theory of derivatives, the *differential calculus* as it is traditionally called. In the process it is necessary to take up the extremely important concepts of *limits* and *continuity*, which have a significance transcending their origin in the differential calculus and will be encountered repeatedly in subsequent chapters.

1. *Rates of Change.* The concept of an average rate of change is very familiar from everyday life. If, for instance, a man drives 180 miles in four hours, he normally says that he "averaged" 45 miles an hour on the trip; he doesn't mean by this that the speedometer showed a reading of 45 miles an hour for the whole trip, but (among other things) that if it had, he would have covered the same distance in the same time. The average speed is an example of an average rate of change—the rate of change of distance covered with respect to time. Average rates are defined over *intervals* (of time, distance, or whatever the independent variable may be.)

The reading on the speedometer, however, indicates something rather different: the *instantaneous* rate of change of distance covered with respect to time. We need not tarry over the manner in which the speedometer succeeds in measuring this rather elusive quantity; but it will be important for us to understand precisely what this quantity is.

We may think of the relation between distance covered and time elapsed as a function $x = f(t)$, where t is time (in hours) and x represents distance covered (in miles). If the driver watched his mileage meter and a stop watch throughout his trip, and recorded their readings at intervals, then at the end of his trip he could plot successive pairs of readings as points on a co-ordinate system, and by drawing a likely-looking curve through them

213

could obtain a graph of the function. Indeed, if he were really interested in the matter he could install a mechanical contrivance in his car which would draw the entire curve automatically.

Let us suppose that the curve so obtained is that in Figure 1.1. What is the graphical meaning of the average speed? It is that *on the average* the curve rises 45 units for every advance of one unit to the right. This average is not attained on every part of the curve; in the second hour, for instance,

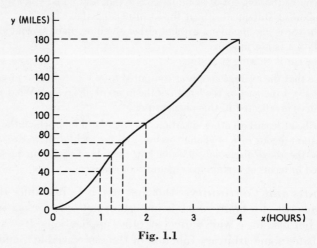

Fig. 1.1

the rise (distance covered) is actually 50 miles, so the average speed over that period is not 45 but 50 miles an hour; in the third half-hour, the rise is not $22\frac{1}{2}$ but 30 units, so over that period the average speed is 60 ($= 30 \div \frac{1}{2}$) miles an hour. In the fifth quarter-hour, the rise is from 40 to 56 miles, or 16 miles, so that the average speed for that period is 64 ($= 16 \div \frac{1}{4}$) miles an hour. If one went on in this way, calculating the average speed over ever-shortening time intervals starting at the end of the first hour (at the point where $t = 1$ on the graph), one would find that these average speeds approached closer and closer to a certain number, which for this curve would be 65; and it is *this* number which is meant by the instantaneous speed of the car at the instant when $t = 1$.

This may seem to be a roundabout way of arriving at the notion of an instantaneous speed; but it turns out to be essentially the only way of arriving at a useful definition.

It is easy to see that this general set of ideas does not depend upon the particular interpretation given to the variables involved; x might be any variable depending on the variable t; and if one replaced the word "speed" by the phrase "rate of change of x with respect to t" throughout our discussion, changed the units, and so on, the discussion would retain its cogency.

The object of this chapter is to expand upon these ideas. More particularly, we shall be concerned with three principal problems: (*a*) the problem of making the definitions implicit in this discussion precise and general; (b) the problem of developing a set of rules (a calculus) for calculating rates of change when the function $f(t)$ is given by means of an explicit formula; and (c) the problem of establishing the graphical meaning of rates of change.

EXERCISES

1.1. In terms of the concept of instantaneous speed, how could you express each of the following statements about the car discussed above?

a) The car is moving along without either speeding up or slowing down.

b) The car is not moving.

c) The car is slowing to a stop.

1.2. Notice that the average speeds as computed from Figure 1.1 for intervals starting at $t = 1$ increase as the length of the intervals decreases. What property of the curve is reflected in this phenomenon?

1.3. Describe at least two other situations of everyday life in which the concept of an instantaneous rate of change occurs, and for each of these situations paraphrase the above discussion, showing how the rate of change in question can be defined in terms of certain average rates of change.

2. Limits and Continuity. Our first step is to introduce the mathematical concept of a limit, which is important not only for our immediate purposes but also for a wide variety of other applications. In what follows $f(t)$ stands for some arbitrary function of the real variable t, and t_0 stands for a fixed but arbitrary value of this variable. The function $f(t)$ may or may not be defined when $t = t_0$; but we assume that $f(t)$ *is* defined for all values of t (with the possible exception of t_0 itself) in some interval ($t_1 < t < t_2$) containing t_0.

Example 2.1. Suppose that

$$f(t) = \frac{t^2 - 1}{t - 1}, \quad t_0 = 1 .$$

Since $f(t)$ is defined for *all* values of t except t_0, this example satisfies the conditions just mentioned. What happens to the value of $f(t)$ for values of t *near* t_0? A table will be instructive:

t	$f(t)$
1.100	2.100
1.050	2.050
1.010	2.010
1.005	2.005
1.001	2.001
etc.	etc.

The numbers in the t column approach t_0 as one reads downwards; and, as it turns out, the numbers in the $f(t)$ column approach a certain number also, namely, 2. Indeed, for all values of t but 1, $f(t) = t + 1$, so that this result is not surprising. The real point of the example is that *one can be sure that $f(t)$ will be as near 2 as one wishes if t differs by a sufficiently small amount from* 1.

The situation may be described briefly by saying that $f(t)$ approaches 2 as t approaches 1; or, in more mathematical language, that the *limit of* $f(t)$ *at* 1 is 2. There are two conventional ways of expressing this relation symbolically: by means of the equation

$$\lim_{t \to 1} f(t) = 2 ,$$

or by means of the expression

$$f(t) \to 2 \quad \text{as} \quad t \to 1 .$$

Both ways of expressing the fact are common in the literature, but we shall usually use the second.

The general definition of a limit is obtained by abstracting from the numerical details of this example. In general, one says that the number A is the limit of a function $f(t)$ at t_0, or

$$f(t) \to A \quad \text{as} \quad t \to t_0 ,$$

if the value of $f(t)$ differs by an arbitrarily small amount from A when t differs by a sufficiently small amount from t_0.

The meaning of the words "arbitrarily" and "sufficiently" in the last statement, though probably clear in a general way, is nevertheless somewhat ambiguous, so that the definition is still imprecise. Any possible ambiguity is removed by the following, and final, definition of the limit concept and of the associated notation:

$$f(t) \to A \quad \text{as} \quad t \to t_0$$

if, for any positive number ϵ, *there exists a positive number* δ *(depending, usually, on* ϵ*) such that*[1] $|f(t) - A| < \epsilon$ *for every value of* t *other than* t_0 *which satisfies* $|t - t_0| < \delta$.

In this definition, the inequality $|f(t) - A| < \epsilon$ expresses the fact that $f(t)$ is "arbitrarily" near A, for the value of ϵ is arbitrary, and the inequality states that $f(t)$ differs from A by at most ϵ; and the inequality $|t - t_0| < \delta$ expresses the fact that t is "sufficiently" near t_0. The strength of the definition lies in the fact that one is allowed to make ϵ as small as he wishes.[2]

It should be noticed that the definition doesn't require that $f(t_0)$ be

---

[1] If u is any real number, $|u|$ denotes the *absolute value* of u; that is, u itself if u is positive or zero, $-u$ if u is negative. If the real numbers are represented in the usual way by points on a straight line, then the absolute value of the difference between two real numbers u_1 and u_2, $|u_1 - u_2|$, is the distance between the corresponding points on the line.

[2] Analogously, one can define what is meant by the limit of a function as the independent variable increases beyond all bounds or, as one says, "approaches infinity." The function $f(t) = 1/t^2$, for instance, assumes values nearer and nearer to 0 as t gets larger. This situation is expressed by writing $f(t) \to 0$ as $t \to \infty$; the symbol "∞," read "infinity," should not be taken to represent a number; it is an inseparable part of the whole expression. In general, one says that $f(t) \to A$ as $t \to \infty$ if, for any positive number ϵ, there exists a number N such that $|f(t) - A| < \epsilon$ for every value of t which satisfies $t > N$. The inequality $t > N$ expresses the fact that "t is sufficiently large."

defined, although it is (implicitly) necessary that $f(t)$ be defined for all values of t *but* t_0 in some interval containing t_0.

Indeed, it is instructive to consider the following three statements:

a) $f(t) \rightarrow A$ as $t \rightarrow t_0$;
b) $f(t_0)$ is defined;
c) $f(t_0) = A$.

Example 2.1 shows that (a) may be true while (b) and (c) are both false. Other examples may be constructed to show that (a) and (b) may both be true while (c) is false.[3] If all three of these statements are true, so that one may meaningfully say

$$f(t) \rightarrow f(t_0) \quad \text{as} \quad t \rightarrow t_0 \, ,$$

the function $f(t)$ is said to be *continuous at* t_0. If a function $f(t)$ is continuous for *all* values of t in some interval, one simply says that it is *continuous* on that interval. Roughly speaking, a function is continuous on an interval if one can draw that part of its graph which lies over the interval without lifting the pencil from the paper. We shall have further use for the concept of continuity in later chapters.

When combined with the ordinary operations of arithmetic, the operation of "passing to the limit" behaves very well. More precisely, if $f(t) \rightarrow A$ and $f(t) \rightarrow B$ as $t \rightarrow t_0$, then

(L_1) $f(t) + g(t) \rightarrow A + B$,

(L_2) $f(t) - g(t) \rightarrow A - B$,

(L_3) $f(t) \cdot g(t) \rightarrow AB$,

(L_4) $\dfrac{f(t)}{g(t)} \rightarrow \dfrac{A}{B}$ (provided that $B \neq 0$) ,

(L_5) $c.f(t) \rightarrow c.A.$ (c being any constant),

all as $t \rightarrow t_0$. These relations all follow directly from the definition of a limit, and should appear plausible. The proofs will not be given here.[4] We shall, however, outline the proof of the following theorem, for which we shall have use in subsequent pages:

A polynomial involving only one variable is a continuous function of that variable. In the first place, constants and the "identical function" $f(t) = t$ are continuous functions of t, as reference to the definition of continuity will readily show. Since t is a continuous function of t, it follows from (L_3), by regarding both f and g as the identical function, that t^2 is a continuous function of t; applying (L_3) again, now regarding f as t^2 and g as t, it may be shown that t^3 is a continuous function of t; and so on. Thus t^n is a continuous function of t whenever n is a positive integer. But then, by (L_5), the

---

[3] For instance, if $f(t)$ is defined by saying $f(t) = 0$ if $t \neq 0$, while $f(0) = 1$, then $f(t) \rightarrow 0$ as $t \rightarrow 0$, but $f(0) \neq 0$.

[4] For these proofs, together with a very careful discussion of other aspects of the limit concept, see E. Landau, *Differential and Integral Calculus* (New York: Chelsea Publishing Co., 1950), chaps. i–iv.

function ct^n, where n is any positive integer and c is any constant, is also continuous. The function ct^n (or a constant c by itself), however, is the most general monomial in one variable. By applying (L_1) enough times, it may finally be shown that the sum of any set of monomials (i.e., any polynomial) is in turn a continuous function of t; and this completes the proof of the theorem. The reader who finds this proof too concise will find it profitable to work out the details.

EXERCISES

2.1. Find the limit of each of the following functions of t as $t \to 0$:

(a) $t^2 + 1$,   (b) $\dfrac{t^2}{t}$,   (c) t^t.

2.2. Find the limit of each of the following functions as $t \to \infty$:

(a) $\dfrac{1}{t^2 + 1}$,   (b) $\dfrac{2t + 1}{3t}$,   (c) t^{-t}.

2.3. Using the facts about continuity stated in this section, prove that a rational function (i.e., any function that can be written as the quotient of two polynomials) is continuous at any value of the independent variable for which the denominator is not zero. Can such a function be continuous even at a value of t for which the denominator is zero?

2.4. Construct a function which is continuous at every value of t other than 2 but is not continuous at 2.

3. Derivatives. We might return now to the example described in Section 1, but in order to broaden the intuitive basis for what follows, as well as to make the economic reader feel more at home, we shall consider a second, parallel example which is more germane to economics. The amount of a certain commodity existing in a given economy is a function of the time t; if the commodity is a stock commodity, this function has a constant value, but in general it is some more flexible function which we may denote by $f(t)$. If x represents the stock of the commodity, therefore, we may write

$$x = f(t) .$$

There is nothing to be gained by specifying the units in which x and t are measured, but it must be assumed that these have been decided on. It is also assumed, merely for the sake of simplicity, that the (gross) quantity of the commodity newly produced in any period of time exceeds the (gross) quantity consumed during the same period, so that x increases steadily with the passage of time. We now wish to recur to the question raised in Section 1: What is to be meant by the rate of change of x with respect to t? In general, we should expect this rate—whatever it is—to change from time to time. Hence, our question may be restated more precisely as: What is to be meant by the rate of change of x with respect to t *at any instant* t_0? This rate may be called the *instantaneous rate of investment*.

The stock variable x corresponds to the distance covered in the example of Section 1, while the instantaneous rate of investment corresponds to the reading on the speedometer. Our direction of attack will therefore be in essence the same as that in Section 1.

We begin by considering what happens over an interval of time starting at t_0 and ending at some later instant $t_0 + h$, where h is an arbitrary positive number. The stock of the commodity existing at the beginning of this interval is $f(t_0)$, while the stock existing at the end is $f(t_0 + h)$; thus the net increase in the stock of the commodity over this time interval is $f(t_0 + h) - f(t_0)$. It will be in perfect accord with ordinary language if we agree to call the quantity

$$\frac{f(t_0 + h) - f(t_0)}{h}$$

the *average rate of change* of x over the interval; for it is the total investment over the interval, divided by the length of the interval. Now whatever is meant by the rate of investment *at* the instant t_0, it is certainly natural to regard the above average rate of investment as an approximation to it; and we should be able to make the approximation as close as we please by making the length of the interval (i.e., the value of h) sufficiently small. But if one attempts to make this idea more precise, he is driven to the conclusion that the *limit* of the above quotient as h approaches zero should be the rate of investment at t_0 itself. This is of course not a proof, merely a vindication of a certain usage; but having vindicated it, we now make it precise by putting it in the form of a definition.

The limit of the quotient

$$\frac{f(t_0 + h) - f(t_0)}{h}$$

as $h \rightarrow 0$, if it exists, is called the rate of change *(with respect to t) of $f(t)$ at the instant t_0; if this limit does not exist, the rate of change is undefined.*

In this example, the phrase "rate of change of $f(t)$" which appears in the definition can be replaced by the term "(instantaneous) rate of investment," in the example of Section 1 by the term "speed;" and by analogous terms in similar examples. Indeed, the definition has been stated so as to apply to *any* function $f(t)$ of t.

Observe that the restriction that h be positive does not appear in the definition. This is intentional. Indeed, if one uses a negative value of h in the example of the stock function, this merely amounts to considering a time interval *ending* at t_0 instead of beginning at that instant. In this case the total investment over the interval would be $f(t_0) - f(t_0 + h)$, and the length of the interval would be $-h$ (h itself being negative), so that the average rate of increase of x over the interval would be

$$\frac{f(t_0) - f(t_0 + h)}{-h} \; ;$$

but this quotient is algebraically identical with the quotient which appears in the definition. Thus, allowing h to assume negative values merely amounts to saying that one can approximate the rate of change of $f(t)$ at t_0 by means of average rates over intervals ending at t_0 as well as by means of average rates over intervals beginning at t_0.

A more troublesome aspect of the definition is that because the denominator in the quotient approaches zero as h approaches zero (for the denominator *is* h), it may seem that we are somehow dividing by zero, which is a meaningless procedure. To put such doubts at rest it is enough to impress oneself with the fact that the separate limits of the numerator and denominator of the above quotient (which we shall hereafter call the *difference quotient*) as h approaches zero are themselves irrelevant; it is the limit of the function represented by the *whole* quotient which is in question. We have already seen (in Example 2.1) that a quotient may have a perfectly good limit even though the limit of the denominator is zero.

It has already been pointed out that the rate of change of $f(t)$ is itself a function of time. In our notation, it has actually been given as a function of t_0. The role of the subscript on t_0, however, was merely to pin down a certain instant; t_0 is simply another way of writing t, so we may drop the subscript 0 and say that we have defined the rate of change of $f(t)$ as a function of t itself, which we shall provisionally denote by $f'(t)$. The limit-taking process which appears in the definition of the rate of change thus leads from a given function $f(t)$ to a new function $f'(t)$. This process is called *differentiation*, and the resulting function $f'(t)$ is called the *derivative of $f(t)$ with respect to t*.

A function $f(t)$ for which the derivative is defined for a certain value of t is said to be *differentiable* at that value of t. If $f(t)$ is differentiable for every value of t in a certain interval, it is said to be differentiable over that interval. It is always possible to interpret a derivative as a rate of change, but it is sometimes convenient to interpret it otherwise, as we shall see later; thus the more abstract term "derivative" is preferable to the term "rate of change," which commits one to a certain interpretation.

By way of summary, and for future reference, we shall now give the complete definition of the term "derivative."

If, for any fixed value of t, the difference quotient

$$\frac{f(t + h) - f(t)}{h}$$

has a limit as h approaches zero, this limit is called the derivative of $f(t)$ for that value of t. The derivative is not defined for values of t for which this limit does not exist.

There are several notations for the derivative besides $f'(t)$. Of these the most convenient for our purposes is this: if $x = f(t)$, the derivative of x (i.e., of $f[t]$) is denoted by dx/dt. This notation has the advantage that it displays both the dependent variable and the independent variable; it has the further advantage that it can be extended easily to "partial" derivatives, which will be explained in a later section. It is to be emphasized that this symbol for the derivative, although it is written in the form of a quotient, is *not* a quotient; the symbol is to be regarded as an irreducible whole, and should not be operated with as if it were a fraction unless explicit justification is given for such operations.

EXERCISES

3.1. Give a verbal interpretation for the derivative dx/dt if in $x = f(t)$

    a) t represents the distance (in feet) down a certain mine shaft, and x represents the temperature (in degrees Fahrenheit) at that distance;

    b) t is the tariff (measured as a percentage) on raw cotton, and x is the number of tons that will be imported at the rate t;

    c) t is the distance covered by an accelerating car, and x is the time at which the distance t was covered.

3.2. Prove that if the value of $f(t)$ is independent of t, then $f'(t) = 0$ for all values of t.

4. The Technique of Differentiation. We are now in a position to discuss methods for differentiating specific types of functions. The central idea of the technique of differentiation is to reduce the problem of finding the derivative of a complicated function to that of finding the derivatives of simpler functions of which it is composed; and then to obtain the derivatives of the simpler functions from a set of standard formulas. All of the theorems (formulas) which are required for this purpose follow almost directly from the definition of the derivative. In this section we shall list, prove, and illustrate the use of the most fundamental of these theorems.

    (D_1) *If $f(t)$ and $g(t)$ are functions which have derivatives for a certain value of t, and a and b are constants, then the function $F(t) = af(t) + bg(t)$ has a derivative for that value of t, which is given by $F'(t) = af'(t) + bg'(t)$.*[5]

PROOF: By assumption,

$$\frac{f(t + h) - f(t)}{h} \to f'(t) \quad \text{and} \quad \frac{g(t + h) - g(t)}{h} \to g'(t) \quad \text{as } h \to 0 .$$

Therefore

$$\frac{F(t + h) - F(t)}{h} = \frac{af(t + h) + bg(t + h) - af(t) - bg(t)}{h}$$

$$= a\left[\frac{f(t + h) - f(t)}{h}\right] + b\left[\frac{g(t + h) - g(t)}{h}\right] \to af'(t) + bg'(t) \quad \text{as } h \to 0 ,$$

as was to be shown. Here we have used the properties (L_1) and (L_5) of limits stated in Section 2.

    A similar statement could be made and proved for the function obtained by multiplying n functions $f_i(t)$ $(i = 1, 2, \ldots, n)$ by corresponding constants c_i and then adding.

---

    [5] In mathematical parlance, this theorem says that the operation of differentiation is *linear*.

Two important special implications of this theorem should be noted: if one sets $a = b = 1$, it appears that *the derivative of the sum of two functions is the sum of their derivatives;* and if $b = 0$, it appears that *the derivative of a constant times a function is that constant times the derivative of that function.* Conversely, these two statements together imply (D_1).

(D_2) *If $f(t)$ and $g(t)$ are functions which have derivatives for a certain value of t, then the function $F(t) = f(t) \cdot g(t)$ has a derivative for that value of t, which is given by*

$$F'(t) = f(t) \cdot g'(t) + f'(t) \cdot g(t) .$$

This means that, in general, the derivative of the product of two functions is *not* the product of their derivatives.

PROOF: By assumption,

$$\frac{f(t + h) - f(t)}{h} \to f'(t) \quad \text{and} \quad \frac{g(t + h) - g(t)}{h} \to g'(t) \quad \text{as } h \to 0 .$$

Therefore

$$\frac{F(t + h) - F(t)}{h} = \frac{f(t + h) \cdot g(t + h) - f(t) \cdot g(t)}{h}$$

$$= \frac{f(t + h) \cdot g(t + h) - f(t + h) \cdot g(t) + f(t + h) \cdot g(t) - f(t) \cdot g(t)}{h}$$

$$= f(t + h)\frac{g(t + h) - g(t)}{h} + \frac{f(t + h) - f(t)}{h}g(t) \to f(t) \cdot g'(t) + f'(t) \cdot g(t)$$

as $h \to 0$.

In the last step, which is the only one that involves anything more than simple algebra, we have used properties (L_1), (L_3), and (L_5) of limits (Section 2) and the further fact that $f(t + h) \to f(t)$ as $h \to 0$. This fact follows from the assumption that $f(t)$ has a derivative for the value of t in question; for this assumption may be written

$$\frac{f(t + h) - f(t)}{h} = f'(t) + r(h) ,$$

where $r(h) \to 0$ as $h \to 0$. $r(h)$ is simply the error produced in approximating the derivative $f(t)$ by the difference quotient $[f(t + h) - f(t)]/h$, and it is part of the definition of the derivative that this should tend to 0 as $h \to 0$. Multiplying on both sides by h, we obtain

$$f(t + h) - f(t) = h \cdot f'(t) + h \cdot r(h) .$$

Since $f'(t)$ is a definite number which does not depend on h, the right side of this equation clearly has 0 as its limit as $h \to 0$; thus

$$f(t + h) - f(t) \to 0 \quad \text{as} \quad h \to 0 ,$$

as claimed.[6]

---

[6] This constitutes a proof of the following theorem: *If $f(t)$ has a derivative for a certain value of t, it is continuous at that value of t;* for the statement that $f(t + h) \to f(t)$ as $h \to 0$ simply asserts that $f(t)$ is continuous for the value of t in question. Briefly, differentiability implies continuity.

(*D₃*) *If f(t) and g(t) are functions which have derivatives for a certain value of t, and g(t) ≠ 0 for that value of t, then the function F(t) = f(t)/g(t) has a derivative for that value of t, which is given by*

$$F'(t) = \frac{g(t) \cdot f'(t) - f(t) \cdot g'(t)}{[g(t)]^2}.$$

PROOF: Again, we have

$$\frac{f(t+h) - f(t)}{h} \to f'(t) \quad \text{and} \quad \frac{g(t+h) - g(t)}{h} \to g'(t) \quad \text{as } h \to 0,$$

by assumption. Therefore

$$\frac{F(t+h) - F(t)}{h} = \frac{\dfrac{f(t+h)}{g(t+h)} - \dfrac{f(t)}{g(t)}}{h} = \frac{f(t+h) \cdot g(t) - f(t) \cdot g(t+h)}{g(t) \cdot g(t+h) \cdot h}$$

$$= \frac{1}{g(t) \cdot g(t+h)} \cdot \frac{f(t+h) \cdot g(t) - f(t) \cdot g(t) + f(t) \cdot g(t) - f(t) \cdot g(t+h)}{h}$$

$$= \frac{1}{g(t) \cdot g(t+h)} \cdot \left[g(t) \frac{f(t+h) - f(t)}{h} - f(t) \frac{g(t+h) - g(t)}{h} \right] \to$$

$$\frac{1}{[g(t)]^2} \cdot [g(t) \cdot f'(t) - f(t) \cdot g'(t)]$$

as $h \to 0$, as claimed. The last step, which is again the only difficult one, follows for reasons which should be clear from the preceding proofs.

Now suppose that x is a certain function $f(t)$ of t, *and that t in turn is a certain function g(u) of some variable u.* In this situation, x may be regarded, in a natural way, as a function of u. To obtain the value of x corresponding to some value u_0 of u, one first determines the value t_0 of t which corresponds to u_0 according to the function g, and then finds the value x_0 of x which corresponds to t_0 according to the function f. The function $x = F(u)$ so set up is defined for a certain value u_0 of u if (a) $g(u_0)$ is defined and (b) $f[g(u_0)]$ is also defined. Such a function is called a *composite* function, and one can write $x = F(u) = f[g(u)]$. The next theorem in our list relates to composite functions and is perhaps the most frequently used of the lot:

(*D₄*) *If g(u) has a derivative for a certain value of u, and if f(t) has a derivative for t = g(u), where u has that value, then the composite function F(u) = f[g(u)] has a derivative for that value of u, which is given by*

$$F'(u) = f'(t) \cdot g'(u).$$

The proof of this theorem is rather more delicate than those of the preceding theorems in this section, but it also rests squarely on the definition of the derivative.

PROOF: The assumption that $g'(u)$ exists may be expressed by saying that

$$\frac{g(u+h) - g(u)}{h} = g'(u) + d(h),$$

or, equivalently,

$$(4.1) \quad g(u + h) - g(u) = h[g'(u) + d(h)],$$

where $d(h)$ is a function with the property that

$$d(h) \to 0 \quad \text{as} \quad h \to 0.$$

Similarly, the assumption that $f'(t)$ exists may be written

$$(4.2) \quad f(t + k) - f(t) = k[f'(t) + e(k)],$$

where $e(k)$ is a function with the property that

$$e(k) \to 0 \quad \text{as} \quad k \to 0.$$

We make the variable k a function of h by putting $k = g(u + h) - g(u)$. We know that $k \to 0$ as $h \to 0$ because $g(u)$, being differentiable for the value of u in question, is continuous for that value of u. Moreover, since $k = g(u + h) - g(u)$, equation (4.1) gives

$$k = h[g'(u) + d(h)];$$

and using this to eliminate k as the first factor in the right side of (4.2), we obtain

$$(4.3) \quad f(t + k) - f(t) = h[g'(u) + d(h)][f'(t) + e(k)].$$

However, since $t = g(u)$ and $t + k = g(u) + [g(u + h) - g(u)] = g(u + h)$, the left side of (4.3) is merely $f[g(u + h)] - f[g(u)]$, i.e., $F(u + h) - F(u)$. Using this fact, and dividing both sides of (4.3) by h, we get finally

$$(4.4) \quad \frac{F(u + h) - F(u)}{h} = f'(t) \cdot g'(u) + d(h) \cdot f'(t) + e(k) \cdot g'(u).$$

Now as $h \to 0$, $d(h) \to 0$; and since $k \to 0$ as $h \to 0$, while $e(k) \to 0$ as $k \to 0$, we also have $e(k) \to 0$ as $h \to 0$. On the other hand, $f'(t)$ and $g'(u)$ are fixed numbers which do not depend on h; thus, by the properties (L_5) and (L_1) of limits stated in Section 2, the expression within square brackets in the right side of (4.4) has the limit 0 as $h \to 0$. Therefore

$$\frac{F(u + h) - F(u)}{h} \to f'(t) \cdot g'(u) \quad \text{as } h \to 0,$$

and this is merely another way of writing the conclusion of (D_4). This completes the proof.

(D_4), which in rough paraphrase states that the derivative of a composite function is the product of the derivatives of the constituent functions, is a special instance of the so-called *chain rules* which we shall encounter in Section 6. For this reason (D_4) itself is sometimes called the chain rule; however, in order to preserve the distinction without concealing the connection, we shall refer to (D_4) as the *simple* chain rule.

The theorems (D_1)–(D_4) provide the basic instruments for expressing the derivatives of many complicated functions by means of those of simpler functions of which they are somehow made up: the derivative of a product by means of the derivatives of its factors (D_2), etc. But so far we have stated no theorems which give the actual derivatives of even the simplest explicit functions, so that on the basis of the theorems which have been proved it is not yet possible to compute any actual derivatives. The two remaining theorems of this section will remedy this defect to some extent.

(D_5) *If* $f(t) \equiv C$, *where* C *is a constant—i.e., if the value of* $f(t)$ *does not depend on* t—*then* $f'(t) \equiv 0$. *More briefly, the derivative of a constant is zero.*

The problem of proving this theorem has been given as Exercise 3.2.

(D_6) *If* $f(t) = t^n$, *where* n *is any positive whole number, then* $f'(t) = nt^{n-1}$. Thus the derivative of t^2 is $2t$, the derivative of t^5 is $5t^4$, etc.

PROOF: This theorem is most conveniently proved by the method of *mathematical induction:* one first proves that it is true for the smallest value of n in question, namely, $n = 1$, and then proves that *if* it is true for any particular value of n, say m, then it must also be true for the next value of n, $m + 1$. These two steps together imply that the statement is true for all (positive whole) values of n.

First, the statement is true for $n = 1$: if $f(t) = t$, then $f'(t) = 1 \cdot t^0 = 1$. In this case the difference quotient

$$\frac{f(t + h) - f(t)}{h} = \frac{(t + h) - t}{h} = \frac{h}{h} = 1 \quad (h \neq 0) ;$$

so the limit as $h \to 0$ of the difference quotient certainly exists and is 1. This is what had to be shown.

Next, we *assume* that the derivative of t^m is mt^{m-1}, and wish to show that the derivative of t^{m+1} is $(m + 1)t^m$. Now $t^{m+1} = t^m \cdot t$; thus the product rule (D_2) may be used, and it says that this function has a derivative given by

$$t^m \cdot 1 + (mt^{m-1}) \cdot t ;$$

but simplifying this gives $(m + 1)t^m$.

The importance of (D_6) lies in the fact that, taken together with (D_1) and (D_5), it makes possible the differentiation of any polynomial. The theorems (D_2) and (D_4) frequently enable one to shorten the differentiation of a given polynomial, although of course these theorems (as well as[D_1]) have a much wider usefulness. The following examples will serve to illustrate these remarks.

Example 4.1.   Suppose that

$$f(t) = 2t^4 + 5t .$$

According to (D_6), the derivatives of t^4 and t are $4t^3$ and 1, respectively. Therefore, by (D_1), the derivative of $f(t)$ is $2(4t^3) + 5(1)$, or simply $8t^3 + 5$:

$$f'(t) = 8t^3 + 5 .$$

Example 4.2.   Suppose that

$$f(t) = 16t^3 - 3t^2 + 2t - 17 .$$

The derivatives of t^3, t^2, and t are, respectively, $3t^2$, $2t$, and 1, by (D_6); the derivative of -17, by (D_5), is 0. Therefore applying (D_1) several times gives

$$f'(t) = 16(3t^2) - 3(2t) + 2(1) + 0 = 48t^2 - 6t + 2.$$

Example 4.3. If it were necessary to differentiate the function given by

$$F(t) = (t^2 + 3t - 2)^{12},$$

the straightforward way to proceed would be to "expand" the expression $(t^2 + 3t - 2)^{12}$ by dogged multiplication and then to differentiate the resulting polynomial (whose degree would be 24) in the manner of Example 4.2. A more humane way, however, is to use (D_4): if one defines

$$s = g(t) = t^2 + 3t - 2,$$

then $F(t) = f(s) = s^{12}$. It should now be easy to see that

$$g'(t) = 2t + 3,$$
$$f'(s) = 12s^{11}.$$

Consequently, by (D_4),

$$F'(t) = f'(s) \cdot g'(t) = 12s^{11}(2t + 3) = 12(t^2 + 3t - 2)^{11}(2t + 3).$$

Example 4.4. Likewise, there are two ways of differentiating the function $F(t)$ given by

$$F(t) = (t^4 + 3t - \tfrac{1}{2})(t^2 - t + 4).$$

The straightforward way is to carry out the indicated multiplication and then differentiate the resulting polynomial (of degree 6) as in Example 4.2. The shorter alternative is to regard the two factors as separate functions of t:

$$f(t) = t^4 + 3t - \tfrac{1}{2},$$
$$g(t) = t^2 - t + 4;$$

then differentiation gives

$$f'(t) = 4t^3 + 3,$$
$$g'(t) = 2t - 1.$$

Finally, by (D_2), one gets the derivative of $F(t)$:

$$F'(t) = f(t) \cdot g'(t) + f'(t) \cdot g(t) = (t^4 + 3t - \tfrac{1}{2})(2t - 1) + (4t^3 + 3)(t^2 - t + 4).$$

This is the answer, though naturally it could be simplified.

One final example will be given to illustrate the use of (D_3).

Example 4.5. In a certain hypothetical economic system, the stock of wheat in millions of bushels is given by

$$(4.6) \quad x(t) = \frac{65t^2 + 40}{t^2 + 8},$$

where t is the time in years measured from a certain initial year (e.g., 1947). What then is the rate of net investment in wheat (in millions of bushels per year) when $t = 15$?

This example takes us back to Section 3, where it was seen that the rate of net investment is simply the derivative of $x(t)$. If one regards the two terms of the fraction in (4.6) as separate functions, say

$$f(t) = 65t^2 + 40,$$
$$g(t) = t^2 + 8,$$

then by (D_1), (D_5), and (D_6), as in the other examples,

$$f'(t) = 130t,$$
$$g'(t) = 2t,$$

and by (D_3),

$$x'(t) = \frac{g(t) \cdot f'(t) - f(t) \cdot g'(t)}{g(t)^2} = \frac{(t^2 + 8)(130t) - (65t^2 + 40)(2t)}{(t^2 + 8)^2}.$$

Replacing t by 15 gives finally

$$x'(15) = \frac{14{,}400}{54{,}289},$$

or approximately 265,000 (0.265 million) bushels per year.

EXERCISES

4.1. Differentiate each of the following functions of t:

(a) $t + 2$, (b) t^7, (c) $t^3 - 5t^2 + 6t + 1$,
(d) $(t - 1)^3$, (e) $(t^2 + 1)^9$, (f) 2^{30},

(g) $\dfrac{t^2 - 2}{t + 1}$, (h) $\dfrac{1}{t^2 + a^2}$ (a is a constant).

4.2. If $f(t)$, $g(t)$, and $h(t)$ are three differentiable functions of t, use (D_2) to find a formula for the derivative of

$$F(t) = f(t) \cdot g(t) \cdot h(t)$$

in terms of the three functions f, g, h, and their derivatives.

4.3. An alternative proof for (D_3) is this: since $F(t) = f(t)/g(t)$, $f(t) = F(t) \cdot g(t)$. Applying (D_2) to this equation gives

$$f'(t) = F(t) \cdot g'(t) + F'(t) \cdot g(t).$$

Replacing $F(t)$ by $f(t)/g(t)$ in this equation and solving for $F'(t)$ gives the formula for (D_3). In what way is this proof less satisfactory than the proof given in the text?

5. Graphical Interpretation of Derivatives. The natural way of explaining the graphical meaning of the derivative of a function is by way of the difference quotient; for if we can establish the graphical meaning of the latter concept, it should be easy to "pass to the limit" and learn the significance of the derivative itself.

Figure 5.1 shows part of the graph of a certain function $f(t)$. To the value t_0 of t there corresponds a point P on the curve: the co-ordinates of P are $(t_0, f(t_0))$. The value $t_0 + h$ of t likewise determines a point Q on the curve, its co-ordinates being $(t_0 + h, f(t_0 + h))$. The point R is obtained as the

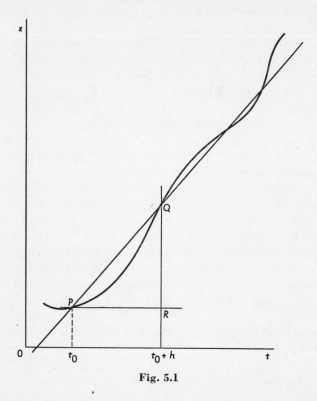

Fig. 5.1

point of intersection of the vertical line through Q and the horizontal line through P; its co-ordinates are $(t_0 + h, f(t_0))$. We shall be interested in the straight line passing through P and Q. Clearly, a point moving along this line from P to Q rises by the amount QR as it advances horizontally by the amount PR.[7] The ratio of the rise to the horizontal advance, QR/PR, is characteristic of the whole line in the sense that advancing from any point on the line to any other would yield a rise-to-advance ratio with the same value. We may therefore call this ratio the *slope of the line*, for it may be computed using any two points on the line, and therefore depends solely on the line itself.

---

[7] We shall take QR to be positive if Q is above R, negative if below; similarly, PR is taken to be positive if P lies to the left of R, negative if to the right. Only the positive cases occur in Figure 5.1, but there is nothing to prevent the other possible combinations from occurring.

It should be clear that the slope of the line measures the *steepness* of the line: when the slope is large and positive, the line is inclined steeply upward to the right; when the slope is small and positive, the line is relatively flat and inclined upward to the right; when the slope is zero, the line is horizontal; and finally, when the slope is negative the line is inclined *downward* to the right, since for a positive (rightward) horizontal advance the "rise" must be negative, and this means that Q is below the horizontal line through P.

This establishes the *graphical* significance of the slope. Its *functional* significance in this context is equally easy to establish. From what has been said about the co-ordinates of P, Q, and R it follows that $PR = h$ and $QR = f(t_0 + h) - f(t_0)$; therefore

$$\text{slope of } PQ = \frac{QR}{PR} = \frac{f(t_0 + h) - f(t_0)}{h} \ ;$$

in words, the slope of the line through P and Q is exactly the difference quotient corresponding to t_0 and h.

If one now chooses smaller and smaller values of h, on the one hand, the difference quotient will approach nearer and nearer to the derivative of $f(t)$ at t_0, while, on the other hand, Q will move nearer and nearer to P, so that the line through P and the moving point Q will come nearer and nearer to a line T which is *tangent* to the curve at P. (Indeed, the tangent line to a general curve is defined in this way.) It therefore follows that *the value of the derivative of $f(t)$ at t_0 is the slope of the tangent line to the graph of $f(t)$ at the corresponding point P*, provided that both the derivative and the tangent line exist.

In view of this fact, one defines the *slope of the curve* at P as the slope of the tangent line to the curve at P. With this definition, one may immediately say that *the value of the derivative of $f(t)$ at t_0 is the slope of the graph of $f(t)$ at the corresponding point;* this is merely a paraphrase of the last italicized clause.

It follows that whenever $f'(t) > 0$, $f(t)$ is *increasing* as t increases (its graph is moving upward to the right), and that whenever $f'(t) < 0$, $f(t)$ is *decreasing* as t increases (its graph is moving downward to the right). The various possible graphical situations which may correspond to the case $f'(t) = 0$ will be explored in a subsequent chapter.

One note of caution: in certain economic contexts, it has become traditional to measure the independent variable (usually price) along the vertical co-ordinate axis and the dependent variable (usually some quantity variable) along the horizontal axis. The above remarks should be applied to this situation with care. The relation between the two situations may be seen by mentally rotating the co-ordinate system in the second case through half a revolution about the line which passes through the origin and makes an angle of 45° with the positive halves of the axes; this will restore the variables to their usual positions, with the independent variable on the horizontal axis, etc. In this way one may see that the relation between the sign of the derivative and the direction in which the curve is inclined is the same in both cases; even in the second case (with the independent variable on the vertical axis) a point moving rightward along the graph moves upward or downward according as the derivative is positive or negative. The same cannot be said in the matter of steepness: the graph of a function in the second case will be inclined *more* steeply, not less, the nearer the derivative is to zero.

EXERCISES

5.1. Draw some graphs which illustrate the points made in the last paragraph above.

5.2. Find the slope of the graph of the function $x = t^2 - 6t$ at the points where $t = 0, 3$, and 5. Graph the function, and draw the lines tangent to the graph at the given points.

5.3. Without drawing a graph, find at which values of t the function $f(t) = 4 - t^2$ is increasing, and at which values it is decreasing. What does this show about the behavior of the function at $t = 0$?

6. Partial Derivatives and the Chain Rule. The material in the preceding five sections deals only with functions of one independent variable. In this section some of the ideas developed there will be extended to cover functions of several independent variables; but for the sake of simplicity the discussion will be confined to the case of *two* independent variables. The reader should experience no difficulty in extending the ideas to functions involving three or more.

To say that

$$(6.1) \quad x = f(s,t)$$

represents a function of the two variables s and t is to say that a definite value of x is determined by any pair of values of s and t lying within a certain set of pairs of numbers (the domain of the function, which may be depicted as some part of the s,t plane).

But if s is regarded as having some fixed given value, $f(s,t)$ becomes a function of t alone which is defined for those values of t which, combined with the given value of s, lie in the domain of $f(s,t)$. This function of t may be differentiable; the derivative, if it exists, is given by the limit of the *partial* difference quotient

$$\frac{f(s, t + h) - f(s, t)}{h}$$

as $h \to 0$. This limit will in general depend not only on t but on s, and it may be viewed as a function of these two variables. This function is called the *partial derivative of* $f(s,t)$ (*or of* x) *with respect to* t, and is denoted by any one of the symbols $\partial x/\partial t$, $\partial f(s,t)/\partial t$, x_t, $f_t(s,t)$. The first of these notations is the one generally used in this book.[8] The symbol ∂ is merely a stylized d, and its use serves to emphasize both the relation and the difference between the partial derivatives and derivatives as defined in Section 3 with the notation dx/dt. Whenever it is necessary to distinguish verbally the latter derivatives from partial derivatives, they are called *ordinary* derivatives.

The partial derivative of $f(s,t)$ with respect to s is defined analogously and is denoted by $\partial x/\partial s$, etc.

Example 6.1. If $f(s,t) = s^3 + 5s^2t^2 + t^3$, the partial derivative $\partial x/\partial t$ may be found as in Section 4, treating s as a constant. By (D_5), the derivative of s^3 will be zero; and by (D_6), the derivatives of t^2 and t^3 are $2t$ and $3t^2$, respectively. Thus, by (D_2), the derivative sought is $0 + 5s^2(2t) + 3t^2$, or $10s^2t + 3t^2$. Likewise, the derivative $\partial x/\partial s$ is $3s^2 + 10st^2$.

It may happen that the variables s and t appearing in the relation (6.1) are themselves functions of some variable, say z:

$$(6.2) \begin{cases} s = u(z), \\ t = v(z). \end{cases}$$

In this case x may be regarded as a function of z alone; any value of z (in an appropriate domain) determines values of s and t which in turn determine a value of x. Therefore, x may have an ordinary derivative with respect to z, and the problem we shall now take up is that of expressing this derivative by means of those of the intermediate functions $f(s,t)$, $u(z)$, $v(z)$.

The solution to this problem is given by the following theorem:

(D_7) *If the functions f, u, and v are as in (6.1) and (6.2), and if all three functions have continuous derivatives $(\partial x/\partial s, \partial x/\partial t, ds/dz, dt/dz)$ for the values of the variables z, s, and t involved, then x, regarded as a function of z, has a derivative which is given by*

$$(6.3) \quad \frac{dx}{dz} = \frac{\partial x}{\partial s}\frac{ds}{dz} + \frac{\partial x}{\partial t}\frac{dt}{dz}.$$

We shall not give the proof of this theorem; it is a direct extension of the proof of (D_6) (Section 4), with some additional refinements, and it may be found in any good textbook on the calculus (see the *Suggestions for Further Reading*). With (D_6) in mind, however, one may interpret the first term in the right side of (6.3) as the "contribution" made to the total rate of change of x with respect to z by the intermediate variable s; and of the second term as the similar "contribution" made by the intermediate variable t. It is therefore not surprising that the whole rate of change of x with respect to z is the sum of these two "contributions," and this is what one proves in proving (D_7). (D_7), or more briefly (6.3), is called a *chain rule;* the chain rules for cases where there are more than two intermediate variables like s

---

[8] When the independent variables are indexed, as in the functions $U(x_1, \ldots, x_n)$ and $x(v_1, v_2)$, it is sometimes convenient to write the partial derivatives of U with respect to $x_i (i = 1, \ldots, n)$ and of x with respect to $v_i (i = 1, 2)$ as U_i and x_i, respectively. This notation is used extensively in Chapters Five and Six. Whether an index is being used in this way, or to distinguish different variables, should be clear from the context.

and t have analogous forms. In general, if $x = f(s_1, s_2, \ldots, s_n)$, where $s_i = u_i(z)$ ($i = 1, 2, \ldots, n$), and if these functions have the appropriate properties of continuity and differentiability, then dx/dz exists and is given by

$$(6.4) \quad \frac{dx}{dz} = \sum_{i=1}^{n} \frac{\partial x}{\partial s_i} \frac{ds_i}{dz}.$$

We shall have particular use for the special case of (6.3) in which $s = z$. In this case, (D_6) implies that $ds/dz = 1$, so (6.3) reduces to

$$(6.5) \quad \frac{dx}{dz} = \frac{\partial x}{\partial z} + \frac{\partial x}{\partial t} \frac{dt}{dz}.$$

This equation incidentally shows the importance of distinguishing $\partial x/\partial z$ from dx/dz when both derivatives are defined.

EXERCISES

6.1. Compute the partial derivatives $\partial x/\partial s$ and $\partial x/\partial t$ for each of the following functions:

(a) $x = s + t$,   (b) $x = 2st$,   (c) $x = (s - t)^2$,
(d) $x = s^2/t^2$,   (e) $x = 5t^{10}$,   (f) $x = 60$.

6.2. If p is the price of a certain commodity, t is the rate of luxury tax on the commodity, and consumer demand for the commodity is given by the equation $d = f(p,t)$, describe in words the economic interpretation of the partial derivatives $\partial d/\partial p$ and $\partial d/\partial t$. In what units would these derivatives be measured? What signs would you expect them normally to have?

6.3. If s and t are assumed to be functions of a variable z, how can dx/dz be expressed for each of the functions in Exercise 6.1 in terms of s, t, ds/dz, and dt/dz?

6.4. Let $x = 5 - (s + 2t)^2$, $s = z + 3$, $t = 1 - z^2$. Find dx/dz first by expressing x explicitly as a function of z and then differentiating with respect to z; then find dx/dz by use of the chain rule (6.3). Your two answers should be the same. Why?

6.5. If $x = z(t + 1)$ and $t = \frac{1}{2}z^2$, find $\partial x/\partial z$ and dx/dz. For what value(s) of z, if any, are the two derivatives equal?

6.6. If $x = f(s_1, s_2, s_3)$ and $s_1 = z^2$, $s_2 = 1 - z$, and $s_3 = 7$, express $\partial x/\partial z$ in terms of z and the three derivatives $\partial x/\partial s_i$.

7. Higher Derivatives. It has been emphasized in previous sections that derivatives of functions are themselves functions; this applies to partial as well as to ordinary derivatives. Accordingly, the derivatives themselves may in turn have derivatives, and these *higher* derivatives— when they exist—are often of great importance. The idea is a simple one, and the principal task of this section is to explain the notations and terminology most frequently used.

First, consider a function of a single real variable t given by $x = f(t)$. If this function has a derivative, it is denoted by $f'(t)$ or dx/dt. Now suppose that the function $f'(t)$ has a derivative of its own which is defined at least for certain values of t; then this derivative of the derivative of $f(t)$, or more briefly the *second derivative* of $f(t)$, is denoted by $f''(t)$, or d^2x/dt^2. The notation $f''(t)$ should seem quite natural, but the notation d^2x/dt^2 requires a word of explanation. When the notation dx/dt is used for the first (i.e., the usual ordinary) derivative, the second derivative can be denoted quite logically by $d(dx/dt)/dt$. Now although dx/dt and similar expressions should not be regarded as fractions, their fractional *form* can be exploited for the sake of notational convenience. If $d(dx/dt)/dt$ is treated as a fraction, it can be rewritten as $d^2x/(dt)^2$; and omission of the parentheses in the "denominator" leads to the notation given.

The second derivative $f''(t)$ (or d^2x/dt^2) may in its turn have a derivative, and if it does this *third derivative* of $f(t)$ [which is also the second derivative of $f'(t)$ and the first derivative of $f''(t)$] is denoted by $f'''(t)$ or d^3x/dt^3, as might be expected.

This process may be repeated as many times as one wishes—provided that the derivatives encountered do exist—and the result of submitting $f(t)$ to the operation of differentiation n successive times is called the nth *derivative*, or *derivative of order n*, of $f(t)$. When n is at all large, the first notation, if extended in the straightforward way, leads to an unsightly and unmanageable proliferation of primes; this difficulty is avoided by writing $f^{(n)}(t)$ for the nth derivative. The parentheses around the n serve to distinguish this symbol from $f^n(t)$, which might be interpreted as the nth *power* of $f(t)$, or otherwise. Thus $f'(t) = f^{(1)}(t), f''(t) = f^{(2)}(t)$, etc. The prime notation is usually used for the first two or three derivatives, but the other is available for all values of n. For the derivatives following the third some writers replace the (n) in $f^{(n)}(t)$ by the Roman numeral for n, so that $f^{vii}(t)$ would denote the seventh derivative; but the advantages of this system are not clear.

The notation using the d's generalizes without the least difficulty: d^nx/dt^n stands for the nth derivative of $f(t)$.

When one starts with a function of several variables, say $x = f(s,t)$, the matter is somewhat complicated by the fact that at each stage it is possible to differentiate with respect to either of the independent variables. For instance, there are four possible ways of differentiating twice:

a) first with respect to s, then with respect to s again;
b) first with respect to s, then with respect to t;
c) first with respect to t, then with respect to s;
d) first with respect to t, then with respect to t again;

and there is no reason to suppose that these four processes will yield the same result. By a natural extension of the ∂ notation for partial derivatives, one writes

$$(7.1) \quad \frac{\partial^2x}{\partial s^2}, \quad \frac{\partial^2x}{\partial t\partial s}, \quad \frac{\partial^2x}{\partial s\partial t}, \quad \frac{\partial^2x}{\partial t^2},$$

respectively, for the results of these four processes. Notice that in the cases (*b*) and (*c*) the terms ∂s and ∂t in the "denominators" should be read *from right to left;* $\partial^2 x/\partial t \partial s$, for example, denotes the function obtained by differentiating x first with respect to s, then with respect to t. The functions (7.1) are called the second (partial) derivatives, or derivatives of order 2, of the given function. The derivatives of higher orders are defined analogously, and the notation appearing in (7.1) is extended in the obvious way: thus one of the fourth derivatives of $x = f(s,t)$ would be $\partial^4 x/\partial t^2 \partial s^2$, the result of differentiating the given function twice with respect to s and then twice with respect to t.

Example 7.1.   Consider the function $x = s^2 + st + t^3$. Then, as explained in Section 6,

$$\frac{\partial x}{\partial s} = 2s + t , \quad \frac{\partial x}{\partial t} = s + 3t^2 .$$

Differentiation of *these* functions gives

$$\frac{\partial^2 x}{\partial s^2} = 2 , \quad \frac{\partial^2 x}{\partial s \partial t} = 1 , \quad \frac{\partial^2 x}{\partial t \partial s} = 1 ,$$

$$\frac{\partial^2 x}{\partial t^2} = 6t .$$

When the order n is fairly large, especially if there are more than two independent variables, the number of different derivatives of that order may be very large indeed. This unfortunate phenomenon is somewhat counterbalanced by the truth of the next theorem.

Theorem 7.1.   If two partial derivatives of a certain order of a given function involve differentiation with respect to each independent variable the same number of times, then they are equal if they are continuous.

In other words, the *sequence* of the successive differentiations leading to higher derivatives of a function of several variables is irrelevant to the outcome if all the possible outcomes are continuous functions: if all the derivatives of order 3 of the function $x = f(s,t)$ were known to be continuous, we could say:

$$\frac{\partial^3 x}{\partial t^2 \partial s} = \frac{\partial^3 x}{\partial t \partial s \partial t} = \frac{\partial^3 x}{\partial s \partial t^2} ,$$

$$\frac{\partial^3 x}{\partial t \partial s^2} = \frac{\partial^3 x}{\partial s \partial t \partial s} = \frac{\partial^3 x}{\partial s^2 \partial t} ,$$

etc.

Theorem 7.1 will not be proved here.

EXERCISES

7.1. Find the second and third derivatives of each of the functions given in Exercise 4.1.

7.2. It has been shown that any polynomial in a single variable t is differentiable, and the derivative of a polynomial is itself always a polynomial. Thus a polynomial has derivatives of all possible orders. Show that the derivatives of a polynomial of all sufficiently large orders (i.e., of orders n not less than a certain number n_0) are identically zero. How is n_0 related to the degree of the polynomial?

7.3. Express in words the geometrical meaning of $f''(t)$, referring to a figure like Figure 5.1.

7.4. Find all second derivatives of each of the functions given in Exercise 6.1.

7.5. Discuss the questions raised by Exercise 7.2 as applied to polynomials in several independent variables.

SUGGESTIONS FOR FURTHER READING

The two most reputable treatises in English which deal with the subjects of this chapter are perhaps *A Course of Pure Mathematics* by G. H. Hardy (New York: Cambridge University Press; of the ten editions, the last is best because it has an index); and R. Courant's *Differential and Integral Calculus* (2d ed.; London and New York: Interscience, 1937). The book by Landau referred to in Section 2 emphasized logical rigor, and it is best suited to people who prefer to take their mathematics neat. All of these books are rather difficult for beginners, and many readers may choose to begin with a more conventional textbook, e.g., *Calculus* by C. R. Wylie, Jr. (New York: McGraw-Hill Book Co., Inc., 1953); or W. L. Ferrar, *Differential Calculus* (New York: Oxford University Press, 1955).

Chapter Ten

DEFINITE INTEGRALS AND
TAYLOR SERIES

THE ideas developed in Chapter Nine will now be used to elaborate two further concepts which are historically and logically closely related to them: the *definite integral* and the *Taylor series*. The definite integral is the mathematical notion corresponding to the economic process of capital formation: if the rate of investment in a certain commodity is represented by a given function of time, the amount of that commodity which will have accumulated over an interval of time will be given by the definite integral of the given investment function over the given interval. It goes without saying that processes of this kind are of considerable interest to the economist.

The Taylor series of a function enables one to replace a given function, the explicit expression for which may be very complex, by a simple polynomial of some suitable degree which approximates the function adequately, at least for some restricted range of the variables. The systematic use of this principle permits a number of important simplifications in dealing with problems in economic dynamics.

1. The Definite Integral. Suppose that the rate of net investment (= production − consumption) in a commodity is given by a certain function $f(t)$, where t is the time measured according to some time scale. Here the term *rate* means *instantaneous* rate, as defined in Chapter Nine. The function need not be restricted to positive values. If $f(t)$ has a negative value at some time this merely means that at that time previously existing stocks of the commodity are being consumed faster than they are being replenished: consumption exceeds production, so that capital disinvestment occurs.

If $f(t)$ is given, then intuition suggests that the change in existing stocks over any time interval can be determined from the knowledge of $f(t)$. In other words, if one knows the amount of the commodity actually in existence at any one time, one should be able to determine, knowing $f(t)$, what that amount will be at any subsequent time; or if not to determine this quantity, then at least to feel sure that there is but one possible value for it. The problem at issue is to develop a mathematical procedure for finding that value; or, more precisely, to find an expression for the investment in stocks over the interval starting when $t = T_1$ and ending when $t = T_2$ ($T_1 < T_2$) if the rate of net investment is given by a function $f(t)$ which is continuous over that interval.

The first step is to find an *approximate* value for the quantity in question. Imagine that the interval from T_1 to T_2 is subdivided into a number of shorter intervals with ends at the instants denoted by $t_0, t_1, \ldots, t_n$, where $T_1 = t_0 < t_1 < \ldots < t_n = T_2$ (see Fig. 1.1). Here it is convenient to suppose that the subintervals are numerous and short, and to concentrate on one of them, say the interval from t_{k-1} to t_k (k is any integer between 1 and n inclusive). Since this subinterval, the "kth," is short, and since $f(t)$ is con-

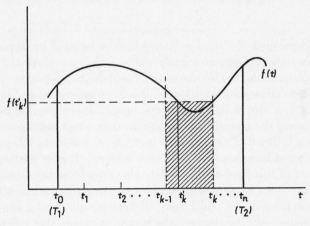

Fig. 1.1

tinuous, the value of $f(t)$ does not change very much as t changes from t_{k-1} to t_k. Equivalently, if t'_k is any value of t between t_{k-1} and t_k (i.e., $t_{k-1} \leqslant t'_k \leqslant t_k$), then $f(t'_k)$ will be a good approximation to the value of $f(t)$ over the whole subinterval; that is to say, we may consider $f(t)$ to have the constant value $f(t'_k)$ over the given interval even though this is not precisely true. If the rate of net investment is a constant, however, the total capital formation over an interval may be obtained simply by multiplying the rate of investment by the length of the interval. Thus the actual capital formation over the kth subinterval is approximately equal to $f(t'_k)(t_k - t_{k-1})$, for $t_k - t_{k-1}$ is the length of the subinterval. In Figure 1.1, this quantity is represented by the area of the shaded rectangle, for its dimensions are precisely $f(t_k)$ and $t_k - t_{k-1}$. If this procedure is carried out for each of the n subintervals, which amounts merely to choosing a number t'_k for each value of k from 1 to n subject to the condition $t_{k-1} \leqslant t'_k \leqslant t_k$, and adding together the resulting products $f(t'_k)(t_k - t_{k-1})$, one obtains a certain sum

$$(1.1) \qquad \sum_{k=1}^{n} f(t'_k)(t_k - t_{k-1})$$

as the desired approximation to the total capital formation over the whole interval from T_1 to T_2.

What keeps this approximation from being exact is that (1.1) was arrived at by replacing $f(t)$ by a constant over each of the subintervals, and this introduces errors which will cancel out only in exceptional cases. However, these errors (and therefore the total error) may be expected to be small if the subintervals are all short enough; indeed, the total error can be made less than any prescribed amount by making the subintervals sufficiently short (and correspondingly numerous). The notion of the limit of a sequence is implicit in this idea and will now be made explicit.

Suppose that I_m stands for a particular subdivision (collection of subintervals) of the interval from T_1 to T_2, obtained in the manner described above. Suppose, moreover, that such a subdivision of the interval from T_1 to T_2 has been chosen corresponding to each positive integer m, so that we have a sequence of different subdivisions $I_1, I_2, \ldots$ There is no need to assume that each subdivision I_m is obtained from the preceding ones in the sequence according to any particular rule, but it may be supposed that the subdivisions get finer as m increases. More exactly, it is assumed that for any prescribed positive number ϵ, however small, every subinterval belonging to I_m is less than ϵ in length for all values of m exceeding a certain value, which will depend upon ϵ.

If a sum (1.1) is formed for each of the subdivisions I_m, then according to our discussion these sums (denoted respectively by J_m) may be expected to approach, as $m \to \infty$, a certain limit J, namely, the exact amount of net capital formation over the interval from T_1 to T_2; each J_m is an approximation to this quantity, and the approximation gets better as the subdivision gets finer (i.e., as the value of m increases).

As a matter of fact, the assumptions underlying this argument are such that the existence of the limit of the sequence $J_1, J_2, \ldots$ may be *proved*. Moreover, it can be shown that the limit J does not depend on the particular sequence of subdivisions I_m used, nor yet on the manner in which the numbers t'_k associated with each J_m are chosen. J depends only on the function $f(t)$ itself and the numbers T_1 and T_2—this being as it should be if J is to be given the intended interpretation. This limit is called the *definite integral of $f(t)$ from T_1 to T_2*, and is conventionally denoted by the symbol

$$(1.2) \quad \int_{T_1}^{T_2} f(t) \, dt \, .$$

This is nothing but an abbreviation for the italicized phrase just defined, and the component symbols $\int$ and dt should not be given any independent significance.

Geometrically, this quantity represents the area of the figure bounded by the $f(t)$ curve, the t-axis, and the vertical lines $t = T_1$, $t = T_2$ in Figure 1.1. The sums J_m represent approximations to this area obtained by slicing the figure into vertical strips, squaring off the tops of these strips, and adding together the areas of the resulting set of rectangles. The existence of the limit (1.2) corresponds to the fact that the error involved in approximating the area of the figure in this way can be made as small as one wishes by making all of the vertical slices sufficiently thin. If the graph of $f(t)$ happens to dip below the t-axis, the corresponding area (the area approximated by the rectangles extending *downward* from the t-axis) will count negatively, so that the definite integral will represent the area of that part of the figure lying above the axis with the area of that part of the figure lying below the axis subtracted from it.

The definition of (1.2) is independent of the interpretation attached to $f(t)$, and may therefore be applied to any function for which the limit in question exists. Even the continuity of $f(t)$ is not strictly necessary; the definite integral will still exist if the graph of $f(t)$ takes a finite number of finite jumps and is otherwise continuous.

The theory of the definite integral is called the *integral calculus*, and it is to the elements of this subject that the next three sections are devoted.

EXERCISES

1.1. If $f(t)$ represents the speed of an object moving in one direction along a certain straight line, what is the significance of (1.2)?

1.2. If $f(t)$ is a linear function of t ($= at + b$), and if the numbers t'_k are always chosen to be the midpoints of the corresponding subintervals, the value of (1.1) will be exactly equal (and not merely an approximation) to the definite integral. Why?

1.3. Let $f(t)$ be defined to have the value 1 if t is a rational number, 0 if t is irrational. Show that by a suitable choice of the numbers t_k, given any sequence of subdivisions of the interval $0 \leqslant t \leqslant 1$ as described in the text, one can bring it about that the corresponding sums J_m have as their limit any prescribed number between 0 and 1. (Hint: Any interval of the t-axis, however short, contains both rational and irrational values of t.)

2. *Properties of the Definite Integral.* In Chapter Nine it was shown how the very definition of the derivative of a function could be used to obtain formulas for the derivatives of functions of certain types. It might be expected that something of the same sort would be possible for the definite integral—that values for the definite integrals of given functions over given intervals could be obtained by a more or less direct application of the definition. This is true, however, only to a very limited degree. The values of a few definite integrals may be obtained in this way, but for most functions this line of attack leads nowhere. It is fortunate, therefore, that there exists a general principle for finding definite integrals *without* the direct application of the definition. The principle will be stated, partially proved, and illustrated in the next section. By way of preparation, this section is devoted to some of the basic properties of the definite integral.

The first such property is directly evident on intuitive grounds. In terms of the example of the net investment function used in Section 1, the property may be stated as follows: If T_1, T_2, and T_3 are successive instants of time, then the total increase in commodity stocks between the instants T_1 and T_3 is the sum of the total increase between T_1 and T_2 and that between T_2 and T_3. In the definite integral notation,

$$(2.1) \quad \int_{T_1}^{T_3} f(t) \, dt = \int_{T_1}^{T_2} f(t) \, dt + \int_{T_2}^{T_3} f(t) \, dt \, .$$

The proof of this assertion may be sketched in a few sentences. Suppose that I_1, I_2, ... , is a sequence of subdivisions of the interval from T_1 to T_3 leading to the definite integral $\int_{T_1}^{T_3} f(t) \, dt$. Nothing is lost by assuming that each of the subdivisions I_m includes T_2 among the values of t separating its subintervals; we assume, therefore, that this is the case. Now the terms in the sum (1.1), i.e., J_m, corresponding to subintervals of I_m involving values of t less than T_2 yield a certain sum which we may call J'_m; and the terms corresponding to values of t larger than T_2 yield a similar sum J''_m. Clearly,

$$J_m = J'_m + J''_m \, .$$

But if we take the limit as $m \to \infty$ on both sides of this equation, we obtain (2.1); for by definition $J'_m \to \int_{T_1}^{T_2} f(t) \, dt$ as $m \to \infty$, and similarly for J''_m.

Strictly speaking, the expression $\int_{T_1}^{T_1} f(t) \, dt$, in which the interval degenerates to a single point, remains to be defined; but it is consistent with the spirit of the principal definition to put

$$(2.2) \quad \int_{T}^{T} f(t) \, dt = 0 \, ,$$

where T is any value of t, and this is what is done.

This suggests the question: What meaning, if any, should be assigned to the symbol (1.2) when T_1 is *greater* than T_2? One point of view leading to the natural answer to this question is this: We have seen that when $T_1 < T_2 < T_3$, and the integrals involved exist, the formula (2.1) holds true. The chief reason for assuming $T_1 < T_2 < T_3$ was that the integrals concerned had been defined in this case only. In view of the complementary definition (2.2), it is easy to verify that (2.1) remains valid if $T_1 = T_2 < T_3$, $T_1 < T_2 = T_3$, or $T_1 = T_2 = T_3$. One would like to carry this process further, so as to make (2.1) valid for any possible order of T_1, T_2, and T_3; in particular, it would be desirable to have (2.1) hold true when $T_3 = T_1 > T_2$. In this case formula (2.1) becomes

$$\int_{T_1}^{T_2} f(t) \, dt = \int_{T_1}^{T_2} f(t) \, dt + \int_{T_2}^{T_1} f(t) \, dt \, ,$$

but according to (2.2) the left side of this equation is zero. Transposing therefore gives

$$(2.3) \quad \int_{T_1}^{T_2} f(t) \, dt = - \int_{T_2}^{T_1} f(t) \, dt \, .$$

The definite integral on the right side has already been defined, since $T_2 < T_1$. Therefore (2.3) may be, and is, taken as the definition of the definite integral on the left side when $T_1 > T_2$; it is then valid regardless of the relative values of T_1 and T_2. Among other things, it follows from this that *interchanging the numbers at the tips of the "integral sign"* $\int$ *is equivalent to changing the sign of the definite integral.*

It has already been shown that the defining formula (2.3) is *necessary* in order for (2.1) to hold true for all possible values of T_1, T_2, and T_3. It is also *sufficient;* for assuming that (2.1) is valid when $T_1 < T_2 < T_3$ (as has been proved), and using (2.2) and (2.3), one can show that (2.1) is valid for any combination of values of T_1, T_2, and T_3—assuming always that the three integrals appearing in (2.1) do exist.

Finally it is worth while to consider the important *Mean-Value Theorem* for integrals, which runs as follows: *If $f(t)$ is continuous for all values of t satisfying $T_1 \leqslant t \leqslant T_2$, then there exists at least one value of t, say t', such that $T_1 < t' < T_2$ and*

$$(2.4) \qquad \int_{T_1}^{T_2} f(t) \, dt = f(t')(T_2 - T_1) \ .$$

The proof of this theorem depends on some rather subtle aspects of continuity and will not be given here; but a few words about its meaning may make it easier both to remember and to believe. For this purpose it may be helpful to return once more to the interpretation provided by the net investment function. The integral on the left side of (2.4) represents the total increase in stocks over the time interval from T_1 to T_2. The right side of (2.4) is the rate of net investment at the instant t', multiplied by the length of the time interval, and therefore represents the total increase in stocks that would occur if the rate at the instant t' were to prevail throughout the interval. In other words, $f(t')$ is that rate of net investment which, if it were to prevail throughout the time interval under consideration, would result in a total of net capital formation exactly equal to that given by the varying rate $f(t)$. It is therefore natural to call $f(t')$, or more generally the value of the quotient $\int_{T_1}^{T_2} f(t) \, dt/(T_2 - T_1)$, the *average*, or *mean* rate of net production over the interval; and what the theorem asserts under the present interpretation of $f(t)$ is that *there is at least one instant within the interval at which the actual rate of net investment is equal to the mean rate for the interval.* One should remember that this need not be true if $f(t)$ is not continuous. This is shown by the example in which $T_1 = 0$, $T_2 = 2$, $f(t) = 0$ if $0 \leqslant t < 1, f(t) = 1$ if $1 \leqslant t \leqslant 2$. Here the net increase in stocks is 1, so that the mean rate is $\frac{1}{2}$; but there is no instant within the interval at which $f(t) = \frac{1}{2}$. The trouble is caused by the discontinuity of $f(t)$ at $t = 1$.

EXERCISES

2.1. Use the definitions and the formulas proved in the text to show that (2.1) holds if $T_2 < T_3 < T_1$, and illustrate the situation graphically.

2.2. *Why* is (2.2) "consistent with the spirit of the principal definition"?

2.3. What can you conclude if the mean value of a continuous function over an interval is 0?

3. *The Fundamental Theorem of the Calculus.* A comparison between the discussion in Section 1 of this chapter and that in Chapter Nine, Section 3, indicates the existence of a close connection between the definite integral concept and the derivative concept. In forming the derivative, one starts with the function representing the accumulated stock of a commodity and arrives at the rate of net investment; while in forming the definite integral one starts with the rate of net investment and arrives at a means of describing the growth of stock over intervals of time. Thus, the two processes are, in a sense, inverse to each other; forming the definite integral undoes differentiation and *vice versa*. And this should be provable as a mathematical statement about the derivative and the definite integral; for if it were not, our interpretation of the limit process leading to the definite integral would have to be re-examined for fallacies. The statement is provable, and it is most conveniently expressed in the form of the theorem:

If $F(t)$ is any function whose derivative $F'(t)$ is the continuous function $f(t)$, then

$$\int_{T_1}^{T_2} f(t)\, dt = F(T_2) - F(T_1).$$

In terms of the examples used earlier, this means that if $F(t)$ is any function whose derivative is the given rate of net investment $f(t)$—any function, in other words, which, if regarded as the function giving the size of the accumulated stock as a function of time t, yields $f(t)$ as the corresponding *rate* of growth of stocks—then the growth of stock over the interval from T_1 to T_2 is given as the difference between the values of $F(t)$ at the ends of the interval.

In general, this theorem provides a strong link between the differential calculus, on the one hand, and the integral calculus, on the other; it is therefore frequently called the *Fundamental Theorem of the Calculus*, and its discovery was one of the most important achievements of seventeenth-century mathematics.

With a few of the fine points omitted, the proof of the Fundamental Theorem runs as follows:

The definite integral $\int_{T_1}^{T_2} f(t)\, dt$, where T_1 is held fixed and T_2 is allowed to vary, defines a function of T_2. In order to emphasize the variability of T_2, we drop the subscript and write simply T. Thus there is defined a function

$$(3.1) \quad \mathfrak{F}(T) = \int_{T_1}^{T} f(t)\, dt.$$

The next step is to compute the derivative of this function (cf. Chapter Nine, Section 3). The difference quotient is given by

$$\frac{1}{h}[\mathfrak{F}(T + h) - \mathfrak{F}(T)] = \frac{1}{h}\left[\int_{T_1}^{T+h} f(t)\, dt - \int_{T_1}^{T} f(t)\, dt\right].$$

However, the difference of the two definite integrals on the right is merely $\int_T^{T+h} f(t)\, dt$, according to formula (2.1); and this integral in turn, by the Mean-Value Theorem, is equal to

$$f(t')(T + h - T) = hf(t'), \text{ where } T < t' < T + h\,;$$

so

$$(3.2) \quad \frac{1}{h}[\mathfrak{F}(T + h) - \mathfrak{F}(T)] = f(t'),\quad (T < t' < T + h)\,.$$

Now as $h \to 0$, the value of t' (which depends on h) is forced to approach T. Therefore, since $f(t)$ is continuous, $f(t') \to f(T)$ as $h \to 0$. This means that the right side of (3.2) has a limit as $h \to 0$, namely, $f(T)$. The same is therefore true of the left side; but since the left side is the difference quotient for $\mathfrak{F}(T)$, this shows that the derivative of $\mathfrak{F}(T)$, the limit of the difference quotient as $h \to 0$, exists and is equal to $f(T)$:

(A) *If $\mathfrak{F}(T)$ is defined by (3.1), $\mathfrak{F}'(T) = f(T)$.*

This statement is itself of considerable importance, but in order to obtain the Fundamental Theorem one must go a bit further. We note that *any* function whose derivative is $f(T)$ must differ from $\mathfrak{F}(T)$ by a constant:

(B) *If $F'(T) = f(T)$, then $F(T) \equiv \mathfrak{F}(T) + C$, where C is a certain constant.*

This follows from the fact that $F(T) - \mathfrak{F}(T)$ has the derivative $f(T) - f(T) \equiv 0$, so that the value of $F(T) - \mathfrak{F}(T)$ does not change with T—i.e., is some constant C.

All that remains is to tie these threads together. By (3.1) and (2.2),

$$(3.3) \quad \mathfrak{F}(T_1) = 0\,,$$

and by (3.1) alone

$$(3.4) \quad \mathfrak{F}(T_2) = \int_{T_1}^{T_2} f(t)\, dt\,.$$

Now if $F(T)$ if any function whose derivative is $f(T)$, (B) says that for some constant C, $F(T) \equiv \mathfrak{F}(T) + C$. Therefore

$$\begin{aligned}
F(T_2) - F(T_1) &= [\mathfrak{F}(T_2) + C] - [\mathfrak{F}(T_1) + C] \\
&= \mathfrak{F}(T_2) - \mathfrak{F}(T_1) \\
&= \int_{T_1}^{T_2} f(t)\, dt - 0 \\
&= \int_{T_1}^{T_2} f(t)\, dt\,,
\end{aligned}$$

by (3.3) and (3.4). This establishes the theorem.

EXERCISES

3.1. State the Fundamental Theorem in your own words, using no mathematical symbols at all.

3.2. In the statement and proof of the Fundamental Theorem nothing is said about the relative size of T_1 and T_2. Are there any points at which the possibility that T_1 might be greater than T_2 could cause trouble? Explain.

3.3. Derive formulas (2.1) and (2.2) directly from the Fundamental Theorem. (Note that this will not constitute a proof of these formulas, since they are both used in the proof of the Fundamental Theorem.) 𝒶

4. Antiderivatives: the Integration of Polynomials. The most important practical consequence of the Fundamental Theorem is that it reduces the problem of finding the definite integral of a continuous function $f(t)$ to that of finding a function $F(t)$ whose derivative is $f(t)$. A function of this kind is called an *antiderivative*[1] of $f(t)$, and the process of finding some antiderivative of a given function is called *integration*.

It follows from the proposition (B) of Section 3 that any two antiderivatives of a given function $f(t)$ must differ by a constant; conversely, if $F(t)$ is an antiderivative of $f(t)$, so is $F(t) + C$, where C may be any constant, for $F(t)$ and $F(t) + C$ always have the same derivative, the derivative of C being zero. It follows that if $F(t)$ is *any* antiderivative of $f(t)$, the expression $F(t) + C$ gives *all* antiderivatives of $f(t)$ if C is regarded as an arbitrary constant; a constant, that is, which is allowed to have (and may be thought of as having) any value whatever. Accordingly, the expression $F(t) + C$ may be called the *general* antiderivative of $f(t)$; it is frequently denoted by $\int f(t)\, dt$, but we shall not use the notation in this book.

In large measure, then, the technique of calculating definite integrals is composed of methods for finding antiderivatives. This is a very large subject, and we shall only scratch its surface here. There exist extensive tables of antiderivatives, and these often include lists of special definite integrals. A very convenient one is *A Short Table of Integrals* by B. O. Peirce (Boston: Ginn & Co., 1929), and anyone who has occasion to know specific definite integrals will do well to obtain the appropriate antiderivative from such a collection as this. For our purposes, however, it will suffice to develop the theory of a very special class of antiderivatives, namely, those of polynomials; this will enable us to set up a number of examples here and elsewhere.

Because of the intimate connection between derivatives and antiderivatives, some of the rules for differentiation obtained in Section 4 of Chapter Nine lead directly to useful statements about antiderivatives. Two of them will suffice for our purposes:

(I_1) *If $F(t)$ and $G(t)$ are respectively antiderivatives of $f(t)$ and $g(t)$, and if a and b are constants, then $aF(t) + bG(t)$ is an antiderivative of $af(t) + bg(t)$.*

PROOF: By assumption, $F'(t) = f(t)$ and $G'(t) = g(t)$. Therefore, by (D_1) (Chapter Nine, Section 4), the derivative of $aF(t) + bG(t)$ is $af(t) + bg(t)$, and this is what had to be shown.

Like (D_1), (I_1) may be extended directly to functions formed by adding

---

[1] Terms in common use which are more or less synonymous with "antiderivative" include *primitive* and *indefinite integral*.

together more than two constant multiples of functions: if $F_i(t)$ is an anti-derivative of $f_i(t)$ and c_i is a constant $(i = 1, 2, \ldots, n)$, then

$$c_1F_1(t) + c_2F_2(t) + \ldots + c_nF_n(t)$$

is an antiderivative of $c_1f_1(t) + c_2f_2(t) + \ldots + c_nf_n(t)$. This statement may be proved directly by use of the extended form of (D_1), or it may be proved by applying (I_1) several times.

(I_2) *If n is any positive whole number or zero, $t^{n+1}/(n + 1)$ is an anti-derivative of t^n.*

PROOF: When n is a positive whole number, the derivative of

$$\frac{t^{n+1}}{(n + 1)} \text{ is } \frac{1}{n + 1}(n + 1)\, t^{(n+1)-1} = t^n .$$

When n is zero, $t^{n+1}/(n + 1) = t$, and the derivative of t is 1, which is t^0.

The assumption that n is a positive whole number or zero could be re-placed by the much lighter assumption that $n \neq -1$, and the conclusion of (I_2) would remain true; but we shall not prove this more general form of the rule.

Unfortunately, there are no theorems about antiderivatives analogous to (D_2) and (D_3); i.e., there is no general formula which gives an antiderivative of the product of two functions in terms of antiderivatives of those func-tions, nor is there one which gives an antiderivative of a quotient in terms of the antiderivatives of numerator and denominator. It is primarily this fact which makes integration an altogether more difficult process than dif-ferentiation. Nevertheless, the rules (I_1) and (I_2) suffice for the integration of polynomials.

Example 4.1. We shall find the antiderivative of the function

$$f(t) = 3t^2 - 8t.$$

By (I_2), antiderivatives of t^2 and t are $t^3/3$ and $t^2/2$, respectively. Therefore, by (I_1), an antiderivative of $f(t)$ is

$$3\frac{t^3}{3} - 8\frac{t^2}{2},$$

or simply

$$t^3 - 4t^2 .$$

The *general* antiderivative of $f(t)$ is therefore

$$t^3 - 4t^2 + C ,$$

where C is an arbitrary constant. This conclusion may be checked by dif-ferentiation.

Example 4.2. We shall now evaluate the definite integral

$$\int_0^1 (t + 1)^2 \, dt .$$

The first step is to find an antiderivative of $(t + 1)^2$. This is the same as $t^2 + 2t + 1$, and according to (I_2) t^2, t, and 1 ($= t^0$) have the antiderivatives $t^3/3$, $t^2/2$, and t, respectively, so that by (I_1) (in the extended form) an antiderivative of $(t + 1)^2$ is given by

$$\frac{t^3}{3} + 2\frac{t^2}{2} + t,$$

or

$$\frac{t^3}{3} + t^2 + t.$$

If this function is denoted by $F(t)$, the Fundamental Theorem asserts that

$$\int_0^1 (t + 1)^2 \, dt = F(1) - F(0) = \tfrac{1}{3} + 1 + 1 - (0 + 0 + 0) = \tfrac{7}{3}.$$

Following the pattern set by this example, one can calculate the definite integral of any polynomial over any interval.

EXERCISES

4.1. Find an antiderivative for each of the following functions:
(a) 2,   (b) $t - 5$,   (c) $3t^2 - 5t^4$,   (d) $(t^2 + 2)^2$.
Check each answer by differentiation.

4.2. Prove that $(x^2 + 2)/(x^2 + 1)$ is an antiderivative of $-2x/(x^2 + 1)^2$. Use this result to find

$$\int_0^1 \frac{2x}{(x^2 + 1)^2} dx.$$

4.3. Evaluate each of the following definite integrals:
(a) $\displaystyle\int_0^2 (-1) \, dt$,   (b) $\displaystyle\int_{-1}^1 t^4 \, dt$,   (c) $\displaystyle\int_1^2 (t^2 + 3t) \, dt$,

(d) $\displaystyle\int_1^{\frac{3}{2}} (t - 1)^2 dt$,   (e) $\displaystyle\int_{-1}^0 (t + 1)(t - 2) dt$,   (f) $\displaystyle\int_{-1}^1 t(t + 2)^3 dt$.

4.4. Calculate the three definite integrals:
(a) $\displaystyle\int_0^a (t + 1) dt$,   (b) $\displaystyle\int_0^a (t - 1) dt$,   (c) $\displaystyle\int_0^a (t^2 - 1) dt$.

Your results should constitute a *dis*proof of the nontheorem

$$\int_0^a f(t)g(t) dt = \left(\int_0^a f(t) \, dt \right)\left(\int_0^a g(t) \, dt \right).$$

5. *Approximation by Polynomials.* If for no reason other than the ease with which they may be differentiated and integrated, polynomials are extremely convenient functions with which to work. However, many of the functions which one encounters in the applications of mathematics are not polynomials; indeed, many arise from fitting a curve to empirical data, and it may be impossible to give any explicit formula for functions of this kind.

Nevertheless, since applied mathematics always involves some amount of idealization and approximation under the best of circumstances, one is frequently justified in replacing a given function $f(t)$ by a polynomial $P(t)$

which approximates it with a suitably high degree of accuracy, and then working with the polynomial $P(t)$ as if it were the function $f(t)$ itself. In other words, it is frequently possible to act as if a given function were a polynomial even though one knows that in fact it is not, for this assumption introduces a negligibly small error into the calculations. The mathematical justification for this procedure is provided in many cases by the following theorem.

If $f(t)$ *is a function which is continuous over an interval* $T_1 \leqslant t \leqslant T_2$, *and* ϵ *is an arbitrarily small positive number, there exists a polynomial* $P(t)$ *such that*

$$|f(t) - P(t)| < \epsilon$$

for every value of t in the interval.

The proof of this theorem, the so-called *Weierstrass Approximation Theorem*, is rather difficult and will not be given here. It should be pointed out, however, that despite its great generality the theorem has a number of shortcomings from the practical point of view: for instance, nothing is said about how the polynomial $P(t)$ may be found, and nothing is said about the size of the degree which $P(t)$ must have for a given function $f(t)$, a given interval, and a given value of ϵ. These shortcomings, as well as others, can in fact be removed to some extent, but the theory is not simple.

For our purposes, however, a different kind of approximation by polynomials is more useful. This is the kind of approximation which might be called *approximation at a point:* instead of trying to find a polynomial which approximates a given function well over a (possibly very long) interval, one tries to find a polynomial which approximates the function for values of the independent variable at and near a certain value t_0. In this case the sense of the word "approximate" is changed somewhat. Instead of requiring simply that the approximating polynomial $P(t)$ should differ from $f(t)$ by less than some prescribed constant ϵ for values of t near t_0 (this problem would be covered by the Weierstrass Approximation Theorem), one requires that *the functions $f(t)$ and $P(t)$ and their derivatives of orders* $1, 2, \ldots, n$ *should have the same values at t_0.* Here n is merely some positive integer which is suggested by the particular circumstances; and the higher the value of n, the more stringent the requirement. It is easy to show that if $f(t)$ has all the necessary derivatives, a polynomial $P(t)$ can always be found which approximates $f(t)$ in this sense. Moreover, *it is never necessary that the degree of $P(t)$ be greater than n.*

The proof of this last statement actually shows how $P(t)$ may be found: Let $f(t)$ be the given function, and t_0 a value of t at which the first n derivatives of $f(t)$ exist. We write $P(t)$ in the form[2]

$$(5.1) \quad P(t) = a_0 + a_1(t - t_0) + a_2(t - t_0)^2 + \ldots + a_n(t - t_0)^n,$$

where $a_0, \ldots, a_n$ are constant coefficients to be determined.

---

[2] Any polynomial of degree n (or less) can be written in this form; however, it suffices to observe that (5.1) does give a polynomial in t of degree at most n. If $a_n \neq 0$, the degree is exactly n, otherwise less.

If t is replaced by t_0 in (5.1), this equation reduces to

$$P(t_0) = a_0 .$$

However, since we want it to be true that $f(t_0) = P(t_0)$, this means that we must choose

(5.2) $a_0 = f(t_0) .$

If (5.1) is differentiated on both sides with respect to t, the result is

(5.3) $P'(t) = a_1 + 2a_2(t - t_0) + 3a_3(t - t_0)^2 + \ldots + na_n(t - t_0)^{n-1} .$

Replacing t by t_0 in (5.3) gives $P'(t_0) = a_1$; but since we want $P'(t_0) = f'(t_0)$, we must choose a_1 according to the formula

(5.4) $a_1 = f'(t_0) .$

Differentiating both sides of (5.3) gives

(5.5) $P''(t) = 2a_2 + 6a_3(t - t_0) + 12a_4(t - t_0)^2 + \ldots + n(n - 1)a_n(t - t_0)^{n-2} ,$

and putting $t = t_0$ here leads to $P''(t_0) = 2a_2$, so we must take

(5.6) $a_2 = \frac{1}{2}f''(t_0) .$

Continuing in this way, one obtains the formulas, similar to (5.6),

(5.7) $a_3 = \dfrac{f^{(3)}(t_0)}{6}, \quad a_4 = \dfrac{f^{(4)}(t_0)}{24}, \ldots, a_n = \dfrac{f^{(n)}(t_0)}{n(n - 1) \cdots 1} .$

The product of the positive whole numbers from 1 to n inclusive is conventionally denoted by the symbol $n!$ (read "factorial n"). If this symbol is used here, the formulas (5.2), (5.4), (5.6), and (5.7) can be collapsed into the single general formula

(5.8) $a_k = \dfrac{f^{(k)}(t_0)}{k!}, \quad (k = 1, 2, \ldots, n) .$

[Here it is to be understood that $f^{(0)}(t)$ means simply $f(t)$, and that $0! = 1$. This notation—which is also customary—enables one to include the formula (5.2) with the others.]

This shows that if the coefficients a_k in (5.1) are chosen according to the formula (5.8), then (5.1) approximates $f(t)$ in the sense described. In summary, then, we may say: *If the function $f(t)$ has derivatives of orders 1 through n at t_0, then a polynomial whose value at t_0 is the same as that of $f(t)$, and whose derivatives of orders 1 through n have the same values at t_0 as the corresponding derivatives of $f(t)$ is given by*

(5.9) $P(t) = f(t_0) + f'(t_0)(t - t_0) + f''(t_0)\dfrac{(t - t_0)^2}{2} + \ldots + f^{(n)}(t_0)\dfrac{(t - t_0)^n}{n!} .$

Moreover, $P(t)$ is the only polynomial whose degree is less than or equal to n which has this property.

Example 5.1.   Take $f(t) = 5/(1 + 4t^2)$ and $t_0 = 1$; then $f(t_0) = 1$,

$f'(t_0) = -8/5$, $f''(t_0) = 88/25$, and $f^{(3)}(t_0) = -1152/125$, as one may verify by the methods of Chapter Nine. The first few polynomials given by (5.9) are therefore those shown in Table 5.1.

TABLE 5.1

n	$P(t)$
0	1
1	$1 - \frac{8}{5}(t-1)$
2	$1 - \frac{8}{5}(t-1) + \frac{44}{25}(t-1)^2$
3	$1 - \frac{8}{5}(t-1) + \frac{44}{25}(t-1)^2 - \frac{192}{125}(t-1)^3$

The polynomials in Table 5.1, together with the function $f(t)$ itself, are graphed in Figure 5.1. It should be observed in this diagram that the higher

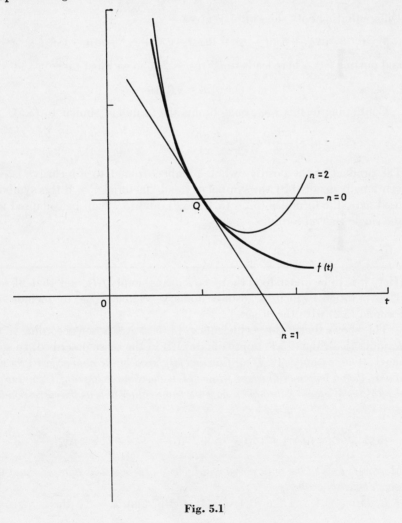

Fig. 5.1

the value of n, the closer the fit of the corresponding polynomial $P(t)$ to $f(t)$. When $n = 0$, $P(t)$ is merely a horizontal straight line through the point Q at which the approximation is taking place; but when $n = 1$, the polynomial agrees with $f(t)$ not only in value but also in slope at t_0, and its graph is the line tangent to the graph of $f(t)$ at Q. When $n = 2$, the fit is still better, for (geometrically speaking) the polynomial and $f(t)$ then agree not only in height and slope at t^0 but also in the rate at which the slope is changing (the second derivative); and so on. These remarks apply to any function $f(t)$, and not merely to the example depicted.

As a consequence, or at least a concomitant, of this phenomenon of an improving fit with increasing n, the range of values of t over which $P(t)$ approximates $f(t)$ with a given degree of accuracy also increases as n increases. This raises the interesting question of whether a polynomial approximating $f(t)$ over a prescribed interval including t_0 with a prescribed degree of accuracy can be found in this way—i.e., whether the problem of finding a polynomial which approximates $f(t)$ at t_0 leads to a solution of the problem implicit in the Weierstrass Approximation Theorem. This is a difficult question, and it leads to the concept of the Taylor formula and Taylor series, which we discuss in the next section.

EXERCISES

5.1. Find the polynomial of degree 2 or less which agrees in value and in the value of the first two derivatives with each of the following functions at the specified value of t.

a) $f(t) = \dfrac{1}{1 + t}$, $t_0 = 0$

b) $f(t) = \dfrac{1}{t^2}$, $t_0 = 2$

c) $f(t) = t^3$, $t_0 = 0$

d) $f(t) = t^3$, $t_0 = -1$

5.2. If a function $f(t)$ given in Exercise 5.1 were itself a polynomial of degree 2 or less, one would naturally expect that the answer should be that polynomial. Working with the general polynomial $at^2 + bt + c$ and an unspecified t_0, show that this expectation will always be fulfilled.

5.3. Draw a figure which illustrates the meaning of the Weierstrass Approximation Theorem.

5.4. Tabulate the values of $n!$ for $n = 0, 1, 2, \ldots, 12$. What does this lead you to conjecture about the relative significance of the terms in the right side of formula (5.9)?

6. *Taylor's Formula.* In Section 5 we have seen how a polynomial may be found which agrees with a given function $f(t)$ in value, and in the values of all derivatives up to and including a given order n, at a given value t_0 of t. For different values of n, the polynomials are (in general) different. In order to emphasize this dependence on n, we shall now begin writing $P_n(t)$ for the polynomial defined by (5.9). We define the *remainder function of order n*, $R_n(t)$, by means of the equation

$$(6.1) \quad R_n(t) = f(t) - P_n(t) .$$

Since $R_n(t)$ is the difference between the given function $f(t)$ and the approximating polynomial $P_n(t)$, the size of $R_n(t)$ indicates the excellence of the approximation; the smaller the values of $R_n(t)$ over a certain interval, the better the approximation of $P_n(t)$ to $f(t)$ over that interval. It would therefore be valuable to have some fairly simple way of estimating the size of $R_n(t)$ in terms of the function $f(t)$ itself. This may be done in various ways, of which we shall mention but one. We assume that $f(t)$ has continuous derivatives up to and including the order $n + 1$ over an interval $T_1 \leqslant t \leqslant T_2$ containing the number t_0. On this assumption, if t is any number in the interval,

$$(6.2) \quad R_n(t) = f^{(n+1)}(t')\frac{(t - t_0)^{n+1}}{(n + 1)!},$$

where t' is some number between t_0 and t. This is called *Lagrange's form* of the remainder.

If one combines equations (5.9), (6.1), and (6.2), the result is

$$(6.3) \quad f(t) = f(t_0) + f'(t_0)(t - t_0) + \tfrac{1}{2}f''(t_0)(t - t_0)^2 + \cdots$$
$$+ f^{(n)}(t_0)\frac{(t - t_0)^n}{n!} + f^{(n+1)}(t')\frac{(t - t_0)^{n+1}}{(n + 1)!} .$$

This equation is called *Taylor's formula with Lagrange's form of the remainder*. The statement that (6.3) is valid under the assumptions stated is called *Taylor's Theorem,* and it is an important instrument of mathematical analysis. We shall not prove this theorem, although the proof is not very difficult.

One should note the resemblance between the expression on the right side of (6.3) and the expression for $P_{n+1}(t)$; they differ only in the point at which the highest derivative is evaluated. This resemblance makes (6.3) easy to remember.

For our purposes, the value of the formula (6.2) is that it may be possible to estimate the size of $f^{(n+1)}(t)$ over the interval in question, and therefore to estimate the maximum possible error committed in replacing $f(t)$ by $P_n(t)$ over that interval. This idea will become clear upon consideration of an example.

Example 6.1. Take $f(t) = 1/(4 - t)$, $T_1 = -1$, $T_2 = 1$, $t_0 = 0$. The conditions under which (6.2) is valid are satisfied for any value of n. We shall use (6.2) to form an idea of the error committed in replacing $f(t)$ by $P_3(t)$ over the interval from T_1 to T_2. By the methods of Chapter Nine, one may find: $f^{(4)}(t) = 24/(4 - t)^5$. Clearly, the largest value of this function on the interval will occur when $4 - t$ has its smallest value on that interval, namely, 3; therefore

$$|f^{(4)}(t)| \leqslant \frac{24}{3^5} \quad \text{for} \quad -1 \leqslant t \leqslant +1 .$$

Since $t_0 = 0$, the largest possible value of $(t - t_0)^4$ on the interval is 1. Finally, $(n + 1)! = 4! = 24$. Therefore

$$|R_n(t)| \leqslant \frac{24}{3^5} \cdot 1 \cdot \frac{1}{24} = \frac{1}{3^5} < 0.0042 \,,$$

and we may accordingly say that the error committed by using $P_3(t)$ [which is $(t^2 + 4t + 16)/64$] in place of $1/(4 - t)$ over the interval from -1 to $+1$ will never exceed 0.0042. For many practical purposes, an error of this size would be negligibly small.

One observation that should be made in connection with this example is that the estimate for the maximum error would be smaller still if the interval from T_1 to T_2 were shorter: for instance, suppose now that $T_1 = -\frac{1}{4}$, $T_2 = +\frac{1}{4}$, the other data being as before. On this interval, the smallest value of $4 - t$ is 3.75, so that the largest value of $f^{(4)}(t)$ is $24/(3.75)^5$. At the same time, the largest possible value of $(t - t_0)^4$ on this interval is $\frac{1}{4}^4$. Therefore, when $-\frac{1}{4} \leqslant t \leqslant +\frac{1}{4}$,

$$|R_n(t)| \leqslant \frac{24}{3.75^5} \cdot \frac{1}{4^4} \cdot \frac{1}{24} \leqslant 0.00001.$$

This improvement is not an arithmetical accident; for the effect on (6.2) of contracting the interval will, in general, be this: the term $1/(n + 1)!$ will of course be unaltered, but the maximum possible value of $f^{(n+1)}(t')$ cannot be increased, and the maximum possible value of the factor $(t - t_0)^{n+1}$ will definitely decrease. The maximum possible value of $R_n(t)$ must therefore decrease. Roughly speaking,

(A) *for a fixed value of n, the shorter the interval, the better the approximation of $P_n(t)$ to $f(t)$.*

This remark is a companion to a remark made in connection with Example 5.1, which may be stated in the form:

(B) *for a fixed interval, the larger the value of n, the better the approximation of $P_n(t)$ to $f(t)$.*

Both of these statements are subject to qualifications, but they express the normal state of affairs.

EXERCISES

6.1. Find a value of t' between t_0 and t for which (6.3) is true if $f(t) = 1 + t^3$, $t_0 = 1$, $t = 3$, and $n = 1$.

6.2. The special case of Taylor's Theorem that occurs when $n = 0$ is called the *Mean-Value Theorem for Derivatives*. Can you find a geometrical interpretation for this theorem?

6.3. Estimate the error committed by approximating $f(t) = 1/t$ by $P_2(t)$ on the interval $1 \leqslant t \leqslant 3$, where $t_0 = 2$.

6.4. Use the equation (6.2) to obtain yet another proof (cf. Exercise 5.2) of the fact that if $f(t)$ is a polynomial of degree 2 or less, then $P_2(t) \equiv f(t)$.

7. The Taylor Series. We have not yet made any use of a certain interesting property of the polynomials $P_n(t)$, namely, that for a given function $f(t)$, if $m > n$ then $P_m(t)$ may be obtained from $P_n(t)$ by merely appending a suitable number $(m - n)$ of new terms without altering those already occurring in $P_n(t)$; the same terms occur in all of the polynomials $P_n(t)$, the difference lying merely in how many are used in each case. This fact is illustrated, for instance, by the entries in Table 5.1. From another point of view, one may describe this phenomenon by saying that $P_n(t)$ is equal to the sum of the first $n + 1$ terms in the schematic expression

$$(7.1) \quad f(t_0) + f'(t_0)(t - t_0) + \tfrac{1}{2}f''(t_0)(t - t_0)^2 + \ldots$$
$$+ f^{(n)}(t_0)\frac{(t - t_0)^n}{n!} + f^{(n+1)}(t_0)\frac{(t - t_0)^{n+1}}{(n + 1)!} + \ldots,$$

where the last three dots indicate that this "sum" does not break off but continues indefinitely, so as to contain all terms of the form

$$f^{(n)}(t_0)\frac{(t - t_0)^n}{n!}, \quad (n = 0, 1, 2, \ldots) .$$

Actually, (7.1) is not a sum in the strict sense at all, even though it is obtained by writing plus signs between definite terms; for there are infinitely many of these terms, and the postulates of algebra apply to "sums" of infinitely many terms neither in intention nor in effect. It should also be remarked that (7.1) has meaning only if all of the derivatives $f^{(n)}(t_0)$ exist; we shall assume that this is the case throughout this section.

The expression (7.1) is called the *Taylor series of* $f(t)$ *at* t_0. (If $t_0 = 0$, the series assumes the especially simple form

$$f(0) + f'(0)\, t + \tfrac{1}{2}f''(0)\, t^2 + \ldots + f^{(n)}(0)\frac{t^n}{n!} + \ldots;$$

this is sometimes called the *Maclaurin series* of $f(t)$.)

On the basis of the discussion in Sections 5 and 6, we may be sure that the Taylor series (7.1) is likely to be useful only if the polynomials $P_n(t)$ do in fact provide good approximations to $f(t)$, at least for all values of t in some interval containing t_0 or, as we shall say, in some *neighborhood* of t_0. When this happens—when, more precisely, the approximation of $P_n(t)$ to $f(t)$ in some neighborhood of t_0 can be made as good as one wishes by taking n sufficiently large—then the expression (7.1) represents $f(t)$ in a stronger sense than we have yet indicated. To make this clearer, it is convenient to introduce a new notion.

We shall denote by t_1 a certain value of t. To say that $P_n(t)$ is a good approximation to $f(t)$ at t_1 is to say that the quantity $f(t_1) - P_n(t_1)$ is near zero; and to say that the approximation of $P_n(t)$ to $f(t)$ at t_1 can be made as good as one wishes by taking n sufficiently large is to say that

$$f(t_1) - P_n(t_1) \to 0$$

as $n \to \infty$, or, by (6.1), that

$$(7.2) \quad R_n(t_1) \to 0 \text{ as } n \to \infty .$$

When this happens, the Taylor series is said to *converge* to $f(t)$ at t_1. Another way of writing (7.2) is

$$(7.3) \quad P_n(t_1) \to f(t_1) \text{ as } n \to \infty .$$

This means that adding up more and more terms of (7.1) (with t replaced by t_1) gets one closer and closer to $f(t_1)$. Consequently, in a certain sense which is being implicitly defined at the moment, adding *all* of the terms of (7.1) gives $f(t_1)$ exactly. In this sense, we may write

$$(7.4) \quad f(t) = f(t_0) + f'(t_0)(t - t_0) + \ldots + f^{(n)}(t_0)\frac{(t - t_0)^n}{n!} + \ldots,$$

for those values of t for which the Taylor series converges. Approximating $f(t)$ by $P_n(t)$ in this case may be regarded as throwing away all but the first $n + 1$ terms on the right side of the "equation" (7.4); and this process, because of (7.2), will introduce only a small error if n is large.

But all this raises a new question: For what values of t will the Taylor series of a given function converge? The basic theorem in this connection is:

Theorem 7.1. For a given function $f(t)$ and a given t_0 either (a) the Taylor series of $f(t)$ converges for all values of t or (b) there exists a nonnegative number T such that the Taylor series of $f(t)$ converges for all values of t between $t_0 - T$ and $t_0 + T$ and fails to converge (diverges) for all values of t outside this interval. In case (b), the series may converge or diverge at the values $t_0 - T$ and $t_0 + T$ themselves.

The number T is called the *radius of convergence*. The worst possibility is case (b) with $T = 0$; then the interval on which the Taylor series converges (*the interval of convergence*) reduces to the single point t_0. The Taylor series (7.1) will always converge at t_0, for $P_n(t_0) = f(t_0)$ for all values of n (cf. [5.9] and [7.3]). The most favorable possibility is of course case (a).

There exists a variety of methods for determining the value of the radius of convergence T once $f(t)$ and t_0 have been given. Sometimes it is possible to accomplish this using the formula (6.2) for the remainder function; sometimes it is necessary to resort to more sensitive methods. The same may be said for the problem of identifying case (a) when it occurs. We shall not discuss any of these methods; nor shall we prove Theorem 7.1, for in order to prove it we would be compelled to enter into a somewhat lengthy digression on the theory of infinite series in general.

Our applications of these ideas in Part I are on a level much lower than that we have now reached, and it may be worth while to describe them in a general way at this point. What we do is simply to use one of the polynomials $P_n(t)$ (usually $n = 0, 1,$ or 2) as a substitute for $f(t)$ in some neighborhood of a point t_0; we call $P_0(t)$ the "constant part," $P_1(t)$ the "linear part," etc., of the Taylor series of $f(t)$ (or of $f(t)$ itself) at t_0. Actually, of course, it is unnecessary to refer to the Taylor series in situations of this kind. Our purposes in referring to it are to unify the mode of expression and to remind the reader of the (frequently tacit and sometimes unnecessary) assumption that the Taylor series of $f(t)$ does converge for the values of t in question, so that $P_0(t)$, etc., are legitimate approximations to $f(t)$. Generally the interval of values of t for which the approximation is made is so short that (in accordance with the remark (A) of Section 6) $P_1(t)$ or at worst $P_2(t)$ is quite adequate. The discussion in this section is intended mainly to give some insight into this procedure.

EXERCISES

7.1. Find the first four terms of the Maclaurin series for each of the following functions. If possible, find a general formula for the coefficient of t^n in the series.

(a) $f(t) = t^2$,   (b) $f(t) = \dfrac{1}{1+t}$,   (c) $f(t) = \dfrac{1-t}{1+t}$.

7.2. Find the first four terms of the Taylor series for each of the following functions, using the indicated value of t_0.

a) $f(t) = t^3 + 1$, $t_0 = 1$.

b) $f(t) = \dfrac{t}{1+t^2}$, $t_0 = 24$.

c) $f(t) = \dfrac{1}{t}$, $t_0 = -2$.

7.3. If a Taylor series converging to a certain function $f(t)$ happens to terminate (i.e., if all terms beyond a certain one are zero), then $f(t)$ must be a polynomial. Prove this statement carefully. Is the converse statement true?

7.4. Find the linear part at $t_0 = 2$ of each of the functions in Exercise 4.1, Chapter Nine.

7.5. How would you interpret graphically the fact that the linear part of the Taylor series of a function at a point is a constant?

8. Taylor Series for Functions of Several Variables. The concepts developed in the last three sections can be extended to apply to a function of several independent variables. As one might expect, however, the details are somewhat more difficult; and in fact there are complications more difficult than one might expect. We shall therefore confine ourselves to the problem of finding the polynomials corresponding to the polynomials $P_1(t)$ and $P_2(t)$ of Section 6, and then sketch further developments very briefly.

Here again the problem is that of finding a polynomial which approximates the given function at a certain point in the sense that corresponding derivatives of orders $0, 1, \ldots, n$ of the given function and of the polynomial have the same values at that point. Since several independent variables are involved, these derivatives are necessarily *partial* derivatives. It will actually simplify matters to make no assumption about the number of independent variables, and to denote them by t_i $(i = 1, 2, \ldots, r)$.

The first problem is that of finding a polynomial whose value and the values of whose derivatives of the first order agree with those of $f(t_1, t_2, \ldots, t_r)$ at a given point $(\bar{t}_1, \bar{t}_2, \ldots, \bar{t}_r)$. In view of the results in the case of one variable, one expects that a first-degree polynomial should be good enough; and so it is. The general first-degree polynomial in the variables t_i may be written in the form

$$(8.1) \quad P(t_1, t_2, \ldots, t_r) = a + \sum_{i=1}^{r} b_i(t_i - \bar{t}_i),$$

where a and the coefficients b_i are constants. If this function is differentiated with respect to any one of the variables t_i, say t_p, the result is

$$(8.2) \quad \frac{\partial P}{\partial t_p} = b_p,$$

since all but one of the terms on the right side of (8.1) are independent of t_p, and the derivative of that term [namely, $b_p(t_p - \bar{t}_p)$] is b_p. However, we are requiring that when $t_i = \bar{t}_i$ $(i = 1, 2, \ldots, r)$,

$$(8.3) \quad \frac{\partial P}{\partial t_p} = \frac{\partial f}{\partial t_p};$$

thus, by (8.2), we are forced to set

$$(8.4) \quad b_i = \frac{\partial f}{\partial t_i},$$

the derivative being evaluated for $t_i = \bar{t}_i$ $(i = 1, 2, \ldots, r)$.

At the same time, it is demanded that the values of the two functions f and P themselves should coincide at $(\bar{t}_1, \bar{t}_2, \ldots, \bar{t}_r)$; and this gives, upon replacing all t_i's by $\bar{t}_i$'s in (8.1),

$$(8.5) \quad a = f(\bar{t}_1, \bar{t}_2, \ldots, \bar{t}_r).$$

Formulas (8.2) and (8.4) embody the solution of this first problem; and using them to eliminate a and the b_i's from (8.1) we find that the desired polynomial P_1 is given by

$$(8.6) \quad P_1(t_1, t_2, \ldots, t_r) = f(\bar{t}_1, \bar{t}_2, \ldots, \bar{t}_r) + \sum_{i=1}^{r} \frac{\partial f}{\partial t_i}(t_i - \bar{t}_i),$$

the derivatives being evaluated at $(\bar{t}_1, \bar{t}_2, \ldots, \bar{t}_r)$. Needless to say, the problem can be solved only if these derivatives exist.

The derivation of the analogous formula for P_2 runs along the same lines, but has a bit more to it. The most general polynomial of degree 2 in the variables t_i may be written

$$(8.7) \quad P(t_1, t_2, \ldots, t_r) = a + \sum_{i=1}^{r} b_i(t_i - \bar{t}_i) + \sum_{j=1}^{r}\sum_{i=1}^{r} c_{ij}(t_i - \bar{t}_i)(t_j - \bar{t}_j),$$

where a, the b_i's, and the c_{ij}'s are all constants. Moreover, it may be assumed that

$$(8.8) \quad c_{ij} = c_{ji} \ (i, j = 1, 2, \ldots, r)$$

—see Chapter Eleven, Section 7. If P and f are to have the same value at $(\bar{t}_1, \bar{t}_2, \ldots, \bar{t}_r)$, then just as before the constant a must be given by formula (8.5). Differentiation of (8.7) by any one of the t_i's, say t_p, gives

$$(8.9) \quad \frac{\partial P}{\partial t_p} = b_p + 2\sum_{j=1}^{r} c_{pj}(t_j - \bar{t}_j).$$

The details of this differentiation, which uses (8.8) and involves a certain amount of cunning, will be left to the reader (Exercise 8.2). We are again requiring that (8.3) be true when $t_i = \bar{t}_i$ $(i = 1, 2, \ldots, r)$; substituting these values in (8.9) accordingly gives $b_p = \partial f/\partial t_p$ (with the derivative calculated at the given point), but since the index p is arbitrary we may call it i, and this takes us back to (8.4).

To find the c_{ij}'s, first differentiate both sides of (8.9) with respect to t_q, where q is any value of the index j; as in the derivation of (8.2), this gives

$$\frac{\partial^2 P}{\partial t_p \partial t_q} = 2c_{pq};$$

but since it is required that $\partial^2 P/\partial t_p \partial t_q = \partial^2 f/\partial t_p \partial t_q$ at the given point, this implies that $c_{pq} = \frac{1}{2}\partial^2 f/\partial t_p \partial t_q$; or, again relabeling the indices,

$$\mathbf{?} \quad (8.10) \quad c_{ij} = \frac{1}{2}\frac{\partial^2 f}{\partial t_i \partial t_j}.$$

Formulas (8.4), (8.5), and (8.10) together yield all of the coefficients in (8.7), and the problem of finding P_2 is solved.

Example 8.1. Take $f(t_1, t_2) = t_1^2 + 2t_1 t_2 + 2t_2^2$, $\bar{t}_1 = 1$, $\bar{t}_2 = -1$. What is P_2 in this case? Since f is itself a polynomial of degree 2, P_2 should be identically equal to f, being nothing but f written in the form (8.7). First, by (8.5), $a = f(1, -1) = 1$. The needed partial derivatives are

$$\frac{\partial f}{\partial t_1} = 2(t_1 + t_2), \qquad\qquad \frac{\partial f}{\partial t_2} = 2(t_1 + 2t_2),$$

$$\frac{\partial^2 f}{\partial t_1^2} = 2, \qquad\qquad \frac{\partial^2 f}{\partial t_2^2} = 4,$$

$$\frac{\partial^2 f}{\partial t_1 \partial t_2} = \frac{\partial^2 f}{\partial t_2 \partial t_1} = 2.$$

Thus, by (8.4) and (8.10), we have

$$b_1 = 0 , \quad b_2 = -2 , \quad c_{11} = 1 , \quad c_{22} = 2 , \quad c_{12} = c_{21} = 1 ,$$

and

$$P_2(t_1,t_2) = 1 - 2(t_2 + 1) + (t_1 - 1)^2 + (t_1 - 1)(t_2 + 1)$$
$$+ (t_2 + 1)(t_1 - 1) + 2(t_2 + 1)^2 .$$

Simplification of this expression will show that it is identical with f. At the same time, P_1 is given by the first two terms of P_2.

A comparison of the expressions we have found for P_1 and P_2, especially if one keeps in mind the matching expressions for the one-variable case, will suggest what terms should be added to P_2 in order to obtain P_3, and so on. In fact, P_3 will be obtained from the right side of (8.7) if one adds on the triple sum

$$(8.11) \qquad \sum_{k=1}^{r} \sum_{j=1}^{r} \sum_{i=1}^{r} d_{ijk}(t_i - \bar{t}_i)(t_j - \bar{t}_j)(t_k - \bar{t}_k) ,$$

where

$$d_{ijk} = \frac{1}{3!} \frac{\partial^3 f}{\partial t_i \partial t_j \partial t_k} ,$$

the derivative being evaluated in the usual way. The verification of this fact is a matter of straightforward but somewhat lengthy calculation. P_4 could then be obtained by adding a further set of terms analogous to (8.11), but involving four indices, four summations, fourth derivatives, and a factor $1/4!$ instead of the $1/3!$. As long as the derivatives last, the process can be continued indefinitely and yields all of the approximating polynomials P_n. Since obtaining any one of these polynomials from its predecessor is merely a matter of adding on further terms of a new kind, one can write down a schematic expression analogous to (7.1) which gives P_n if all terms beyond a certain point are dropped. This is the Taylor series for the given function at the given point, and it is the subject of a substantial theory: one can investigate questions of convergence, ways of writing the remainder, and so on.

As in Section 7, we may call P_1 the *linear part*, P_2 the *quadratic part* of the Taylor series of the given function at the given point, or merely of the function itself.

EXERCISES

8.1. Write out the general expression for P_2 if f is a function of the two variables s and t; do not use summation signs.

8.2. Carry out the differentiation that leads from (8.7) to (8.9), explaining each step.

8.3. Find P_1 and P_2 in each case:

a) $f(t_1, t_2) = \dfrac{1}{t_1 + t_2}$, $\bar{t}_1 = \bar{t}_2 = 1$.

b) $f(t_1, t_2) = t_1 + t_2{}^3$, $\bar{t}_1 = \bar{t}_2 = 0$.

c) $f(t_1, t_2, t_3) = t_1 t_2 t_3$, $\bar{t}_1 = 0$, $\bar{t}_2 = -1$, $\bar{t}_3 = 1$.

SUGGESTIONS FOR FURTHER READING

All of the books listed in the "Suggestions for Further Reading" at the end of Chapter Nine may again be recommended as sources of additional information on the topics discussed in this chapter. A relatively simple proof of the Weierstrass Approximation Theorem (Section 5) is given in E. W. Hobson, *The Theory of Functions of a Real Variable* (2d ed.; New York: Cambridge University Press, 1926), Vol. II, pp. 228–29.

Chapter Eleven

QUADRATIC FORMS AND
DETERMINANTS

THE calculus, with all its extensions and applications, is temporarily abandoned in this chapter, where a return is made to the realm of algebra and descriptions are given of some of the properties and applications of the very special types of polynomials in several variables whose names appear in the title above. Quadratic forms and determinants have a long and honorable history in both pure and applied mathematics, and the reader will find them put to good use not only at many points in Part I but also in later chapters of this Part. They are not quite indispensable; but they enable one to arrive at, state, and apply such a large number of mathematical results in such a convenient way that they are used as a matter of course throughout applied mathematics and, in particular, throughout mathematical economics.

1. Forms in General. The notion of a polynomial has already been discussed at some length in Chapter Eight, Section 4. It will be recalled that a polynomial is a sum of monomials, a monomial being defined as a product of variables (each raised to some power which uses a positive whole number as the exponent) with a constant coefficient. The *degree* of a monomial is the sum of the exponents appearing in its variable factors, and the highest degree found among the monomials occurring in a certain polynomial is defined to be the degree of that polynomial. In general, of course, a polynomial may contain monomials of various degrees; but if all of the monomials happen to have the same degree, the polynomial is said to be a *form*. The degree common to the monomial terms of a form is naturally called the *degree of the form*.[1]

Any form in a single variable (say t) may be written in the form at^n, where a is a constant coefficient and n is a positive integer, the degree of the form. Because of the extreme simplicity of this kind of form, one may rightly expect that the theory of forms will become interesting only when several variables are involved. We shall first briefly consider forms of degrees zero and one.

---

[1] We shall deal here only with *real* forms—forms all of whose coefficients are real numbers, and in which the variables are understood to take on only real values.

Since a constant by itself is regarded as a monomial of degree zero (and there are no other monomials of degree zero), a form of degree zero will be a sum of constants or, what comes to the same thing, a constant alone. The number 0 by itself is not regarded as a form.[2]

A monomial of degree one being the product of a constant and a variable, a form of degree one is an expression of the type

$$at + bu + \ldots + kw,$$

where $a, b, \ldots, k$ are constants (not all zero) and $t, u, \ldots, w$ are variables. This is simply a linear polynomial in which the constant term is zero; forms of this kind are accordingly called *linear* forms.

Next in order of complexity (as measured by the degree) come the forms of degree two or, as they are more commonly called, *quadratic* forms. The general quadratic forms in one and two variables are, respectively, at^2 ($a \neq 0$) and $at^2 + btu + cu^2$, where $a, b,$ and c again stand for constants (not all of which are zero) and t and u are variables. When more than two variables are involved, it is convenient to resort to the subscript notation. If the variables are denoted by $t_1, t_2, \ldots, t_n$, then the general quadratic form in these variables may be written

$$(1.1) \quad a_{11}t_1^2 + a_{12}t_1t_2 + \ldots + a_{nn}t_n^2 = \sum_{i=1}^{n} \sum_{j=1}^{n} a_{ij}t_it_j,$$

where the symbols a_{ij} stand for the coefficients, at least one of which should be different from zero. Some of the terms in (1.1) may be combined; for example, the terms $a_{12}t_1t_2$ and $a_{21}t_2t_1$, since they contain the same variables in essentially the same way, might be combined and written as a single term. Nevertheless, the superficially more prolix notation in (1.1) is preferable.[3]

For the sake of simplicity, we shall write merely $\Sigma_{ij}a_{ij}t_it_j$ for the double sum in (1.1). It is always to be understood that the sum represented by such a symbol is that of the n^2 terms obtained by letting both indices range through all of the integers from 1 to n inclusive.

Forms of higher degree may be written in similar ways. For example, the general form of degree four in n variables may be written

$$\sum_{i=1}^{n} \sum_{j=1}^{n} \sum_{k=1}^{n} \sum_{m=1}^{n} a_{ijkm}t_it_jt_kt_m,$$

or more simply

$$\Sigma_{ijkm}a_{ijkm}t_it_jt_kt_m.$$

---

[2] Some writers prefer to regard 0 as a form which may be assigned any degree, on the ground that 0 may always be written $0t^n$.

[3] In discussions of quadratic forms it is customary to assume that $a_{ij} = a_{ji}$ for all values of the subscripts, i.e., that the quadratic form is *symmetrical*, and this assumption is not so restrictive as it may seem (see Section 7); but in view of certain applications in Part I no such assumption will be made here.

Before proceeding to the particular aspects of forms with which we shall be most concerned, we shall dignify some elementary propositions about forms by listing them as theorems.

Theorem 1.1.   If each variable t_i in a form is multiplied by the same constant λ, the effect is the same as that obtained by multiplying the whole form by λ^d, where d is the degree of the form.

PROOF: When each t_i is multiplied by λ, each monomial term in the form acquires d factors λ; and these may be combined and factored out from the whole polynomial. For example,

$$a(\lambda t)^2 + b(\lambda t)(\lambda u) + c(\lambda u)^2 = a\lambda^2 t^2 + b\lambda^2 tu + c\lambda^2 u^2 = \lambda^2(at^2 + btu + cu^2) .$$

A function of the variables t_i which has the property described in Theorem 1.1 is said to be *homogeneous;* i.e., the function $f(t_1, t_2, \ldots, t_n)$ is homogeneous if there exists a number d (the *degree* of homogeneity) such that

$$f(\lambda t_1, \lambda t_2, \ldots, \lambda t_n) = \lambda^d f(t_1, t_2, \ldots, t_n)$$

is an identity in the variables $t_1, t_2, \ldots, t_n$, and λ.

There is a converse to Theorem 1.1 (Theorem 1.2) which we shall not prove.

Theorem 1.2.   A polynomial which is homogeneous is a form.

As a corollary to Theorem 1.1 (putting $\lambda = 0$), or simply by direct inspection, we have Theorem 1.3.

Theorem 1.3.   The value of a form of positive degree is zero when all of the variables are replaced by zero.

Using Theorems 1.1 and 1.2 together, or by using the definition directly, one can easily prove Theorem 1.4.

Theorem 1.4.   The sum or difference of two forms of the same degree is a form of that degree (or zero); the product of two forms of degrees d_1 and d_2, respectively, is a form of degree $d_1 + d_2$.

Finally, since forms are polynomials and polynomials are continuous functions, we have Theorem 1.5.

Theorem 1.5.   Forms are continuous for all values of the variables.

EXERCISES

1.1. Without using subscripts, write out in full a general expression for a form of degree 3 in two variables.

1.2. Determine which of the following polynomials are forms, and find the degree of each form.
   a) $t^2 - 2$
   b) $(t + u)^2 - (t - u)^2$
   c) $t^3 u^3 v^3 + t^2 u^2 v^2 (t^3 + u^3 + v^3)$
   d) $4tu - (t + u)$

1.3. For what value or values of the constants a and b is $u(au + b) - bu^2$ a form?

1.4. Prove that if $f(t,u)$ is a form of degree d, then

$$\frac{\partial f}{\partial t}t + \frac{\partial f}{\partial u}u = d \cdot f.$$

(Hint: start by using Theorem 1.1 and differentiation with respect to λ.)

1.5. Prove the first part of Theorem 1.4.

2. Definiteness, Indefiniteness, and Semidefiniteness. Theorem 1.3 asserts that the result of replacing all of the variables in any nonconstant form by zero is to get zero. Naturally, there may be other values of the variables which lead to the same result; e.g., the value of the linear form $x - y$ is zero whenever $x = y$. A form for which this does not happen, i.e., a form which assumes the value zero only when all of the variables have the value zero, is said to be *definite*. A definite form cannot assume both positive and negative values; for if it did, say if it were positive at $(t_1', t_2', \ldots, t_n')$ and negative at $(t_1'', t_2'', \ldots, t_n'')$, then because of the continuity of the form there would necessarily be some point "between" these two—a point that could always be chosen not to be $(0, 0, \ldots, 0)$—at which the form would be zero, and the condition for definiteness would be contradicted. Thus definite forms may be classified as positive and negative definite forms: a *positive definite* form is one which assumes positive values for all values of the variables but $(0, 0, \ldots, 0)$, while a *negative definite* form is one which assumes negative values for all values of the variables other than $(0, 0, \ldots, 0)$. For example, $t^2 + u^2$ is a positive definite form in the two variables t and u, while $-t^2 - u^2$ is negative definite.

A form (like $t^2 - tu$, say) which may assume both positive and negative values is said to be *indefinite*.

There is a third possibility intermediate between definiteness and indefiniteness. Conceivably, a form may assume no negative values (thus failing to be indefinite) but nevertheless assume the value zero for values of the variables other than $(0, 0, \ldots, 0)$ (thus failing to be definite). A form of this kind is called a *semidefinite*, or more completely a *positive semidefinite* form. Similarly, a *negative semidefinite* form is one which assumes no positive values but is not definite.

Example 2.1. That the logical category of semidefinite forms is not empty is shown by the example of the quadratic form $t^2 - 2tu + u^2$. This form, which may also be written as $(t - u)^2$, clearly assumes no negative values, but it becomes zero whenever $t = u$.

The five types of forms just defined are mutually exclusive and exhaustive: any given form must be either (positive or negative) definite, indefinite, or (positive or negative) semidefinite. Moreover, there do exist forms of all five types, as the examples mentioned above show. Indeed, these examples show that there are *quadratic* forms of all five types. That the same cannot be said for forms of all degrees follows from the next theorem.

Theorem 2.1. Every form of odd degree is indefinite.

PROOF: Let the form be denoted simply by $f(t_1, t_2, \ldots, t_n)$. Since the form (by definition) is not identically zero, there exists a set of values of the variables, say $(\bar{l}_1, \bar{l}_2, \ldots, \bar{l}_n)$, for which the form attains a nonzero value:

$$f(\bar{l}_1,\bar{l}_2, \ldots ,\bar{l}_n) = c \neq 0 .$$

But then, by Theorem 1.1 (with $\lambda = -1$),

$$f(-\bar{l}_1,-\bar{l}_2, \ldots ,-\bar{l}_n) = (-1)^d c = -c ,$$

d being the (odd) degree of the form. The form thus has both of the numbers c and $-c$ in its range, and since one must be positive while the other is negative, the form is indefinite.

Theorem 2.2. *If a form of degree d is positive definite, all of the terms involving dth powers of the variables must have positive coefficients; if the form is negative definite, all of these coefficients must be negative.*

PROOF: In proving this theorem we shall refer to quadratic forms only. (By Theorem 2.1, d is necessarily even, so $d = 2$ is the simplest case beyond constant forms $[d = 0]$.) If the value 0 is assigned to all of the variables but l_r ($1 \leqslant r \leqslant n$) and the value 1 is assigned to l_r, the form $\Sigma_{ij} a_{ij} l_i l_j$ assumes the value a_{rr}. Thus all of the coefficients of the "square" terms lie in the range of the form, and the form cannot be positive definite unless all of these numbers are positive, or negative definite unless they are all negative.

That the condition given in Theorem 2.2 is not *sufficient* for definiteness, even when forms of odd degree are excluded (as they must be, by Theorem 2.1), is shown by the quadratic form of Example 2.1, which is not definite even though both square terms have positive coefficients.

EXERCISES

2.1. Can there be such a thing as an indefinite form of degree zero? Explain your answer.

2.2. Determine of each of the following forms whether it is positive definite, negative definite, indefinite, positive semidefinite, or negative semidefinite:

    a) $2t^2$
    b) $t^2 + 2tu + u^2$
    c) $-(t - u - v)^2$
    d) $9,000t^2 - u^2$
    e) $t^3 + u^3 + v^3 - 3tuv$
    f) $t^4 + 2t^2 u^2 + u^4$
    g) $t^4 + 2t^2 u^2 - u^4$

2.3. Prove that all of the coefficients of terms involving dth powers of the variables in a positive semidefinite form of degree d must be positive or zero.

3. The Quadratic Form $at^2 + btu + cu^2$. Theorems 2.1 and 2.2 provide necessary conditions for the definiteness of forms, but these conditions, as has been pointed out, are sufficient neither separately nor in combination. As a matter of fact, necessary and sufficient conditions for definiteness which are valid for forms of all degrees are not known. It is possible, nevertheless, to obtain very satisfactory criteria for the definiteness of *quadratic* forms. Most of these criteria are best expressed using determinants, so we shall postpone their description to the end of this chapter; but when only two variables are involved, one can easily discuss the matter without the use of determinants, and this we shall now do. The conclusions reached in this section have some intrinsic importance, and give a helpful foretaste of the more general conclusions to be described later.

It has already been pointed out that the general quadratic form in two variables may be written

$$(3.1) \quad at^2 + btu + cu^2 .$$

The relationship between this expression and the alternative (subscript) expression for the same type of form, $\Sigma_{ij}a_{ij}l_il_j$, is given by the equations:

$$(3.2) \quad t = t_1 , \quad u = t_2 , \quad a = a_{11} , \quad b = a_{12} + a_{21} , \quad c = a_{22} .$$

These formulas may be used to translate the results which we shall obtain for (3.1) into the subscript notation.

Theorem 3.1. If Δ is defined as the value of the expression $b^2 - 4ac$, then the quadratic form (3.1) is definite, indefinite, or semidefinite according as the number Δ is negative, positive, or zero.

PROOF: We shall assume first that $a \neq 0$. Then one may easily verify that

$$(3.3) \quad at^2 + btu + cu^2 = a\,(t + \frac{b}{2a}u)^2 + \frac{4ac - b^2}{4a}u^2 .$$

Now if $\Delta < 0$, $4ac - b^2$ is positive, and both coefficients on the right side of (3.3) have the same sign, namely that of a. Thus the whole quantity cannot be zero unless both u and $t + bu/2a$ are zero, which in turn happens if and only if t and u are both zero. Therefore the form is definite—in fact, positive or negative definite according as a (or c) is positive or negative.

When $\Delta > 0$, then $4ac - b^2$ is negative. If we let $t = 1$, $u = 0$, the form assumes the value a; but if we take $t = -b/2a$, $u = 1$, the first term on the right side of (3.3) vanishes and the form assumes the value $(4ac - b^2)/a$. Since this and the value a have opposite signs, the form must be indefinite.

Finally, when $\Delta = 0$, the form reduces to $a(t + bu/2a)^2$, and this quantity will always have the same sign as a unless $t + bu/2a = 0$, when the value of the form will be zero. Since the equation $t + bu/2a = 0$ has solutions other than $t = u = 0$, the form must be semidefinite.

It remains to consider what happens when $a = 0$. In this case, the identity (3.3) cannot be used, but the desired conclusions can be arrived at more directly. When $a = 0$, $\Delta = b^2$, so the case $\Delta < 0$ can never occur. If $\Delta > 0$ (i.e., $b \neq 0$), the form reduces to $btu + cu^2$, or $(bt + cu)u$. When u is assigned any nonzero value, this expression will have values of one sign if $t > -cu/b$, of the other if $t < -cu/b$. The form is therefore indefinite. On the other hand, when $\Delta = 0$, then $b = 0$, and so $c \neq 0$ (for not all of the coefficients a, b, and c can be zero); the form reduces to cu^2 which, *regarded as a form in both variables t and u*, is clearly semidefinite.

The quantity Δ will be recognized as the "discriminant" of the equation $ax^2 + bx + c = 0$; and its properties as such may be used to obtain an alternative proof of Theorem 3.1.

Once Theorem 3.1 reveals that a particular form $at^2 + btu + cu^2$ is definite, Theorem 2.2 may be used to determine whether it is positive or negative definite; it is positive definite if a and c are both positive, negative definite if they are both negative. That they must have the same sign when the form is definite follows not only from Theorem 2.2 but also from Theorem 3.1, for in the contrary case the quantity $\Delta = b^2 - 4ac$ is necessarily positive or zero, and the form cannot be definite.

Example 3.1. What kind of form is $3t^2 - 5tu + 3u^2$? For this form, $\Delta = (-5)^2 - 4 \cdot 3 \cdot 3 = -11 < 0$; therefore the form is definite. Since the coefficients of both square terms are positive, the form must be *positive* definite.

EXERCISES

3.1. Apply the criterion of Theorem 3.1 to the quadratic forms (a), (b), and (d) of Exercise 2.2, and to that of Example 2.1.

3.2. Using Theorem 3.1, determine whether each of the following forms is definite, indefinite, or semidefinite:

a) $2t^2 - tu + 5u^2$
b) $t^2 + tu - u^2$
c) $t^2 - 4tu + 4u^2$
d) $3t^2 - 4tu + u^2$

3.3. Show that every quadratic form of the type $t^2 + tu + cu^2$, where $c < 0$, is indefinite.

3.4. Write a discussion parallel to that of the last paragraph of this section but dealing with *semidefinite* forms.

4. *Determinants.* Most of the rest of this chapter is concerned, directly or indirectly, with the problem of solving a system of linear equations (cf. Chapter Eight, Sections 5 and 6). Since the number of unknowns involved in a system of this kind when the system arises in economic theory is frequently very large, the more or less *ad hoc* methods of elimination, substitution, etc., which are often taught for the cases in which there are only two or three unknowns are thoroughly inadequate. A general and unified view of the subject requires the use of the notion of determinants; and although the usefulness of this notion in explicitly computing the solutions of given systems is often exaggerated, its value at the theoretical level is immense. In this section and the next determinants are defined, and their most fundamental properties are derived. Then, in Section 6, we shall return to the study of systems of linear equations, where it will be possible for us to state and prove the important "Cramer's Rule" for solving them, and to discuss some related ideas which it is often convenient to be able to use. Finally, in Section 7, we shall apply the determinant concept in stating general criteria for the definiteness of quadratic forms in any number of variables.

We begin by denoting n^2 variables by u_{ij}, where the indices i and j range from 1 to n inclusive. The corresponding determinant (the *determinant of order n*) is a certain form of degree n in these variables with the property that each coefficient in the form is either -1, 0, or $+1$. Which of these numbers is associated with any particular term is given by the following pair of rules:

1. If, among the variable factors in the term, any value of the index i occurs more than once, the coefficient is zero; and likewise for the subscript j. In particular, any term containing any power higher than the first of any variable u_{ij} receives a zero coefficient. From this it follows that each term with a nonzero coefficient in the determinant contains n different variables u_{ij} such that each index takes on each of its possible values $(1, 2, \ldots, n)$ exactly once.

2. In any such term, let the variables be written in order according to the first index:

$$(4.1) \quad u_{1j_1}u_{2j_2} \ldots u_{nj_n} ,$$

where $j_1, j_2, \ldots, j_n$ are the integers $1, 2, \ldots, n$ in some order. Whenever one of the subscripts j_k is larger than one following it in this order, an *inversion* is said to occur. If the number of inversions occurring in (4.1) is even, the term receives the coefficient $+1$; if odd, -1.

Example 4.1. In the determinant of order 5, what coefficient belongs to the term containing the variables

$$u_{23}u_{32}u_{41}u_{14}u_{55} ?$$

Each value of each index occurs just once; so the coefficient is not zero. If the factors are rearranged in order relative to the first index, the above product becomes

$$u_{14}u_{23}u_{32}u_{41}u_{55} .$$

Here we find six inversions among the second indices: 4 before 3, 2, and 1; 3 before 2 and 1; and 2 before 1. Six being an even number, the correct coefficient is $+1$.

The conventional symbol for the determinant of order n is obtained by writing the variables in a square array and then bordering the whole by a pair of vertical straight lines. For example,

$$(4.2) \quad \begin{vmatrix} u_{11} & u_{12} & u_{13} \\ u_{21} & u_{22} & u_{23} \\ u_{31} & u_{32} & u_{33} \end{vmatrix}$$

stands for the determinant of order 3. Notice that the variables (or *elements* of the determinant, as they are usually called) are arranged so that the first index indicates the *row* (as numbered from top to bottom) in which an element occurs, while the second indicates the *column* (as numbered from left to right). This system is used for determinants of all orders.

The notation (4.2) is extremely convenient, as will soon appear; but an alternative notation which has the advantage of brevity is that of writing $det\ (u_{ij})$. When this notation is used, the order of the determinant is either left unspecified or is dictated by the context.

The application of the definition to determinants of orders one through three gives the formulas:

(4.3) $\quad |u_{11}| = u_{11}$

(4.4)
$$\begin{vmatrix} u_{11} & u_{12} \\ u_{21} & u_{22} \end{vmatrix} = u_{11}u_{22} - u_{12}u_{21}$$

(4.5)
$$\begin{vmatrix} u_{11} & u_{12} & u_{13} \\ u_{21} & u_{22} & u_{23} \\ u_{31} & u_{32} & u_{33} \end{vmatrix} = u_{11}u_{22}u_{33} + u_{12}u_{23}u_{31} + u_{13}u_{21}u_{32} \\ - u_{13}u_{22}u_{31} - u_{12}u_{21}u_{33} - u_{11}u_{23}u_{32}$$

If we were to extend this list of formulas to include determinants of higher orders, it would appear that the number of terms in the determinant of order n increases very rapidly as n increases. For example, the formula corresponding to (4.5) with $n = 6$ would have 720 terms on its right side, each with six factors! From the point of view of anyone who wishes to calculate the value of determinants for given values of the variables, this would be an intolerable situation were it not for the fact that there exist various short cuts which enable one to evaluate determinants much more rapidly than this would suggest. These methods are consequently very useful, and very much used, in practice; but a discussion of them here would not advance our argument. We therefore pass them by, making amends to the reader by using only determinants of orders two and three in the examples and exercises.

EXERCISES

4.1. In the determinant of order six, what coefficient should be assigned to the term containing each of the following sets of variables?

$a)\ \ u_{14}u_{23}u_{31}u_{42}u_{56}u_{65}$

$b)\ \ u_{13}u_{24}u_{15}u_{44}u_{31}u_{62}$

$c)\ \ u_{41}u_{35}u_{12}u_{63}u_{24}u_{56}$

4.2. If each number is taken to be the value of the variable in whose place it stands, find the value of the determinant of order three in each case:

$a)$
$$\begin{vmatrix} 2 & 1 & 3 \\ -1 & 1 & 0 \\ 2 & 0 & 4 \end{vmatrix}$$

b) $\begin{vmatrix} \frac{1}{2} & 1 & 2 \\ 2 & 0 & -1 \\ 1 & \frac{1}{4} & \frac{1}{4} \end{vmatrix}$

4.3. Regarded as a form is the determinant of order two definite, indefinite, or semi-definite?

5. Basic Properties of Determinants; the Laplace Expansion. In this section a number of basic theorems about determinants in general will be proved. From now on we shall regard the elements of a determinant as *numbers*, so that when we say "determinant" we shall actually mean the *value* of the determinant (of the appropriate order) when the variables are assigned certain numerical values.

Each of the next three theorems contains the phrase "row (or column)." Proofs will be given for rows only; the proofs for columns are strictly analogous.

Theorem 5.1. A determinant in which one row (or column) consists entirely of zeros has the value zero.

PROOF: Every term in the determinant contains exactly one element of the kth row, i.e., one element for which the value of the first subscript is k. Thus if all such elements are zero, all of the terms and therefore the determinant itself will have the value zero.

Theorem 5.2. If two rows (or columns) in a determinant are interchanged, the value of the determinant is multiplied by -1.

PROOF: Consider first the effect of interchanging two *adjacent* rows. The effect on each of the terms of the determinant, written with the variables in the order of the rows in which they occur, will be to interchange two adjacent factors, and thus to change by exactly one the number of inversions in the column subscripts; thus the sign attached to each term will be reversed, and the value of the whole determinant will in effect be multiplied by -1.

Now if the rows to be interchanged (which will be called the "upper" and "lower" rows for the moment) have some other rows between them, say p in number, the interchange may be carried out by interchanging adjacent pairs of rows $2p + 1$ times, as follows: first interchange the upper row with the one just below it, then with the one just below it in its new position, and so on, until the upper row is just above the lower one. This process clearly requires p interchanges of adjacent pairs of rows. Then the lower row should be interchanged with the one just above it (which was originally the upper row), and then the first p interchanges should be carried out in the reverse order. At the end of this process, the upper row is where the lower row originally was, the lower row is where the upper one originally was, and the intervening rows are in their original positions. Since each of these interchanges multiplies the value of the determinant by -1, according to the preceding paragraph, the determinant is multiplied by $(-1)^{2p+1}$, or simply -1, when the whole process is carried out.

Theorem 5.3. If corresponding elements of two rows (or columns) in a determinant have the same values, the value of the determinant is zero.

PROOF: Interchanging the two rows leaves the determinant unchanged, since they are identical; but by Theorem 5.2 interchanging these rows must change the sign of the value of the determinant. The value of the determinant must accordingly equal -1 times itself, and the only number which has this property is zero.

If, in the square array of numbers representing a determinant of order n, one strikes out all the elements in the ith row and the jth column, there results a square array of elements (with $n - 1$ rows and columns) which may itself be regarded as representing a certain determinant. This determinant is called the *minor* of the element u_{ij}—the element common to the deleted row and column. Thus, in the determinant

$$\begin{vmatrix} 1 & 3 & -5 \\ 2 & 6 & 4 \\ 1 & -3 & 2 \end{vmatrix}.$$

the minor of the element -3 is the determinant

$$\begin{vmatrix} 1 & -5 \\ 2 & 4 \end{vmatrix}.$$

Theorem 5.4. If $A = \det(a_{ij})$, and A_{ij} is the minor of a_{ij}, then the value of A is given by each of the following formulas:

$$(5.1) \quad A = \sum_{j=1}^{n} (-1)^{i+j} a_{ij} A_{ij} \quad (i = 1, \ldots, n),$$

$$(5.2) \quad A = \sum_{i=1}^{n} (-1)^{i+j} a_{ij} A_{ij} \quad (j = 1, \ldots, n).$$

In words, the formula (5.1) says this: take the jth element in the ith row, multiply it by the corresponding minor, and multiply the product by -1 if $i + j$ is odd.[4] The sum of all such products, one for each element of the specified row, is the value of the determinant. Formula (5.2) gives the analogous rule for columns. It should be noticed that these formulas enable one to reduce the problem of calculating the value of an nth-order determinant to that of calculating the values of n suitably chosen determinants of order $n - 1$. Formula (5.1) is said to give the *Laplace expansion of A by minors of the ith row;* formula (5.2), that of the jth column.

---

[4] The quantity $(-1)^{i+j} A_{ij}$ is called the *cofactor* of a_{ij}. The content of formula (5.1) may thus be expressed by saying that the sum of all the elements of the ith row, each multiplied by its cofactor, is the value of the determinant.

The proof of Theorem 5.4 is best taken in short steps, by using two lemmas:

Lemma A. The sum of all the terms of A containing the factor a_{11} is $a_{11}A_{11}$.

PROOF: Each such term is obtained by multiplying a_{11} by $n - 1$ elements of A, one from each row and column of A_{11}. The product of these elements is (except possibly for sign) one of the terms in A_{11}. Thus any term in A containing a_{11} is (except possibly for sign) a product of a_{11} with a term of A_{11}, and vice versa. However, the signs also agree; for writing a_{11} in front of a term from A_{11} gives a product with a_{11} in its natural place as regards both indices; the presence or absence of a_{11} has no influence on the number of inversions in the terms, and the associated signs are therefore the same. This completes the proof of Lemma A.

Lemma B.   The sum of all the terms of A containing the element a_{ij} is $(-1)^{i+j}a_{ij}A_{ij}$.

PROOF: By $i - 1$ successive interchanges of adjacent pairs of rows, a_{ij} can be brought into the first row; and then by $j - 1$ successive interchanges of adjacent pairs of columns this element can be brought into the upper left-hand corner of the determinant. The new determinant thus obtained, by Theorem 5.2, has the value $(-1)^{(i-1)+(j-1)}A$, or $(-1)^{i+j}A$. However, the sum of the terms containing a_{ij} in the new determinant, by Lemma A, is $a_{ij}M$, where M is the minor of a_{ij} in this determinant. Moreover, as one may easily see, M is exactly the same as A_{ij}, the minor of a_{ij} in the original determinant. Thus, since the terms in the old determinant are those in the new multiplied (or, equivalently, divided) by $(-1)^{i+j}$, we have the relation asserted.

The formula (5.1) can now be established in a few words: Each term in A contains exactly one factor from the ith row; therefore the sum of the terms of A (i.e., A itself) can be obtained by adding together the sums of terms containing the elements a_{ij} ($j = 1, \ldots, n$). This, by Lemma B, leads at once to (5.1). The formula (5.2) follows from Lemma B in the same way.

Theorem 5.5.   With the same notations as in Theorem 5.4,

$$(5.4) \quad \sum_{j=1}^{n} (-1)^{i+j}a_{kj}A_{ij} = 0 \quad if \quad k \neq i,$$

and

$$(5.5) \quad \sum_{i=1}^{n} (-1)^{i+j}a_{ik}A_{ij} = 0 \quad if \quad k \neq j.$$

In words, if one "expands" A by minors of some row (or column), but uses the elements of the wrong row (or column) as coefficients in the "expansion," the result is not A but zero. This follows at once from Theorem 5.4. For instance, by that theorem, the left side of (5.4) is exactly the Laplace expansion by minors of the kth row of the determinant A' obtained from A by replacing the ith row by the kth row. Such a determinant, however, has two identical rows and therefore, by Theorem 5.3, has the value zero.

Example 5.1. The Laplace expansion of

$$(5.5) \qquad \begin{vmatrix} 2 & 1 & 3 \\ 4 & -1 & 2 \\ 1 & -2 & -3 \end{vmatrix}$$

by minors of the second column is

$$-(1)\cdot \begin{vmatrix} 4 & 2 \\ 1 & -3 \end{vmatrix} + (-1)\cdot \begin{vmatrix} 2 & 3 \\ 1 & -3 \end{vmatrix} - (-2)\cdot \begin{vmatrix} 2 & 3 \\ 4 & 2 \end{vmatrix} .$$

The values of the second-order determinants appearing here (as computed using formula [4.4]) are -14, -9, and -8, respectively. The value of the determinant is therefore given by

$$-(1)\cdot(-14) + (-1)(-9) - (-2)(-8) = +7 .$$

Note that if the elements of another column are used with the same minors, the result is zero; for instance, with the first column,

$$-(2)(-14) + (4)(-9) - (1)(-8) = 0 .$$

EXERCISES

5.1. Obtain the value of each of the following determinants by forming the Laplace expansion by minors of the second row and check by recalculating the value using the Laplace expansion by minors of the first column:

$$(a) \begin{vmatrix} 2 & -2 & 30 \\ 1 & 0 & 5 \\ 4 & -1 & 2 \end{vmatrix} \quad (b) \begin{vmatrix} 1 & 2 & 3 \\ 4 & 5 & 6 \\ 7 & 8 & 9 \end{vmatrix} \quad (c) \begin{vmatrix} 1 & -1 & 3 & 2 \\ 0 & 4 & -2 & 0 \\ 2 & 1 & -1 & 6 \\ 0 & 0 & 5 & -3 \end{vmatrix}$$

5.2. On the basis of your experience with part (c) of Exercise 5.1, formulate a rule for choosing a row or column on which to base a Laplace expansion in order to obtain the value of the determinant with the least calculation.

5.3. Prove that a determinant in which the elements of one row may be obtained by multiplying those of another by a constant k must have the value zero.

6. *Systems of Linear Equations.* The general question of solving systems of equations has already been discussed in Chapter One. In this section the matter will be examined in greater detail on the assumption that the equations involved are *linear*. More precisely, we shall deal with the problem of solving the system of equations

$$(6.1) \begin{cases} a_{11}t_1 + a_{12}t_2 + \ldots + a_{1n}t_n = c_1 , \\ a_{21}t_1 + a_{22}t_2 + \ldots + a_{2n}t_n = c_2 , \\ \ldots\ldots\ldots\ldots\ldots\ldots\ldots\ldots\ldots\ldots , \\ a_{m1}t_1 + a_{m2}t_2 + \ldots + a_{mn}t_n = c_m ; \end{cases}$$

or, more briefly,

$$(6.2) \quad \sum_{j=1}^{n} a_{ij}t_j = c_i \quad (i = 1, \ldots, m) .$$

It is assumed that the constants a_{ij} and c_i are given, so the problem is that of determining whether there exist values of the variables t_j for which the equations (6.1) or (6.2)) are simultaneously satisfied, and, if they exist, of finding them. When $m = n$ (there are as many equations as "unknowns"), the basic result is Theorem 6.1.

Theorem 6.1 (Cramer's Rule). If, in (6.1), $m = n$, and if the value of the determinant $A = \det(a_{ij})$ is different from zero, then the system (6.1) has exactly one solution, which is given by the formulas

$$(6.3) \quad t_j = \frac{A_j}{A} \quad (j = 1, \ldots, n) ,$$

where A_j is the determinant obtained from A by replacing a_{ij} by c_i ($i = 1, \ldots, n$), i.e., by replacing the jth column of A by the column made up of the numbers $c_1, \ldots, c_n$.

PROOF: We shall first show that the numbers given by (6.3) do satisfy the equations (6.1). It will be convenient to refer to the case $m = n = 3$; but the idea of the proof may be used for any value of n. Consider the determinant

$$\begin{vmatrix} c_1 & a_{11} & a_{12} & a_{13} \\ c_1 & a_{11} & a_{12} & a_{13} \\ c_2 & a_{21} & a_{22} & a_{23} \\ c_3 & a_{31} & a_{32} & a_{33} \end{vmatrix} ;$$

its value is zero, since the first two rows are identical (Theorem 5.3). Using the Laplace expansion by minors of the first row, we may therefore write

$$c_1 \begin{vmatrix} a_{11} & a_{12} & a_{13} \\ a_{21} & a_{22} & a_{23} \\ a_{31} & a_{32} & a_{33} \end{vmatrix} - a_{11} \begin{vmatrix} c_1 & a_{12} & a_{13} \\ c_2 & a_{22} & a_{23} \\ c_3 & a_{32} & a_{33} \end{vmatrix} +$$

$$a_{12} \begin{vmatrix} c_1 & a_{11} & a_{13} \\ c_2 & a_{21} & a_{23} \\ c_3 & a_{31} & a_{33} \end{vmatrix} - a_{13} \begin{vmatrix} c_1 & a_{11} & a_{12} \\ c_2 & a_{21} & a_{22} \\ c_3 & a_{31} & a_{32} \end{vmatrix} = 0 .$$

If one now interchanges columns in the last two determinants and uses Theorem 5.2, one obtains

$$c_1 A - a_{12}A_1 - a_{12}A_2 - a_{13}A_3 = 0 .$$

Since $A \neq 0$ by assumption, we may divide through in this equation by A. This gives

$$a_{11}\frac{A_1}{A} + a_{12}\frac{A_2}{A} + a_{13}\frac{A_3}{A} = c_1 .$$

This shows that the numbers defined by the equations (6.3) do satisfy the first of the equations (6.1); and in the same way one may show that they also satisfy the other equations of the system (6.1).

This shows that the formulas (6.3) give a solution of the system (6.1). It is still necessary to show that this is the *only* solution of (6.1) or, to put the matter in another way, that any solution of the system (6.1) must satisfy the equations (6.3). This we shall now do, again taking the case $m = n = 3$ as representative. We assume, accordingly, that the symbols t_1, t_2, t_3 stand for numbers such that the equations

$$a_{11}t_1 + a_{12}t_2 + a_{13}t_3 = c_1 ,$$
$$a_{21}t_1 + a_{22}t_2 + a_{23}t_3 = c_2 ,$$
$$a_{31}t_1 + a_{32}t_2 + a_{33}t_3 = c_3 ,$$

do hold true. If one multiplies the first of these equations by A_{11} (the minor of a_{11}), the second by $-A_{21}$, the third by A_{31}, and adds, the result is

$$(a_{11}A_{11} - a_{21}A_{21} + a_{31}A_{31})t_1 + (a_{12}A_{11} - a_{22}A_{21} + a_{32}A_{31})t_2$$
$$+ (a_{13}A_{11} - a_{23}A_{21} + a_{33}A_{31})t_3 = c_1A_{11} - c_2A_{21} + c_3A_{31} .$$

By Theorem 5.4, the coefficient of t_1 and the right side of this equation are A and A_1, respectively; while by Theorem 5.5 the coefficients of t_2 and t_3 are zero. Thus the equation reduces to

$$At_1 = A_1 ,$$

or since $A \neq 0$,

$$t_1 = \frac{A_1}{A} ;$$

and this is the first of the formulas (6.3). The others may be derived similarly. The proof of Theorem 6.1 is thus complete.

When all of the constants c_i are zero, the system (6.1) is said to be *homogeneous*. If a system (6.1) in which $m = n$ is homogeneous, then all of the determinants A_j as defined in Theorem 6.1 are zero, for each one contains a column made up entirely of zeros (Theorem 5.1). Therefore, if $A \neq 0$, all of the numbers t_j given by (6.3) will be zero. This constitutes a proof of Theorem 6.2.

Theorem 6.2. If $m = n$ for a homogeneous system (6.1), and if A ($= det(a_{ij})$) is not zero, then the system has only the trivial solution $t_j = 0$ ($j = 1, \ldots, n$).

The mate to Theorem 6.2 is Theorem 6.3.

Theorem 6.3. If $m = n$ for a homogeneous system (6.1), and if $A = 0$, then the system has infinitely many solutions.

We shall not give a proof of this theorem. We shall show, however, how one may set about finding solutions of a system which satisfies the conditions of Theorem 6.3, even though Cramer's Rule (Theorem 6.1) is inapplicable.

Example 6.1. We shall solve the system

$$(1) \quad t + 2u - v = 0,$$
$$(2) \quad 2t - u + 3v = 0,$$
$$(3) \quad 3t - 2u + 5v = 0.$$

Using formula (4.5) or some Laplace expansion one can verify that the "determinant of the coefficients" A, i.e.,

$$\begin{vmatrix} 1 & 2 & -1 \\ 2 & -1 & 3 \\ 3 & -2 & 5 \end{vmatrix},$$

has the value zero. Since there are as many equations as unknowns, the hypotheses of Theorem 6.3 are satisfied, and there must be infinitely many solutions of the system. We assume, therefore, that the symbols t, u, v actually stand for a solution of the system. Multiplying both sides of the equation (1) by -2 and adding the result to (2) with the object of eliminating t gives

$$-5u + 5v = 0,$$

or equivalently

$$(4) \quad -u + v = 0.$$

Eliminating t from the equation (3) in the same way—by multiplying both sides of (1) by -3 and adding the result to (3)—gives

$$-8u + 8v = 0,$$

which is again equivalent to (4). Thus the given system (1)–(3) is equivalent to the system

$$(1) \quad t + 2u - v = 0,$$
$$(4) \quad -u + v = 0;$$

for, as we have just shown, these equations follow from (1)–(3); and (1)–(3) can be obtained from (1) and (4) by reversing the indicated steps. But the system consisting of equations (1) and (4) may be solved very easily, as follows: assign any value whatever (say a) to v; then in order for (4) to be satisfied, u must also be chosen to be a. When these values are substituted into (1), one gets

$$t + 2a - a = 0,$$

or $t = -a$. Thus all possible solutions of the given system are provided by the formulas

$$t = -a, \quad u = a, \quad v = a,$$

where a is arbitrary. Substitution will show that any such set of values does satisfy (1)–(3); thus the system is completely solved.

The same procedure may be used for systems not satisfying the conditions of Theorem 6.3. Witness the following example.

Example 6.2. We shall solve the *non*homogeneous system

(1) $t + u + \ v = 1$,
(2) $2t - u - 3v = 0$,
(3) $-t + u + 2v = 0$.

Using (1) to eliminate t from (2) and (3), as in Example 6.1, gives the equivalent system

(1) $t + u + \ v = 1$,
(2′) $-3u - 5v = -2$,
(3′) $2u + 3v = 1$.

Now (2′) may in turn be used to eliminate u from (3′)—one multiplies both sides of (2′) by $\frac{2}{3}$ and adds to (3′). This leads to the system

(1) $t + u + \ v = 1$,
(2′) $-3u - 5v = -2$,
(3″) $v = 1$,

which, being equivalent to the system (1)–(2′)–(3′), is also equivalent to the original system. This last system is easily solved. The equation (3″) says that the value of the unknown v must be 1; putting this value into (2′) and solving for u gives -1 as its value; and substituting these two values into (1) gives 1 as the value of t. The solution of the given system is therefore $t = 1, u = -1, v = 1$. This result may be checked by substitution.

The method illustrated in these two examples is sometimes called the "triangular" method for solving a system of equations (6.1), because of the form of the left sides of the equations in the system (1)–(2′)–(3′), which is typical. Even when Cramer's Rule applies (as in Example 6.2), the triangular method is usually a better method, in that it requires less calculation; but its chief strength lies in the fact that it is often effective for systems where Cramer's Rule does not apply, as in Example 6.1.

Theorems 6.1 through 6.3 leave unanswered all questions about what happens (a) when $m \neq n$, or (b) when $m = n$, the system is not homogeneous, and $A = 0$. There is a general theorem which enables one to decide in all such cases whether or not a system (6.1) has at least one solution or, in other words, is consistent. In order merely to state this theorem (we shall not prove it) we shall require the notion of the rank of a matrix. By a *matrix* we mean a rectangular array of numbers (or variable expressions) of the form

$$(6.4) \quad \begin{bmatrix} u_{11} & u_{12} \ldots u_{1n} \\ u_{21} & u_{22} \ldots u_{2n} \\ \ldots\ldots\ldots\ldots\ldots \\ u_{m1} & u_{m2} \ldots u_{mn} \end{bmatrix},$$

where m (the number of rows) and n (the number of columns) need not be equal. Given a matrix, it is possible to obtain from it *square* matrices of various sizes by striking out rows and columns. For instance, if m exceeds n by two, then striking out any two rows leaves a square matrix with n rows and columns; striking out any three rows and any one column leaves a square matrix with $n - 1$ rows and columns; etc. The numbers appearing in any such square matrix may be regarded in a natural way as the elements of a determinant of the appropriate order, and the value of that determinant may be calculated. The *rank* of the matrix (6.4) is defined as the order of the largest such determinant whose value is not zero. It follows at once from this definition that the largest possible value for the rank of (6.4) is the smaller of the two numbers m and n; the smallest possible rank is zero, which is said to occur when all of the elements u_{ij} in the matrix are zero. The systematic way to calculate the rank of a given numerical matrix is to compute the values of the determinants of order N (where N is the smaller of m and n) obtainable from the given matrix, then those of order $N - 1$, then those of order $N - 2$, and so on; as soon as a determinant whose value is not zero is encountered, its order is the rank of the matrix and the computation may be discontinued.

The theorem referred to above is Theorem 6.4.

Theorem 6.4. The system (6.1) is consistent if and only if the two matrices

$$(6.5) \quad \begin{bmatrix} a_{11} & a_{12} \ldots a_{1n} \\ a_{21} & a_{22} \ldots a_{2n} \\ \ldots\ldots\ldots\ldots\ldots \\ a_{m1} & a_{m2} \ldots a_{mn} \end{bmatrix}$$

and

$$(6.6) \quad \begin{bmatrix} a_{11} & a_{12} \ldots a_{1n} & c_1 \\ a_{21} & a_{22} \ldots a_{2n} & c_2 \\ \ldots\ldots\ldots\ldots\ldots\ldots \\ a_{m1} & a_{m2} \ldots a_{mn} & c_m \end{bmatrix}$$

have the same rank. If (6.5) and (6.6) have the common rank r, then the system (6.1) has exactly one solution or infinitely many solutions according as r is equal to or less than n.

It should be observed that this theorem (unlike Theorem 6.1) merely gives a criterion for the existence of solutions and does not tell how a given system may be solved. Once Theorem 6.4 has been used to establish the solvability of a given system of equations, some such technique as the "triangular" method may be used to solve it.

EXERCISES

6.1. Solve each system of equations using Cramer's Rule:

a) $3t + 2u = -3$
     $t + u = -2$

b) $t + 2u - 3v = 2$
     $2t + 5u + v = 3$
     $-t + 4u - 4v = 0$

c) $2x + 3y + 5z = 0$
     $x - 2y - 4z = 1$
     $3x + y + 2z = 3$

6.2. Solve each of the systems of equations in Exercise 6.1 using the "triangular" method.

6.3. Solve each of the following systems using the "triangular" method:

a) $t + 3u + 2v = 2$
     $3t + u - 4v = 0$
     $2t + 2u - v = 1$

b) $t + 3u - v = 3$
     $-t - 4u + v = -3$
     $2t + 5u + v = -1$
     $4t - u + 2v = 0$

6.4. Using Theorem 6.4, determine whether each of the following systems is consistent and solve each system that is consistent:

a) $2t - u + 3v = 7$
     $-t + u - 2v = 4$

b) $4t - 2u = 5$
     $2t - u = 2$

c) $5t - 7u = 3$
     $2t + 4u = -10$
     $4t - 9u = 8$

d) $2t + 3u - 5v = 0$
     $t + 3u + 2v = 4$
     $t + 2u - v = 1$

6.5. Derive each of the following propositions from Theorem 6.4:

a) A system (6.1) in which there are fewer equations than unknowns either is inconsistent or has infinitely many solutions.

b) A system (6.1) which is homogeneous is always consistent.

c) Theorem 6.3.

7. Determinant Conditions for the Definiteness of a Quadratic Form.

The determinant concept may be used to generalize to the case of three or more variables the conditions described in Section 3 for the (positive or negative) definiteness of a quadratic form. Suppose that the given form is

$$(7.1) \quad \Sigma a_{ij}t_i t_j \quad (i,j = 1, 2, \ldots n) .$$

It is convenient to consider the auxiliary quadratic form

$$(7.2) \quad \Sigma b_{ij} t_i t_j,$$

where b_{ij} is defined by

$$(7.3) \quad b_{ij} = \tfrac{1}{2}(a_{ij} + a_{ji}).$$

The form (7.2) has two important properties. First, it is *symmetrical:* $b_{ij} = b_{ji}$ for all values of i and j. This follows at once from the definition (7.3) of b_{ij}. Second, it is equivalent to (7.1) in the sense that it represents the same function of the variables $t_1, \ldots, t_n$. In the first place, by (7.3), the "square" terms in the two forms are identical: $b_{ii} = \tfrac{1}{2}(a_{ii} + a_{ii}) = a_{ii}$ $(i = 1, 2, \ldots, n)$; and in the second place, the two terms involving a particular product $t_i t_j$ (or $t_j t_i$) $(i \neq j)$ in the two forms have the same sum:

$$b_{ij}t_i t_j + b_{ji}t_j t_i = \tfrac{1}{2}(a_{ij} + a_{ji})t_i t_j + \tfrac{1}{2}(a_{ji} + a_{ij})t_j t_i = a_{ij}t_i t_j + a_{ji}t_j t_i.$$

The form (7.2) may be thought of as having been obtained from (7.1) by redistributing the coefficients of the pair of products $t_i t_j$ and $t_j t_i$ so as to make them equal.

Since the forms (7.1) and (7.2) represent the same function of the variables $t_1, \ldots, t_n$, the positive (or negative) definiteness of either form implies that of the other; and if one wishes to investigate the definiteness of a form (7.1), all he needs to do is to investigate the corresponding symmetrical form (7.2). The fact that the conditions we are about to derive apply directly only to symmetrical quadratic forms therefore imposes no real limitation on their applicability to forms in general.

The coefficients of the symmetrical quadratic form (7.2) may be thought of as the elements of a matrix:

$$\begin{bmatrix} b_{11} & b_{12} \ldots b_{1n} \\ b_{21} & b_{22} \ldots b_{2n} \\ \ldots\ldots\ldots\ldots \\ b_{n1} & b_{n2} \ldots b_{nn} \end{bmatrix}.$$

The determinant whose elements constitute the square matrix with k rows and columns in the upper left corner of this matrix will be denoted by D_k; thus

$$D_1 = b_{11}, \quad D_2 = \begin{vmatrix} b_{11} & b_{12} \\ b_{21} & b_{22} \end{vmatrix} = b_{11}b_{22} - b_{12}b_{21}, \text{ etc.}$$

Our first theorem gives a *necessary* condition for definiteness.

Theorem 7.1. If the form (7.2) is definite, all of the determinants D_k $(k = 1, 2, \ldots, n)$ have values different from zero.

PROOF: It will be shown that if $D_k = 0$ for some value of k, then the form is not definite. Suppose that D_k does have the value 0, k being a certain integer between 1 and n inclusive. Then according to Theorem 6.3, the system of equations

$$b_{11}t_1 + b_{12}t_2 + \ldots + b_{1k}t_k = 0$$

$$b_{21}t_1 + b_{22}t_2 + \ldots + b_{2k}t_k = 0$$

$$\ldots\ldots\ldots\ldots\ldots\ldots\ldots\ldots\ldots$$

$$b_{k1}t_1 + b_{k2}t_2 + \ldots + b_{kk}t_k = 0$$

has a solution not consisting entirely of zeros. Call one such solution $(\bar{t}_1, \bar{t}_2, \ldots, \bar{t}_k)$, and put

$$(7.4) \quad \bar{t}_{k+1} = \bar{t}_{k+2} = \ldots = \bar{t}_n = 0 .$$

The form (7.2) assumes the value zero at the point $(\bar{t}_1, \bar{t}_2, \ldots, \bar{t}_n)$, *and is therefore not definite*. To see this, note first that at this point all terms in (7.2) involving indices higher than k will be zero, by (7.4). Thus the value of the form at this point will be simply

$$\sum_{i,j=1}^{k} b_{ij}\bar{t}_i\bar{t}_j \, ;$$

but this is zero, as one can verify by multiplying the equations (which are satisfied by assumption)

$$b_{11}\bar{t}_1 + \ldots + b_{1k}\bar{t}_k = 0$$

$$b_{21}\bar{t}_1 + \ldots + b_{2k}\bar{t}_k = 0$$

$$\ldots\ldots\ldots\ldots\ldots\ldots\ldots$$

$$b_{k1}\bar{t}_1 + \ldots + b_{kk}\bar{t}_k = 0$$

respectively by $\bar{t}_1, \bar{t}_2, \ldots, \bar{t}_k$, and then adding. This proves the theorem.

The principal theorem of this section (Theorem 7.3 below) follows from a well-known theorem in the theory of quadratic forms whose proof is too intricate to belong here. We shall therefore merely state the latter theorem, leaving it to the reader to verify it in the simplest cases (cf. Exercise 7.2).

   Theorem 7.2. *If* $D_k \neq 0$ $(k = 1, 2, \ldots, n)$, *then there exist real numbers*[5]

----

[5] The numbers c_{ij} $(i = 1, 2, \ldots, n; j = i + 1, i + 2, \ldots, n)$ are given by the formula

$$c_{ij} = \frac{E_{ij}}{D_i},$$

where E_{ij} is the determinant obtained from D_i by changing the second index in the last column of D_i from i to j; i.e.,

$$E_{ij} = \begin{vmatrix} b_{11} & b_{12} \ldots b_{1,i-1} \, b_{1j} \\ b_{12} & b_{22} \ldots b_{2,i-1} \, b_{2j} \\ \ldots\ldots\ldots\ldots\ldots\ldots \\ b_{1i} & b_{2i} \ldots b_{i,i-1} \, b_{ij} \end{vmatrix} .$$

$c_{12}, c_{13}, \ldots, c_{1n}; c_{23}, \ldots, c_{2n}; \ldots; c_{n-1,n}$ such that

$$(7.5) \quad \begin{cases} \Sigma b_{ij} t_i t_j = D_1\left(t_1 + \sum_{j-2}^{n} c_{1j} t_j\right)^2 + \frac{D_2}{D_1}\left(t_2 + \sum_{j-3}^{n} c_{2j} t_j\right)^2 \\[2mm] \qquad\qquad + \ldots + \frac{D_{n-1}}{D_{n-2}}(t_{n-1} + c_{n-1,n} t_n)^2 + \frac{D_n}{D_{n-1}} t_n^2. \end{cases}$$

The definiteness conditions are given by Theorem 7.3.

Theorem 7.3. The symmetrical quadratic form (7.2) is positive definite if and only if all of the determinants D_k are positive; it is negative definite if and only if D_1 is negative and subsequent D_k's alternate in sign:

$$(7.6) \quad D_1 < 0, \ D_2 > 0, \ D_3 < 0, \ldots.$$

PROOF: We shall carry the proof through for negative definite forms; the proof for positive definite forms is almost the same and somewhat simpler. Suppose first that (7.6) holds. Then the conditions of Theorem 7.2 are satisfied, and we may use the representation (7.5). The coefficients D_1, $D_2/D_1, \ldots$ on the right side of (7.5) are all negative; and since each is multiplied by the square of a real number, the value of the sum must be nonpositive. To prove that the form is negative definite it will therefore suffice to show that this sum can be zero only if $t_1 = t_2 = \ldots = t_n = 0$. But if the sum is zero, all of the separate terms must be zero, and this implies in turn that each of the linear expressions squared in (7.5) must be zero:

$$(7.7) \quad \begin{cases} t_1 + c_{12} t_2 + \ldots\ldots\ldots + c_{1n} t_n = 0 \\ \qquad t_2 + c_{23} t_3 + \ldots + c_{2n} t_n = 0 \\ \qquad\qquad \ldots\ldots\ldots\ldots \\ \qquad\qquad\qquad\qquad t_n = 0 . \end{cases}$$

This is a homogeneous system of n linear equations in the n variables $t_1, t_2, \ldots, t_n$. However, the determinant of the coefficients can easily be seen to have the value 1 (for all terms in the expansion of the determinant but that made up of the elements of the downward diagonal are zero). Thus, by Theorem 6.2, the only possible values of $t_1, \ldots, t_n$ satisfying this system of equations are $0, \ldots, 0$. This is what had to be shown.

Conversely, if the form is negative definite, the conditions (7.6) must be satisfied. In the first place, by Theorem 7.1, if the form is negative definite the determinants D_k are all different from zero, and the representation (7.5) is possible. Suppose (we shall show that this leads to a contradiction) that there were two consecutive D_k's with the same sign; for simplicity, suppose that $D_1 < 0, D_2 < 0$. Then let $(\bar{t}_1, \bar{t}_2, \ldots, \bar{t}_n)$ be the solution (which exists, by Cramer's Rule) of the system

$$\begin{array}{c} t_1 + c_{12} t_2 + \ldots\ldots\ldots\ldots + c_{1n} t_n = 0 \\ t_2 + c_{23} t_3 + \ldots\ldots\ldots + c_{2n} t_n = 1 \\ t_3 + c_{34} t + \ldots + c_{3n} t_n = 0 \\ \ldots\ldots\ldots\ldots \\ t_n = 0 \end{array}$$

(all the numbers on the right but the second are 0). If this solution is substituted into (7.5), all terms on the right side of (7.5) but the second vanish, and we obtain

$$\Sigma b_{ij} \bar{l}_i \bar{l}_j = \frac{D_2}{D_1} > 0 \; ;$$

but this contradicts the assumption that the form (7.2) is negative definite.

Thus if (7.2) is negative definite, the determinants D_k alternate in sign. The proof will therefore be complete when we show that D_1 must be negative; but this follows at once from Theorem 2.2, according to which D_1 ($= b_{11}$, the coefficient of l_1^2) must be negative if the form is negative definite.

Example 7.1. We shall use Theorem 7.3 to show that the quadratic form $l_1^2 + l_2^2 - l_1 l_2 + 2l_3^2 - l_2 l_3$ ($n = 3$) is positive definite. Here $a_{11} = a_{22} = 1$, $a_{33} = 2$, $a_{12} = a_{23} = -1$, and all the other a_{ij}'s are zero. Using formula (7.3), we obtain the equivalent symmetrical form

$$l_1^2 + l_2^2 - \tfrac{1}{2} l_1 l_2 - \tfrac{1}{2} l_2 l_1 + 2l_3^2 - \tfrac{1}{2} l_2 l_3 - \tfrac{1}{2} l_3 l_2 \, ,$$

for which the matrix of coefficients is

$$\begin{bmatrix} b_{11} & b_{12} & b_{13} \\ b_{21} & b_{22} & b_{23} \\ b_{31} & b_{32} & b_{33} \end{bmatrix} = \begin{bmatrix} 1 & -\tfrac{1}{2} & 0 \\ -\tfrac{1}{2} & 1 & -\tfrac{1}{2} \\ 0 & -\tfrac{1}{2} & 2 \end{bmatrix}.$$

Here $D_1 = 1 > 0$, $D_2 = \tfrac{3}{4} > 0$, $D_3 = \tfrac{5}{4} > 0$; the form is therefore positive definite.

EXERCISES

7.1. Using Theorem 7.3, determine whether each of the following quadratic forms is positive definite, negative definite, or neither.

a) $l_1^2 + l_2^2 + l_2 l_3 + l_3 l_2 + l_3^2$

b) $l_1^2 + l_1 l_2 + l_2^2 + l_2 l_3 + l_3^2$

c) $-l_1^2 + 8l_1 l_2 - l_2^2 - 2l_2 l_3 - 4l_3^2$

d) $(l_1 + l_2)^2 + (l_2 + l_3)^2 + (l_3 + l_1)^2$

7.2. Using the formula for c_{ij} given in footnote 5, prove Theorem 7.2 for the cases $n = 1$, $n = 2$ by working out and simplifying the right side of formula (7.5).

7.3. When $n = 2$, one can express part of Theorem 7.3 by saying that the form is definite if and only if $D_2 > 0$ and $D_1 \neq 0$. Discuss the relation of this statement to Theorem 3.1.

7.4. Show directly (i.e. without reference to the theory of determinants) that the only possible solution of the system (7.7) is that consisting entirely of zeros.

SUGGESTIONS FOR FURTHER READING

The material in this chapter is made up of topics from an area mathematicians call "classical linear algebra," and the reader who is interested in going more deeply will do well to look into any of the many recent books intended to give an introductory treatment of the area. Specifically, we would recommend:

W. L. Ferrar, *Algebra* (Oxford: Clarendon Press, 1941).

L. Mirsky, *An Introduction to Linear Algebra* (Oxford: Clarendon Press, 1955).

M. Bôcher, *Introduction to Higher Algebra* (New York: Macmillan Co., 1907).

Brief treatments of determinants will be found in books of the "College Algebra" type mentioned at the end of Chapter Eight; these books contain descriptions of the methods for shortening the work of calculating the value of a determinant that were referred to at the end of Section 4.

A proof of Theorem 7.2 will be found in H. Hancock, *Theory of Maxima and Minima* (Boston: Ginn & Co., 1917), pp. 89–91.

Chapter Twelve

DIFFERENCE EQUATIONS AND
DIFFERENTIAL EQUATIONS

In Chapters Eight and Eleven of this Part we dealt with conditional equations in which the unknowns were numbers. At least as important for modern mathematics and its applications are equations in which the unknowns are *functions* rather than numbers, and appear not only in various algebraic combinations but also differentiated, integrated, evaluated at distinct values of the independent variables, and so on. In the present chapter we shall give brief introductions to two principal types of these functional equations.

In order to be able to state the results most important for our purposes, we have inserted sections containing short digressions on the trigonometric and exponential functions, which occur frequently in solutions of equations of the types with which we are concerned.

1. *A Simple Difference Equation.* We denote by $f(t)$ an unknown function of the discrete variable t, i.e., a variable which takes on only the values of $0, 1, 2, \ldots$. The equation

$$(1.1) \quad a_0 f(t+1) + a_1 f(t) = 0 \quad (a_0 \neq 0)$$

is a *difference equation* for the function $f(t)$, and any function $f(t)$ satisfying this equation is said to be a solution. The problem with which we shall begin this chapter is that of solving this difference equation.

As a first step, divide through in (1.1) by the nonzero constant a_0; then (1.1) becomes

$$(1.2) \quad f(t+1) = cf(t) ,$$

where c stands for $-a_1/a_0$. This equation says simply that the value of the unknown function for any value of t is obtained by multiplying its value at the preceding value of t by the constant c. Thus if $f(0)$ is some number x_0, (1.2) with $t = 0$ gives $f(1) = cf(0) = cx_0$; from this in turn the same equation with $t = 1$ gives

$$f(2) = cf(1) = c^2 x_0 ,$$

with $t = 2$

$$f(3) = cf(2) = c^3 x_0 ,$$

and so on. These results suggest that the whole solution will be given by $f(t) = c^t x_0$; and that this is a solution of (1.2) may be verified by substitution:

$$f(t + 1) = c^{t+1} x_0 = c(c^t x_0) = cf(t) .$$

It should be noticed that this conclusion is quite independent of the value of x_0; in other words, the value of the solution at 0 (or for that matter at any other integer) may be assigned quite arbitrarily, but once it is assigned the entire solution is completely determined. We may express this fact by saying that the *general* solution of (1.2) is given by $f(t) = c^t x_0$, where x_0 is an arbitrary constant. Putting $t = 0$ in this formula gives $f(0) = x_0$, so that the arbitrary constant x_0 is the *initial value* of the solution.

This phenomenon is typical of functional equations in general; instead of obtaining a unique solution one obtains a general solution, i.e., a formula containing one or more arbitrary constants (or sometimes arbitrary functions) which represents a whole family of solutions, each of which is obtained by assigning specific values to those constants. In order to determine a single solution, therefore, it is necessary to impose other conditions in addition to the functional equation itself, conditions which somehow lead to the determination of the arbitrary constants involved. In the case of equation (1.2), the most natural condition serving this purpose is the specification of the initial value of the solution, the number $f(0)$.

The equation (1.1), which has now been solved, is a simple example of the general difference equation

$$(1.3) \quad F(t, f(t), f(t + 1), \ldots, f(t + n)) = 0 ,$$

where F is some function of $n + 2$ variables. An equation of the form (1.3) merely asserts that there exists a certain relation between the values of the unknown function at any $n + 1$ successive values of t. Our work in this chapter will be concerned with a very special case of (1.3), namely, the case of the *linear difference equation with constant coefficients*

$$(1.4) \quad a_0 f(t + n) + a_1 f(t + n - 1) + \ldots + a_n f(t) = b .$$

Here $a_0, a_1, \ldots, a_n$ and b are assumed to be constants. If $b = 0$, the equation (1.4) is said to be *homogeneous*. (1.1) is the homogeneous case of (1.4) with $n = 1$.

Before passing on to the general theory of the equation (1.4), we shall make some further observations about the equation (1.1) and its solutions which foreshadow future, more general conclusions. These concern the behavior of the solutions as $t \to \infty$. If $|c| < 1$, in other words, if c lies between -1 and $+1$, the value of c^t tends to 0 as $t \to \infty$; successive values of c^t alternate in sign if c is negative, have the same sign (are in fact all positive) if c is positive. We may therefore say that—

Any solution $f(t)$ of the equation (1.1) has the property $f(t) \to 0$ as $t \to \infty$ if $|c| < 1$.

Obviously, the only constant solution (equilibrium point) for the equation (1.1) is $f(t) \equiv 0$; thus this statement may be interpreted as saying that if $|c| < 1$, the equilibrium solution of (1.1) is *stable*. (See Chapter Three, Section 2). On the other hand, if $|c| > 1$, any solution (other than the equilibrium solution) of (1.1) attains larger and larger values as $t \to \infty$; so that in this case the equilibrium solution is definitely unstable. The discussion of the cases $c = \pm 1$ will be left as exercises. Suffice it to say that *the equilibrium solution of (1.1) is stable if and only if $|c| < 1$*.

EXERCISES

1.1. What is the meaning of equation (1.4) if $c = 1$? If $c = 0$?

1.2. Discuss the behavior of the solutions of (1.4) as $t \to \infty$ if $c = \pm 1$.

1.3. Find the general solution and discuss the stability properties of the difference equation

$$4f(t + 1) + 3f(t) = 0 .$$

1.4. In our form of the general solution of equation (1.4) the arbitrary constant x_0 represents the value of the solution at 0. Write the same general solution in a form in which the arbitrary constant is $x_1 = f(1)$.

1.5. Find the general solution of the *non*homogeneous equation

$$f(t + 1) - cf(t) = 1 .$$

2. Homogeneous Linear Difference Equations. We shall now investigate, in a more general way, the homogeneous form of equation (1.4):

$$(2.1) \quad a_0 f(t + n) + a_1 f(t + n - 1) + \ldots + a_n f(t) = 0 .$$

Our investigation will show, after a brief digression, how any given equation of this form may be completely solved, or at least how the problem of solving it may be reduced to that of solving a polynomial equation of the kind discussed in Chapter Eight. It is well to observe in advance that all of the theorems of *this* section remain valid if the coefficients $a_0, a_1, \ldots, a_n$ are allowed to be functions of t, not merely constants.

We continue to assume that $a_0 \neq 0$, for otherwise the first term in (2.1) would be spurious. At the same time, we shall assume that $a_n \neq 0$. This may seem to be a more arbitrary assumption, but in fact it is not. If we were confronted with an equation (2.1) in which $a_n = 0$, we could put $g(t) = f(t + 1)$—this is merely a matter of renaming the unknown function —and put $m = n - 1$; then the equation would become

$$a_0 g(t + m) + a_1 g(t + m - 1) + \ldots + a_m g(t) = 0 .$$

This is an equation of the form (2.1) which is fully equivalent to the given equation; and if a_m ($= a_{n-1}$) $\neq 0$, the given equation has been reduced to a form satisfying our assumption. If $a_m = 0$, the process may be repeated, and after a certain number of repetitions one will arrive at an equation equivalent to the given one in which the last coefficient is not zero. Thus the assumption $a_n \neq 0$ is essentially a restriction on the form in which a given equation is written, not on the equation itself.

When an equation (2.1) satisfies the conditions $a_0 \neq 0$, $a_n \neq 0$ (as we shall assume henceforth), then n is called the *order* of the equation.

The fundamental theorem on the existence of solutions of the equation (2.1) is Theorem 2.1.

Theorem 2.1. If x_0, x_1, . . . , x_{n-1} are any numbers whatever, and t_0 is any integer, then there exists exactly one solution $f(t)$ of the difference equation (2.1) such that

$$(2.2) \quad f(t_0) = x_0, \quad f(t_0 + 1) = x_1, \ldots, f(t_0 + n - 1) = x_{n-1}.$$

In other words, there is always one and only one solution of (2.1) taking on prescribed values at a given set of n successive integers.

PROOF: Put $t = t_0$ in (2.1). Since the conditions (2.2) are to be satisfied by the function $f(t)$ we are seeking, this gives

$$a_0 f(t_0 + n) + a_1 x_{n-1} + \ldots + a_n x_0 = 0.$$

Since $a_0 \neq 0$, this may be solved for $f(t_0 + n)$, so the value of the solution at $t_0 + n$ is uniquely determined. Once this value is known, putting $t = t_0 + 1$ in (2.1) leads to an equation which uniquely determines $f(t_0 + n + 1)$; and so on. Proceeding in this way indefinitely, one finds a unique value of $f(t)$ for every t satisfying $t \geqslant t_0$. Doing the same thing backwards leads one to the values of $f(t)$ for smaller values of t—the process cannot fail, since $a_n \neq 0$. Thus the conditions (2.2) generate a unique solution of the equation (2.1).

COROLLARY: *Any solution of (2.1) which has the value zero at n successive values of t must be identically zero.*

For the function $f(t) \equiv 0$ is evidently a solution of (2.1) with this property (no matter what the n successive values of t may be), and according to Theorem 2.1 there is only one such solution.

The next two theorems lead up to the all-important Theorem 2.4, according to which one needs to find only n solutions of (2.1) in order to find all solutions.

Theorem 2.2. If $f(t)$ and $g(t)$ are any solutions of (2.1), and c and d are any two constants, the function $h(t) = cf(t) + dg(t)$ is also a solution of (2.1).

PROOF: By assumption,

$$a_0 f(t + n) + \ldots + a_n f(t) = 0,$$
$$a_0 g(t + n) + \ldots + a_n g(t) = 0.$$

But then

$$a_0 h(t + n) + \ldots + a_n h(t)$$
$$= a_0 [cf(t + n) + dg(t + n)] + \ldots + a_n [cf(t) + dg(t)]$$
$$= c[a_0 f(t + n) + \ldots + a_n f(t)] + d[a_0 g(t + n) + \ldots + a_n g(t)]$$
$$= c \cdot 0 + d \cdot 0 = 0.$$

This shows that $h(t)$ is indeed a solution of (2.1). Clearly, the analogous statement for more than two functions can be proved in the same way; so we may say that in general *any linear combination of solutions of* (2.1) *is a solution of* (2.1).

We shall say that k functions $f_1(t), \ldots, f_k(t)$, k being any positive integer, are *linearly dependent* if there exist k constants $c_1, \ldots, c_k$, not all of which are zero, such that

$$(2.3) \quad c_1 f_1(t) + c_2 f_2(t) + \ldots + c_k f_k(t) \equiv 0 \,.$$

In the contrary case, i.e., if the identity (2.3) is true only if all of the constants $c_1, \ldots, c_k$ are zero, the functions are *linearly independent*.

Theorem 2.3. The n solutions $f_1(t), f_2(t), \ldots, f_n(t)$ of the equation (2.1) *are linearly dependent if and only if the determinant*

$$W(t) = \begin{vmatrix} f_1(t) & f_2(t) & \ldots f_n(t) \\ f_1(t+1) & f_2(t+1) & \ldots f_n(t+1) \\ \hdotsfor{3} \\ f_1(t+n-1) & f_2(t+n-1) & \ldots f_n(t+n-1) \end{vmatrix}$$

is identically zero.

PROOF: Suppose first that the solutions are linearly dependent; this means that there exist constants $c_1, \ldots, c_n$, not all zero, such that the identity (2.3) (with $k = n$) holds; but if t_0 is an arbitrary value of t, substituting $t_0, t_0 + 1, \ldots, t_0 + n - 1$ into this identity gives the equations

$$(2.4) \begin{cases} c_1 f_1(t_0) + c_2 f_2(t_0) + \ldots + c_n f_n(t_0) = 0 \,, \\ c_1 f_1(t_0+1) + c_2 f_2(t_0+1) + \ldots + c_n f_n(t_0+1) = 0 \,, \\ \hdotsfor{1} \\ c_1 f_1(t_0+n-1) + c_2 f_2(t_0+n-1) + \ldots + c_n f_n(t_0+n-1) = 0 \,. \end{cases}$$

This may be regarded as a system of n linear equations in the n unknowns $c_1, \ldots, c_n$; and by assumption, this system has a solution not made up entirely of zeros. By Theorem 6.2 of Chapter Eleven, this means that the determinant of coefficients must have the value zero. But the determinant of coefficients is exactly $W(t_0)$. Since t_0 was an arbitrary value of t, we conclude that $W(t) \equiv 0$.

Conversely, suppose that $W(t) \equiv 0$. Then for any particular value t_0 of t, the system of equations (2.4) has a solution $c_1, \ldots, c_n$ not consisting entirely of zeros, by Theorem 6.3 of Chapter Eleven. Using these values of the c's, put

$$g(t) = c_1 f_1(t) + c_2 f_2(t) + \ldots + c_n f_n(t) \,.$$

In the first place, by the remark at the end of the proof of Theorem 2.2, we know that this is a solution of (2.1); and in the second place, by (2.4), we have $g(t_0) = 0, g(t_0 + 1) = 0, \ldots, g(t_0 + n - 1) = 0$. These two facts together imply, by the corollary to Theorem 2.1, that $g(t) \equiv 0$. In view of the definition of $g(t)$, however, this means that the functions $f_1(t), f_2(t), \ldots, f_n(t)$ are linearly dependent.

This completes the proof.

A similiar line of reasoning will prove Theorem 2.4.

Theorem 2.4. If $f_1(t), \ldots, f_n(t)$ are n linearly independent solutions of (2.1), and if $g(t)$ is any solution of (2.1) whatever, there exist constants c_1, $c_2, \ldots, c_n$ such that

$$g(t) \equiv c_1 f_1(t) + c_2 f_2(t) + \ldots + c_n f_n(t).$$

In other words, if $f_1(t), \ldots, f_n(t)$ are linearly independent solutions of (2.1), and $c_1, \ldots, c_n$ are thought of as arbitrary constants, then $c_1 f_1(t) + \ldots + c_n f_n(t)$ is the *general* solution of (2.1); for (as we have seen in the proof of the Theorem 2.2) any such function will be a solution of (2.1); and Theorem 2.4 asserts that *all* solutions of (2.1) may be written in this form.

PROOF: By assumption, $f_1(t), \ldots, f_n(t)$ are linearly independent. It then follows from Theorem 2.3 that there is at least one value of t, say t_0, such that $W(t_0) \neq 0$. Consider the system of equations

$$(2.5) \begin{cases} c_1 f_1(t_0) + c_2 f_2(t_0) + \ldots + c_n f_n(t_0) = g(t_0), \\ c_1 f_1(t_0 + 1) + c_2 f_2(t_0 + 1) + \ldots + c_n f_n(t_0 + 1) = g(t_0 + 1), \\ \ldots\ldots\ldots\ldots\ldots\ldots\ldots\ldots\ldots\ldots\ldots\ldots\ldots\ldots\ldots\ldots\ldots\ldots\ldots \\ c_1 f_1(t_0 + n - 1) + c_2 f_2(t_0 + n - 1) + \ldots + c_n f_n(t_0 + n - 1) = g(t_0 + n - 1), \end{cases}$$

where the c's are regarded as unknowns. The determinant of coefficients is $W(t_0)$, which by assumption is not zero; therefore Cramer's Rule gives a unique solution of this system of equations. Using the values of the c's so defined, put

$$h(t) = c_1 f_1(t) + c_2 f_2(t) + \ldots + c_n f_n(t).$$

As we have pointed out, $h(t)$ must be a solution of (2.1); moreover, the equations (2.5) may be written

$$h(t_0) = g(t_0), \ldots, h(t_0 + n - 1) = g(t_0 + n - 1).$$

Thus $h(t)$ and $g(t)$ are two solutions of (2.1) which take on the same values at the n successive values $t_0, t_0 + 1, \ldots, t_0 + n - 1$ of t. Theorem 2.1 then implies that $h(t)$ and $g(t)$ are identical, and this proves the theorem.

The practical significance of Theorem 2.4 lies in the fact that according to this theorem, once one has found n linearly independent solutions of the difference equation, one has effectively found *all* solutions. Moreover, Theorem 2.3 provides a means of determining by direct calculation whether n solutions are in fact linearly independent: all one has to do is to show that $W(t) \neq 0$ for at least one value of t.

EXERCISES

2.1. Using the method suggested in the proof of Theorem 2.1, find the values for $t = 0, 1, 2, 3, 4$ of that solution $f(t)$ of the difference equation

$$f(t + 2) - f(t + 1) + 2f(t) = 0$$

which satisfies the conditions $f(0) = 0$, $f(1) = 1$.

2.2. What is a simpler way of expressing the statement that *two* functions are linearly dependent?

2.3. Show that if any one of the functions $f_1(t), f_2(t), \ldots, f_k(t)$ is identically zero, or if any two of them are identical, then these functions are linearly dependent.

2.4. Verify by substitution that the functions $f_1(t) = 1, f_2(t) = (-1)^t$ are solutions of the difference equation

$$f(t + 2) - f(t) = 0 .$$

Then, using Theorem 2.3, verify that these two solutions are linearly independent.

2.5. If $g(t)$ is defined to be 1 when t is even, 0 when t is odd, it is easily seen to be a solution of the difference equation in Exercise 2.4. According to Theorem 2.4, it must therefore be possible to find constants c_1 and c_2 such that

$$g(t) = c_1 f_1(t) + c_2 f_2(t) ,$$

where $f_1(t)$ and $f_2(t)$ are as given in Exercise 2.4. Find these constants.

2.6. Find that solution of the difference equation in Exercise 2.4 for which $f(2) = 4$, $f(3) = -2$.

3. The Sine and Cosine Functions. Given an ordinary rectangular co-ordinate system with the co-ordinates x and y as in Figure 3.1, any angle

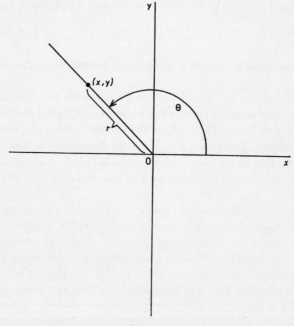

Fig. 3.1

of which the positive half of the x-axis is one side may be thought of as being swept out by a ray starting from the position of the positive half of the x-axis and turning a certain number (not necessarily a *whole* number) of revolutions about the origin. The size of the angle could be measured simply by the number of revolutions involved, but a more convenient measure of angle size is obtained by multiplying the number of revolutions by 2π, where π is the constant 3.15192 . . . familiar from plane geometry.[1] If the direction of rotation is counterclockwise, the measure of the angle is taken to be *positive;* if clockwise, negative. The unit of angle measure so defined is called the *radian;* one revolution is equivalent to 2π radians, a quarter revolution (a right angle) corresponds to $\pi/2$ radians, etc. Thus the angle depicted in Figure 3.1, which is obtained by $\frac{3}{8}$ of a revolution in the positive direction, has as its radian measure $+(2\pi)(\frac{3}{8})$, or $+3\pi/4$ radians.

Now suppose that a real number θ has been given and construct the angle of which θ is the radian measure, in the manner illustrated in Figure 3.1. Let (x,y) be any point on the "terminal side" of this angle, and let r be the distance of this point from the origin. It is easy to see that the ratios x/r and y/r are independent of the manner in which the point (x,y) is chosen on the terminal side of the angle, for choosing any other point merely increases or decreases the three numbers x, y, and r proportionately. In other words, the ratios x/r and y/r depend only on the value of θ, and may be therefore regarded as functions of this quantity. As such, they have special names: the ratio x/r is called the *cosine of* θ (abbreviated cos θ) and y/r is called the *sine of* θ (abbreviated sin θ). Thus, by definition,

$$(3.1) \quad \cos\theta = \frac{x}{r}, \quad \sin\theta = \frac{y}{r},$$

where the variables x, y, and r are related to θ in the manner described above.

The two functions cos θ and sin θ, together with the functions defined by the other four possible ratios of x, y, and r, are called the *trigonometric functions* of θ, and it is to the study of their theory and applications that the traditional subject of trigonometry is chiefly devoted. The values of the six trigonometric functions are extensively tabulated; but (unfortunately, perhaps) θ is almost always expressed in the sexagesimal system in these tables.[2]

One of the uses of the sine and cosine most valuable for our purposes occurs in connection with complex numbers. A complex number, we recall, is one of the form $x + yi$, where x and y are real numbers and i is the "square root of -1," a number which by assumption has the property $i^2 = -1$. Complex numbers can be represented as points in a plane simply by taking x and y, the so-called real and imaginary parts of the number, as the co-ordinates of a point in a rectangular co-ordinate system. But when this is done, we may use (3.1) to represent the complex number in another way:

---

[1] Angles are also measured in the familiar sexagesimal system which uses degrees, minutes, and seconds, but from the mathematical point of view this system is frequently very clumsy and decidedly inferior to the system described in the text.

[2] Cf. footnote 1. If θ is measured in radians, use of these tables of course requires that each radian measure be converted to the sexagesimal equivalent. A large table which gives the sine and cosine with θ in radians is the *Table of Sines and Cosines for Radian Arguments* (Washington, D.C.: National Bureau of Standards, 1940).

if θ is the measure of any angle having the point (x,y) on its terminal side, then by (3.1) $x = r \cos \theta$ and $y = r \sin \theta$, so

$$x + yi = r \cos \theta + i \quad r \sin \theta = r(\cos \theta + i \sin \theta) \, .$$

The expression on the right is called the *trigonometric representation* of the given complex number. It may be defined more directly as follows: In a rectangular co-ordinate system, mark the point whose co-ordinates are the real and imaginary parts of the given complex number. Then draw the ray

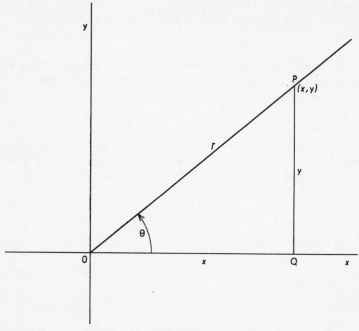

Fig. 3.2

from the origin which passes through this point and measure the angle between the positive half of the x-axis and this ray. If θ is the radian measure of this angle and r is the distance from the origin to the point,

$$r \, (\cos \theta + i \sin \theta)$$

is the trigonometric representation for the given complex number.

Note that θ can be chosen in various ways, since if θ_0 is associated with a certain point in the manner indicated, the same is true of $\theta_0 + 2k\pi$, where k is any integer; the angles measured by these numbers are geometrically indistinguishable, differing as they do by whole numbers of revolutions.

The value of r, on the other hand, is unique. It is called the *absolute value* of the complex number (usually denoted by $|x + yi|$), and it is always real and nonnegative. Its value may be obtained from x and y by means of the formula

$$(3.2) \quad r = \sqrt{x^2 + y^2} \, .$$

The truth of this statement is illustrated in Figure 3.2, where the right triangle POQ has as the lengths of its sides x, y, and r, so that according to the "Pythagorean Theorem" of plane geometry

$$r^2 = x^2 + y^2,$$

and this is equivalent to (3.2).

The value of the trigonometric representation lies in the ease with which it enables one to handle *powers* of complex numbers. The fundamental theorem in this area is Theorem 3.1.

Theorem 3.1 (De Moivre's Theorem). *If n is any whole number,*

$$(\cos \theta + i \sin \theta)^n = \cos n\theta + i \sin n\theta.$$

Since $[r(\cos \theta + i \sin \theta)]^n = r^n(\cos \theta + i \sin \theta)^n$, this theorem implies that in order to raise a complex number in trigonometric form, $r(\cos \theta + i \sin \theta)$, to the nth power, all one has to do is to raise r to that power and replace θ by the multiple $n\theta$.

A proof of this theorem, though not especially difficult, would require us to expend a disproportionate amount of space on the derivation of certain identities involving the sine and cosine; we shall therefore omit it. The interested reader will find De Moivre's theorem proved in any good book on trigonometry.[3]

EXERCISES

3.1. Using formula (3.2) if necessary, find the sine and cosine of the angles whose radian measures are:

$(a)\ 0,\quad (b)\ \dfrac{\pi}{2},\quad (c)\ \dfrac{3\pi}{4},\quad (d)\ 7\pi,\quad (e)\ -\dfrac{\pi}{2}.$

3.2. The *tangent of θ* (abbreviated tan θ) is defined as y/x, where x and y are related to θ in the manner indicated in this section. Explain how this function (which is well tabulated) could be put to use in arriving at the trigonometric representation of a given complex number $x + yi$.

3.3. Derive a formula for converting the size of an angle measured in radians to its size measured in degrees. (There are 360 degrees in one revolution.)

3.4. Find a trigonometric representation for each of the following complex numbers:

$(a)\ i,\quad (b)\ 3,\quad (c)\ \sqrt{2} + \sqrt{2}i,\quad (d)\ \sqrt{2} - \sqrt{2}i.$

3.5. Use De Moivre's theorem to find $(\sqrt{8} + \sqrt{8}i)^7$.

3.6. What can you say about the limit of $(x + yi)^n$ $(n = 0, 1, 2, \ldots)$ as $n \to \infty$ if $|x + yi| < 1$? $|x + yi| > 1$? $|x + yi| = 1$?

4. The Homogeneous Linear Difference Equation with Constant Coefficients.

The theory developed in Section 2 is valid whether the coefficients $a_0, a_1, \ldots a_n$ in equation (2.1) are merely constants or are variable

---

[3] The restriction in De Moivre's theorem that n be a whole number is not necessary; but a proof of the theorem in its most general form is very subtle. The form given above will suffice for our needs.

functions of t; but in the latter case the problem of finding solutions to the equation may be formidable to the point of practical impossibility. When the coefficients are constants, however, the problem is relatively simple.

In Section 1 we have already solved a special case of

$$(2.1) \quad a_0 f(t + n) + a_1 f(t + n - 1) + \ldots + a_n f(t) = 0 ,$$

the case in which $n = 1$. (Here and throughout this section we shall confine our attention to the case of constant coefficients.) There we found that a solution of the equation was a certain constant raised to the tth power, and in fact that any solution could be obtained by multiplying this one by a suitable constant. This suggests that the same kind of function might work here. There is no advance clue this time as to what constant should be raised to the tth power, so we shall begin by calling it λ and substitute λ^t into (2.1) in an experimental way in the hope that the proper value or values of λ will subsequently reveal themselves. We may of course assume that $\lambda \neq 0$, for $\lambda = 0$ would only give the solution $f(t) \equiv 0$, which we already know.

The substitution gives

$$(4.1) \quad a_0 \lambda^{t+n} + a_1 \lambda^{t+n-1} + \ldots + a_n \lambda^t = 0 ,$$

which may be written

$$\lambda^t (a_0 \lambda^n + a_1 \lambda^{n-1} + \ldots + a_n) = 0 .$$

Since $\lambda \neq 0$ by assumption, this equation will be satisfied if and only if

$$(4.2) \quad a_0 \lambda^n + a_1 \lambda^{n-1} + \ldots + a_n = 0 .$$

This is merely a polynomial equation for λ and is quite independent of t; and it follows from the manner in which it was derived that λ^t will be a solution of (2.1) if and only if λ is a solution of this equation.

Equation (4.2) is called the *auxiliary equation* for the difference equation (2.1). Note that it can be thought of as having been obtained from (2.1) by replacing $f(t + k)$ by λ^k in each term of (2.1) $(k = 0, 1, \ldots, n)$.

In general, the equation (4.2) has n roots $\lambda_1, \lambda_2, \ldots, \lambda_n$; if these roots are distinct, the set of functions $\lambda_1^t, \lambda_2^t, \ldots, \lambda_n^t$ accordingly provide n different solutions of the equation (2.1). In fact, when the n roots of the auxiliary equation are distinct, these solutions are linearly independent. This statement follows from Theorem 2.3, for $W(0)$ is:

$$\begin{vmatrix} 1 & 1 & \ldots 1 \\ \lambda_1 & \lambda_2 & \ldots \lambda_n \\ \lambda_1^2 & \lambda_2^2 & \ldots \lambda_n^2 \\ \ldots\ldots\ldots\ldots\ldots\ldots \\ \lambda_1^{n-1} & \lambda_2^{n-1} & \ldots \lambda_n^{n-1} \end{vmatrix} ,$$

and it may be shown that the value of this determinant (the so-called *Vandermonde* determinant) is

$$(\lambda_n - \lambda_1)(\lambda_n - \lambda_2) \ldots (\lambda_n - \lambda_{n-1})\ (\lambda_{n-1} - \lambda_1) \ldots (\lambda_2 - \lambda_1)$$

—the product of all possible quantities of the form $(\lambda_i - \lambda_j)$, where i and j range from 1 to n and $i > j$. In the present case, since the roots are distinct, all of these quantities are different from zero; thus $W(0) \neq 0$, and according to Theorem 2.3 the solutions $\lambda_i{}^t$ $(i = 1, \ldots, n)$ are linearly independent.

Thus, by Theorem 2.4, we have the following theorem:

Theorem 4.1. When the equation (4.2) has n distinct roots $\lambda_1, \ldots, \lambda_n$, the general solution of the difference equation (2.1) is

$$(4.3) \quad c_1\lambda_1{}^t + c_2\lambda_2{}^t + \ldots + c_n\lambda_n{}^t,$$

where $c_1, \ldots, c_n$ are arbitrary constants.

When the roots λ_i of (4.2) are all real, (4.3) gives a general solution of the difference equation (2.1) in a perfectly satisfactory form. But if some of the roots are complex, (4.3) is not satisfactory at all; for in the applications, the coefficients $a_0, \ldots, a_n$ are real numbers, the solutions $f(t)$ are expected to be real-valued functions, and the presence of complex expressions $\lambda_i{}^t$ in the general solution is unwelcome. This difficulty can be overcome by choosing the coefficients c_i in an appropriate way and then using the results of the preceding section. The details follow.

Suppose that the coefficients of (2.1) (and therefore of (4.2)) are real but that the root $\lambda = \alpha + \beta i$ of (4.2) is complex $(\beta \neq 0)$. Then according to Theorem 7.7 of Chapter Eight, the conjugate complex number $\bar{\lambda} = \alpha - \beta i$ must also be a root of (4.2). Corresponding to these two roots of (4.2) the general solution (4.3) contains a pair of terms which may be written

$$(4.4) \quad c(\alpha + \beta i)^t + d(\alpha - \beta i)^t,$$

where c and d are arbitrary constants. If we use the trigonometric representation for the complex numbers $\alpha + \beta i$ and $\alpha - \beta i$, namely,

$$\alpha + \beta i = r(\cos \theta + i \sin \theta),$$
$$\alpha - \beta i = r(\cos \theta - i \sin \theta),$$

and use De Moivre's theorem (Theorem 3.1), the expression (4.4) becomes

$$cr^t(\cos t\theta + i \sin t\theta) + dr^t(\cos t\theta - i \sin t\theta),$$

or

$$(c + d)r^t \cos t\theta + i\,(c - d)\,r^t \sin t\theta.$$

If this component of the solution (4.3) is required to be real, the coefficients $c + d$ and $i(c - d)$ must be real numbers, say A and B, respectively:

$$(4.5) \begin{cases} c + d = A, \\ c - d = -iB. \end{cases}$$

This pair of equations is easily solved for c and d; the solution is

$$c = \tfrac{1}{2}(A - Bi), \quad d = \tfrac{1}{2}(A + Bi).$$

Thus given any real constants A and B, one can find constants c and d such that

$$(4.6) \quad Ar^t \cos t\theta + Br^t \sin t\theta = c(\alpha + \beta i)^t + d(\alpha - \beta i)^t \,;$$

and, conversely, given any constants c and d *for which (4.4) is real*, one can find real constants A and B such that (4.6) holds; they are given by the formulas (4.5). In other words, when the given difference equation has real coefficients, and one is interested only in real solutions, any pair of conjugate roots of (4.2) may be represented in the general solution by the pair of terms on the left side of (4.6) instead of the pair on the right. Since all complex roots of the auxiliary equation occur in conjugate pairs under these assumptions, this enables one to express the entire general solution in terms of real numbers only.

Example 4.1. What is the general solution of the difference equation

$$f(t + 3) - 2f(t + 2) + 4f(t + 1) - 8f(t) = 0 \,?$$

The auxiliary equation is

$$\lambda^3 - 2\lambda^2 + 4\lambda - 8 = 0 \,,$$

and this has the distinct roots (which can be found by factoring) $2i$, $-2i$, and 2. Thus, by Theorem 4.1, the general solution is

$$c_1(2i)^t + c_2(-2i)^t + c_3 2^t \,.$$

But using the ideas developed just above, we can write this general solution in the alternative form

$$A\, 2^t \cos t\frac{\pi}{2} + B\, 2^t \sin t\frac{\pi}{2} + c_3 2^t \,,$$

or

$$2^t\!\left(A \cos t\frac{\pi}{2} + B \sin t\frac{\pi}{2} + c_3\right),$$

since the trigonometric form of $\pm 2i$ is $2[\cos(\pi/2) \pm i \sin(\pi/2)]$.

EXERCISES

4.1. Find the general solution, in real form, of each of the following difference equations:

a) $f(t + 2) - 2f(t + 1) - 3f(t) = 0$
b) $f(t + 2) + f(t) = 0$
c) $6f(t + 2) + f(t + 1) - f(t) = 0$
d) $f(t + 3) - 6f(t + 2) + 11f(t + 1) - 6f(t) = 0$

4.2. By direct calculation, verify that the statement about Vandermonde determinants made in the text is true in the cases $n = 2$ and $n = 3$.

5. Repeated Roots; The Nonhomogeneous Equation. Although the phenomenon is comparatively improbable *a priori*, it may happen that the auxiliary equation (4.2) has repeated roots. For example, the auxiliary equation for

$$(5.1) \quad f(t + 2) - 4f(t + 1) + 4f(t) = 0$$

is

$$\lambda^2 - 4\lambda + 4 = 0 \, ,$$

and the roots of this equation are both equal to 2. In a case of this kind the method of finding the general solution given by Theorem 4.1 certainly breaks down, since the two solutions 2^t, 2^t are obviously not linearly independent (cf. Exercise 2.3); it therefore becomes necessary to find another solution which is linearly independent of 2^t.

Such a solution is provided by $t2^t$. That this function of t is a solution may be verified by direct substitution into (5.1); and that 2^t and $t2^t$ are linearly independent may be established on the basis of the criterion in Theorem 2.3, since

$$W(t) = \begin{vmatrix} 2^t & t2^t \\ 2^{t+1} & (t + 1)2^{t+1} \end{vmatrix} = 2^{2t+1} \neq 0 \, .$$

This is typical of a general situation:

Theorem 5.1.   If λ is a double root of the auxiliary equation (4.2), λ^t and $t\lambda^t$ are linearly independent solutions of the difference equation (2.1).

More generally still, there holds Theorem 5.2.

Theorem 5.2.   If λ is a k-fold root of the auxiliary equation (4.2), then

$$\lambda^t, \, t\lambda^t, \, t^2\lambda^t, \, \dots, \, t^{k-1}\lambda^t$$

are k linearly independent solutions of the difference equation (2.1).

We shall not prove this theorem here, for in order to prove either that the functions listed are solutions or that they are linearly independent requires some fairly elaborate algebra. The significance of the theorem, however, is this: in writing out the general solution when there are repeated roots of the auxiliary equation, each such root λ yields not a block of terms

$$c_1\lambda^t + c_2\lambda^t + \dots + c_k\lambda^t$$

(for this, in effect, is just one term artificially stretched out), but rather a block of *independent* terms

$$c_1\lambda^t + c_2t\lambda^t + \dots + c_kt^{k-1}\lambda^t \, .$$

Since this expression can also be written in the form

$$(c_1 + c_2t + \dots + c_kt^{k-1})\lambda^t \, ,$$

we may say that the contribution of the root λ to the general solution is λ^t multiplied by the general polynomial of degree $k - 1$.

The following theorem summarizes the preceding results:

Theorem 5.3.   *If the auxiliary equation (4.2) has the distinct roots λ_i $(i = 1, 2, \ldots, r \leqslant n)$, and if the multiplicity of λ_i as a root of (4.2) is k_i, then the general solution of the difference equation (2.1) may be obtained by multiplying λ_i^t by the general polynomial of degree $k_i - 1$ and adding the resulting r expressions together.*

When (2.1) has real coefficients, then if some of the roots λ_i are not real, the corresponding terms in the general solution may again be replaced by equivalent real terms in the way described at the end of Section 4; the presence of the various powers of t makes no significant difference in the details.

We turn now to the nonhomogeneous linear difference equation

$$(1.4) \quad a_0 f(t + n) + a_1 f(t + n - 1) + \ldots + a_n f(t) = b,$$

where $b \neq 0$. As in Section 2, our primary concern is with the case in which the coefficients a_i and the term b are all constants; but the next two theorems are also valid if they are variable functions of t.

Theorem 5.4.   *If $f_1(t)$ and $f_2(t)$ are solutions of (1.4), then the function $f(t) = f_1(t) - f_2(t)$ is a solution of the corresponding "reduced" equation*

$$(2.1) \quad a_0 f(t + n) + a_1 f(t + n - 1) + \ldots + a_n f(t) = 0.$$

Conversely, if $f_2(t)$ is any solution of (1.4), and $f(t)$ is any solution of (2.1), then the function $f_1(t) = f(t) + f_2(t)$ is a solution of (1.4).

The two parts of this theorem have proofs closely resembling that of Theorem 2.2; the problem of proving Theorem 5.4 is therefore left as an exercise.

Now let $f(t)$ stand for the general solution of (2.1), and let $f_1(t)$ be any one solution of the nonhomogeneous equation (1.4). It follows from Theorem 5.4 that the expression $f(t) + f_1(t)$ accounts for *all* solutions of the equation; for according to the first part of the theorem, the difference between any solution of (1.4) and $f_1(t)$ is a solution of (2.1), and therefore can be obtained by assigning suitable values to the arbitrary constants in $f(t)$; thus any solution of (1.4) can be obtained from $f(t) + f_1(t)$ by assigning suitable values to the constants in $f(t)$. On the other hand, by the second part of the theorem, any function so obtained must be a solution of (1.4). This constitutes a proof of Theorem 5.5.

Theorem 5.5.   *If $f(t)$ is the general solution of (2.1), and $f_1(t)$ is any particular solution of (1.4), then $f(t) + f_1(t)$ is the general solution of (1.4).*

Thus the problem of completely solving any nonhomogeneous equation (1.4) reduces to two problems: (A) Find the general solution of the reduced equation (2.1); (B) Find any one solution of the complete nonhomogeneous equation (1.4). In the case where all of the coefficients a_i are constants, problem (A) has already been solved; this leaves problem (B).

For the most part, problem (B) is a hook-or-crook matter. Since only one solution of (1.4) is required, many of the mathematical niceties tend to go by the board and the process becomes one of trial and error. Fortunately, in the simplest cases, notably when b is a constant, certain types of trials can be relied on to work in most cases.

When b is a constant, try a constant c in the role of $f_1(t)$. If $f(t) \equiv c$ is substituted into (1.4), one obtains

$$a_0 c + a_1 c + \ldots + a_n c = b.$$

But this may be solved for c:

$$(5.2) \quad c = b / \sum_{i=0}^{n} a_i.$$

Thus, when all the coefficients (including b) in (1.4) are constants, one can take as the $f_1(t)$ of Theorem 5.5 the constant c given by (5.2), *provided that* $\sum_{i=0}^{n} a_i \neq 0$. If $\sum_{i=0}^{n} a_i = 0$ (which means simply that any constant is a solution of the reduced equation (2.1), and so could not possibly be a solution of (1.4)), one should try a solution of the form ct, or (if that fails) ct^2, etc. For some suitable value of m, a value can be assigned to c so that ct^m will indeed be a solution of the equation (1.4) with constant coefficients.

EXERCISES

5.1. Find the general solution (in real form) of each of the following homogeneous linear difference equations:

  a) $f(t + 2) + 6f(t + 1) + 9f(t) = 0$
  b) $f(t + 2) - f(t + 1) + \frac{1}{4}f(t) = 0$
  c) $f(t + 4) + 2f(t + 2) + f(t) = 0$

5.2. Derive Theorem 4.1 from Theorem 5.3.

5.3. Find the general solution (in real form) of each of the following nonhomogeneous linear difference equations:

  a) $f(t + 1) - 4f(t) = 6$
  b) $f(t + 2) - 5f(t + 1) + 6f(t) = 2$
  c) $f(t + 2) - 2f(t + 1) + f(t) = 1$

5.4. What kind of trial solution would you use for the difference equation (1.4) if the coefficients a_i are all constants, but b is a polynomial of degree k in t? Under what circumstances (if any) might you expect this method to break down? Use your method to find the general solution of the difference equation

$$f(t + 1) - 4f(t) = 3t^2 - 2t + 2.$$

5.5. Prove Theorem 5.4.

6. Systems of Difference Equations. Just as, in algebra, one frequently needs to solve a system of equations involving several unknowns, so one sometimes encounters the problem of solving a system of several *difference* equations involving several unknown *functions* of the discrete variable t. This happens in Model VI of Chapter Four, where there arises a system of the form

$$(6.1) \begin{cases} a_{11} f_1(t + 1) + a_{12} f_2(t + 1) + b_{11} f_1(t) + b_{12} f_2(t) + c_1 = 0, \\ a_{21} f_1(t + 1) + a_{22} f_2(t + 1) + b_{21} f_1(t) + b_{22} f_2(t) + c_2 = 0, \end{cases}$$

where $f_1(t)$ and $f_2(t)$ are the unknown functions, and the coefficients a_{ij}, b_{ij}, and c_i $(i, j = 1, 2)$ are constants. Since this is the only kind of system of difference equations to appear in Part I, and since the properties of this system are typical in many ways of difference equation systems in general, we shall confine our attention to it.

A *solution* of the system (6.1) is defined as a pair of functions $(f_1(t), f_2(t))$ which, when substituted into the equations (6.1), make these equations identities in t. On the basis of our experience with the theory of a single difference equation, we may plausibly conjecture that the system (6.1) may be solved by (A) finding two essentially distinct solutions $(f_{11}(t), f_{21}(t))$, $(f_{12}(t), f_{22}(t))$ of the "reduced" homogeneous system

$$(6.2)\begin{cases} a_{11}f_1(t+1) + a_{12}f_2(t+1) + b_{11}f_1(t) + b_{12}f_2(t) = 0, \\ a_{21}f_1(t+1) + a_{22}f_2(t+1) + b_{21}f_1(t) + b_{22}f_2(t) = 0; \end{cases}$$

and (B) finding any one solution, say $(f_{10}(t), f_{20}(t))$, of the complete system (6.1), and then writing

$$(6.3)\begin{cases} f_1(t) = c_1f_{11}(t) + c_2f_{12}(t) + f_{10}(t), \\ f_2(t) = c_1f_{21}(t) + c_2f_{22}(t) + f_{20}(t), \end{cases}$$

for the general solution of (6.1), where c_1 and c_2 are arbitrary constants. The truth of this conjecture is borne out by a proof which simply consists in showing that the line of reasoning that leads to the analogous conclusion for a single difference equation may be adapted to this case. We shall therefore limit our remarks to a discussion of the problems (A) and (B).

First, however, the phrase "essentially distinct" should be defined more precisely. As one might expect, "essential distinctness" is a matter of linear independence. Here the two pairs of functions $(f_{11}(t), f_{21}(t))$, $(f_{12}(t), f_{22}(t))$ are said to be linearly *dependent* if it is possible to find a pair of constants c_1 and c_2, not both zero, such that

$$(6.4)\begin{cases} c_1f_{11}(t) + c_2f_{12}(t) \equiv 0, \\ c_1f_{21}(t) + c_2f_{22}(t) \equiv 0; \end{cases}$$

in other words, if each of the pairs of functions $(f_{11}(t), f_{12}(t))$ and $(f_{21}(t), f_{22}(t))$ is linearly dependent in the sense defined in Section 2, and *the same constants c_1 and c_2 may be used in both cases*. In the contrary case, the two function pairs $(f_{11}(t), f_{21}(t))$ and $(f_{12}(t), f_{22}(t))$ are said to be linearly *independent*.

The above remarks hold true even if the coefficients a_{ij}, b_{ij}, and c_i are functions of t, not merely constants; but it will be assumed here that the coefficients are constants.

The results for a single difference equation might suggest that a promising starting point for solving problem (A) would be to choose (λ^t, μ^t) as a trial solution of (6.2), and by substitution to find the right values for λ

and μ. A moderate amount of experimentation will nevertheless show that the assumption that there exists such a solution of the system (6.2) is at once too broad and too narrow: too narrow, because in general it is necessary to introduce constant coefficients, not necessarily equal, so that the trial solution becomes $(e_1\lambda^t, e_2\mu^t)$, where e_1 and e_2 are to be determined; too broad, because one may always suppose that $\lambda = \mu$. We therefore substitute the trial solution $f_1(t) = e_1\lambda^t$, $f_2(t) = e_2\lambda^t$ into (6.2), in the hope that suitable values may be found for λ, e_1 and e_2. The result of this substitution is

$$(6.5) \begin{cases} a_{11}e_1\lambda^{t+1} + a_{12}e_2\lambda^{t+1} + b_{11}e_1\lambda^t + b_{12}e_2\lambda^t = 0, \\ a_{21}e_1\lambda^{t+1} + a_{22}e_2\lambda^{t+1} + b_{21}e_1\lambda^t + b_{22}e_2\lambda^t = 0. \end{cases}$$

Since we may suppose that $\lambda \neq 0$ [the functions $f_1(t) \equiv 0$, $f_2(t) \equiv 0$ obviously constitute a solution of (6.2), but this solution is linearly independent of no other solution], the common factor λ^t may be removed from both equations (6.5). If the resulting equations are slightly rearranged, one obtains

$$(6.6) \begin{cases} (b_{11} + a_{11}\lambda)e_1 + (b_{12} + a_{12}\lambda)e_2 = 0, \\ (b_{21} + a_{21}\lambda)e_1 + (b_{22} + a_{22}\lambda)e_2 = 0. \end{cases}$$

If these equations are satisfied (and only then), $(e_1\lambda^t, e_2\lambda^t)$ is a solution of (6.2). But the system (6.6) may be regarded as a pair of simultaneous homogeneous linear equations in the unknowns e_1 and e_2, where λ is a parameter. Again, the solution $e_1 = 0$, $e_2 = 0$ of (6.6) is of no interest, for it would lead merely to the trivial solution $f_1(t) \equiv 0, f_2(t) \equiv 0$ of (6.2). Thus in order to get somewhere we must require that (6.6) have solutions other than $e_1 = 0$, $e_2 = 0$. But according to the theory of Chapter Eleven, this will happen if and only if the determinant

$$(6.7) \begin{vmatrix} b_{11} + a_{11}\lambda & b_{12} + a_{12}\lambda \\ b_{21} + a_{21}\lambda & b_{22} + a_{22}\lambda \end{vmatrix} = 0.$$

This is the *auxiliary* or *characteristic equation* for the system of difference equations (6.1). The equation (6.7) is simply a quadratic equation in λ, the roots of which, say λ_1 and λ_2, we shall assume for the present to be distinct. Then when λ has either of these values, the system (6.6) has a nontrivial solution, say (e_{11}, e_{21}) for λ_1, (e_{12}, e_{22}) for λ_2, and we obtain the two solutions of (6.2):

$$(6.8) \quad f_{11}(t) = e_{11}\lambda_1^t, \quad f_{21}(t) = e_{21}\lambda_1^t; \quad f_{12}(t) = e_{12}\lambda_2^t, \quad f_{22}(t) = e_{22}\lambda_2^t.$$

These two solutions may be shown to be linearly independent.

When the roots λ_1 and λ_2 are not real, but the coefficients of the equations (6.2) are, the solutions (6.8) may be put into an equivalent real form along the lines described in Section 4. When $\lambda_1 = \lambda_2$, the solutions (6.8) are of course not linearly independent in general, but they may be made so by allowing e_{12} and e_{22} to be certain linear functions of t rather than constants. In view of the rarity of this case, we shall not dwell on the details.

Thus the complete solution of problem (A) has been outlined, and the procedure for finding a pair of linearly independent solutions of (6.2) in any specific case should be clear.

This leaves problem (B). Here the approach described at the end of Section 5 is again fruitful. Namely, try (g_1, g_2) where g_1 and g_2 are undetermined constants, by substitution in the system of equations (6.1). The result of this substitution is a pair of linear equations which may be written

$$(6.9) \begin{cases} (a_{11} + b_{11})g_1 + (a_{12} + b_{12})g_2 = -c_1, \\ (a_{21} + b_{21})g_1 + (a_{22} + b_{22})g_2 = -c_2. \end{cases}$$

If the determinant of coefficients is not zero (it is zero if and only if 1 is a root of the auxiliary equation, i.e., if and only if one of the solutions of the reduced system (6.2) consists of constants), this pair of equations may be solved for g_1 and g_2, and the desired solution of (6.1) is obtained. If, on the other hand, the determinant of the coefficients is zero, substitution of a trial solution of the form $(g_1 t, g_2 t)$ or, at worst $(g_1 t^2, g_2 t^2)$, will yield a system of equations which can be solved for g_1 and g_2, so that a solution of (6.1) is obtained in one of these forms.

EXERCISES

6.1. Solve the system of difference equations

$$\begin{cases} f_1(t + 1) + f_2(t + 1) + f_1(t) + f_2(t) + 4 = 0 \\ 3f_1(t + 1) - 3f_2(t + 1) - 7f_1(t) + 5f_2(t) - 8 = 0. \end{cases}$$

6.2. Prove the parenthetical remark following (6.5).

6.3. Under what condition does (6.7) fail to be a true quadratic equation? What is it in the theory of a single difference equation that corresponds to this condition?

7. Stability for Difference Equations. The question of the stability of a constant solution of a difference equation (or a system of difference equations) with constant coefficients may be answered quite easily, in principle, with the aid of the following proposition:

Theorem 7.1. If n is any nonnegative whole number, λ is a complex number, and t is a discrete variable ($t = 0, 1, 2, \ldots$), then

$$f(t) = t^n \lambda^t \to 0 \text{ as } t \to \infty$$

if and only if $|\lambda| < 1$.

PROOF: We consider the ratio $f(t + 1)/f(t) = (1 + (1/t))^n \lambda$. The limit as $t \to \infty$ of the first factor, $(1 + (1/t))^n$, is certainly 1. Thus

$$(7.1) \quad \frac{|f(t + 1)|}{|f(t)|} \to |\lambda| \text{ as } t \to \infty.$$

Now if $|\lambda| > 1$, this means that when t is very large, $|f(t+1)| > |f(t)|$, i.e. that the absolute value of $f(t)$ increases with t.

On the other hand, if $|\lambda| < 1$, (7.1) implies that for values of t sufficiently large, say $t \geqslant t_0$, $|f(t+1)|/|f(t)| < \delta$, where δ is some real number satisfying $|\lambda| < \delta < 1$. Thus (putting $t = t_0$ in this relation) we have

$$|f(t_0 + 1)| < \delta|f(t_0)| \; ;$$

putting $t = t_0 + 1$, we get from the same relation

$$|f(t_0 + 2)| < \delta|f(t_0 + 1)| < \delta^2|f(t_0)| \; ;$$

and in general

$$|f(t_0 + n)| < \delta^n|f(t_0)| \; .$$

Since $0 < \delta < 1$, the right side of this inequality tends to zero as $n \to \infty$. The same must therefore be true of the left side, so $f(t) \to 0$ as $t \to \infty$.

Finally, if $|\lambda| = 1$, $|f(t)| = |t^n\lambda^t| = t^n$, and this certainly does not tend to 0 as $t \to \infty$ when n is a nonnegative whole number. This completes the proof.

Now suppose that a difference equation (1.4) with constant coefficients (or, respectively, a system of difference equations (6.1) with constant coefficients) has a constant solution c (or, respectively, (g_1, g_2)). Then the general solution is of the form $f(t) + c$ (or $[f_1(t) + g_1, f_2(t) + g_2]$), where each of the functions $f(t), f_1(t), f_2(t)$ is a sum of terms of the form

$$(7.2) \quad ct^n\lambda^t ,$$

c being an arbitrary constant, n a nonnegative whole number (usually zero), and λ a root of the appropriate auxiliary equation. In order for the constant solution to be stable, *every* solution of the difference equation (or system of difference equations) must approach that solution as $t \to \infty$. But this will happen if *and only if* each of the terms (7.2) approaches 0 as $t \to \infty$, irrespective of the value of c. It follows from Theorem 7.1, however, that this in turn will happen if and only if $|\lambda| < 1$. Thus we have proved the fundamental stability criterion for difference equations which follows.

Theorem 7.2. If a linear difference equation (1.4), or a system of linear difference equations (6.2), with constant coefficients has a constant (i.e., equilibrium) solution, then that solution will be stable if and only if every root λ of the relevant auxiliary equation satisfies the condition $|\lambda| < 1$.

It should be added that when the latter condition is satisfied, a (unique) constant solution will certainly exist, for as we have seen in the course of the preceding sections, a difference equation or system of difference equations of the type described can fail to have a constant solution, or have more than one constant solution, only if the corresponding reduced equation or system of equations has a constant solution other than the zero solution, and this in turn occurs if and only if 1 is a root of the associated auxiliary equation.

Finally, we would point out that the stability guaranteed by the criterion in Theorem 7.2 is *perfect* stability. More precisely, Theorem 7.2 gives a condition which is *necessary* for local *or* perfect stability, *sufficient* for perfect stability (and therefore also for local stability).

EXERCISES

7.1. Without writing out the general solution, show that the equilibrium solution of the difference equation

$$16f(t + 4) - f(t) = 30$$

is perfectly stable. What *is* the equilibrium solution?

7.2. Describe in a general qualitative way the behavior of solutions of a linear difference equation (1.4) with constant coefficients if the roots of the auxiliary equation are all distinct and satisfy the condition $|\lambda| = 1$.

8. The Exponential Function. In elementary algebra one defines $a^{p/q}$, where $a > 0$ and p and q are integers ($q > 0$) as the principal qth root of the pth power of a, i.e., as that positive number x which satisfies the equation $x^q = a^p$. One can therefore think of this as defining a function

$$(8.1) \quad x = a^t,$$

whose domain is the set of all rational numbers t. It may be shown that there is exactly one way of assigning a value to a^t when t is any *ir*rational number so that the function (8.1) is defined and continuous for *all* real values of t. The function (8.1) so defined is called an *exponential function*, or more precisely *the exponential function with base a*. By definition, an exponential function has the set of all real numbers as its domain and is continuous for every value of t. The distinction between the exponential functions (8.1) and the *power functions* $x = t^a$, where the independent variable is the base, not the exponent, is extremely important, and should not be forgotten.

By far the most important exponential function is that corresponding to a certain value of a, namely, the constant e defined by

$$(8.2) \quad e = \lim_{h \to 0} (1 + h)^{1/h}$$

The number e is irrational; its value accurate to six decimal places is 2.718282. The exponential function

$$(8.3) \quad x = e^t$$

is usually referred to simply as *the exponential function*. Its unique importance depends on the curious fact that *this function is its own derivative*.

Theorem 8.1. If $x = e^t$, then $dx/dt = e^t$.

This theorem will not be proved here, since the least tortuous proof makes use of a function called the natural logarithm, an account of which would be an unwelcome digression at this point.

From Theorem 8.1 it at once follows, by the simple chain rule, that if a is any constant, the derivative of e^{at} is ae^{at}; or, more generally, that if $f(t)$ is any differentiable function, the derivative of $e^{f(t)}$ is $f'(t)e^{f(t)}$.

Although e^t is not defined from the outset for complex (nonreal) values of t, its definition can be extended to cover this case in several ways, one of which we shall now briefly sketch. Using Theorem 8.1, one can easily compute the Maclaurin series for e^t; it is

$$(8.4) \quad 1 + t + \frac{t^2}{2!} + \frac{t^3}{3!} + \cdots + \frac{t^n}{n!} + \cdots.$$

This series converges to e^t for all values of t. Now if t is replaced by any complex number $\alpha + \beta i$, the series (8.4) still converges, and the number (usually not real) to which it converges is *defined* as $e^{\alpha + \beta i}$. The function of the complex variable t defined in this way has all the above-mentioned properties of the original exponential function. In particular, it is differentiable, and obeys Theorem 8.1.

When t is a pure imaginary, say βi, then (8.4) becomes

$$1 + \beta i - \frac{\beta^2}{2!} - \frac{\beta^3}{3!}i + \frac{\beta^4}{4!} - \cdots$$

which, upon rearranging terms, becomes

$$(8.5) \quad \left(1 - \frac{\beta^2}{2!} + \frac{\beta^4}{4!} - \cdots\right) + \left(\beta - \frac{\beta^3}{3!} + \frac{\beta^5}{5!} - \cdots\right)i.$$

Now the two infinite series within parentheses happen to be the (always convergent) Maclaurin series for the cosine and sine, respectively. Thus (8.5) may be written

$$\cos \beta + i \sin \beta,$$

and we have the result

$$(8.6) \quad e^{\beta i} = \cos \beta + i \sin \beta.$$

This relation is called *Euler's formula;* it enables one to express the value of $e^{\beta i}$ as an explicit complex number. The operations with infinite series used in deriving this formula may be justified with the aid of the general theory of infinite series.

EXERCISES

8.1. Taking t to be a real variable, describe the general behavior of the function a^t when (a) $0 < a < 1$, (b) $a = 1$, (c) $a > 1$.

8.2. Find the derivative of each of the following functions:
(a) e^{-t}, (b) e^{-t^2}, (c) e^{e^t}, (d) $(t - 1)e^t$.

8.3. Using Euler's formula (8.6), find the explicit value of
(a) $e^{\pi i}$, (b) $e^{\frac{1}{2}(1 + 3\pi i)}$, (c) i^i (Hint: by [8.6], $i = e^{\frac{1}{2}\pi i}$).

8.4. Derive De Moivre's Theorem from Euler's formula.

8.5. Prove that $|e^{\beta i}| = 1$ if β is any real number.

9. Linear Differential Equations. *A linear differential equation of order n* is a relation of the form

$$(9.1) \quad a_0 f^{(n)}(t) + a_1 f^{(n-1)}(t) + \ldots + a_n f(t) = b,$$

where $f(t)$ is an unknown function of the continuous variable t, and the coefficients a_i and b are given functions of t (or, more particularly, constants). The problem associated with (9.1) is of course that of finding a solution, or better yet all possible solutions of the equation, a solution being defined as a function of t (with the necessary derivatives) which, when substituted for $f(t)$ in (9.1), reduces the latter to an identity in t.

The theory of (9.1), right down to the arrangement of proofs, is so closely similar to that of the analogous difference equation (1.4) that we are justified in merely giving its outlines. Our ultimate concern is with the case in which all coefficients are constants, but Theorems 9.1–9.5 are true more generally, namely, when the coefficients a_i and b are any continuous functions of t, and $a_0 \neq 0$. The assumption that these conditions are satisfied will be taken for granted in what follows.

Theorem 9.1. If $x_0, x_1, \ldots, x_{n-1}$ are any numbers, and t_0 is any value of t, there exists exactly one solution $f(t)$ of (9.1) satisfying the conditions

$$f(t_0) = x_0, \ f'(t_0) = x_1, \ f''(t_0) = x_2, \ldots, f^{(n-1)}(t_0) = x_{n-1}.$$

In other words, there is a unique solution of (9.1) assuming a prescribed value, and whose first $n - 1$ derivatives assume prescribed values, at any given value of t. This is the fundamental existence and uniqueness theorem for solutions of (9.1); but unlike its difference equation counterpart, it can be proved only with considerable difficulty. We shall omit the proof entirely.

The equation (9.1) is said to be *homogeneous* if the term b is identically zero. As an immediate consequence of Theorem 9.1, we have Theorem 9.2.

Theorem 9.2. A solution of the homogeneous equation

$$(9.2) \quad a_0 f^{(n)}(t) + a_1 f^{(n-1)}(t) + \ldots + a_n f(t) = 0$$

which has the value zero, and whose first $n - 1$ derivatives all have the value zero, at any given value of t must be identically zero.

From this, as in Section 2, one may derive Theorem 9.3.

Theorem 9.3. Any n solutions $f_1(t), f_2(t), \ldots, f_n(t)$ of (9.2) are linearly dependent if and only if the "Wronskian" determinant

$$W(t) = \begin{vmatrix} f_1(t) & f_2(t) & \ldots & f_n(t) \\ f_1'(t) & f_2'(t) & \ldots & f_n'(t) \\ \ldots\ldots\ldots\ldots\ldots\ldots\ldots\ldots\ldots \\ f_1^{(n-1)}(t) & f_2^{(n-1)}(t) & . & f_n^{(n-1)}(t) \end{vmatrix}$$

is identically zero.

Or, in other words, the n solutions are linearly *in*dependent if and only if there exists at least one value of t such that $W(t) \neq 0$. From this fact in turn one can derive Theorem 9.4.

Theorem 9.4. If $f_1(t), f_2(t), \ldots, f_n(t)$ are n linearly independent solutions of (9.2), then the expression

$$(9.3) \quad c_1 f_1(t) + c_2 f_2(t) + \ldots + c_n f_n(t) ,$$

where the coefficients c_i are arbitrary constants, is the general solution of (9.2).

The practical consequence of this theorem is that in order to find *all* solutions of (9.2), all one has to do, in effect, is to find n linearly independent solutions of that equation.

Another proposition whose statement and proof are almost identical with those of its difference equation counterpart is the next theorem.

Theorem 9.5. If $f(t)$ is the general solution of (9.2), and $f_1(t)$ is any one solution of (9.1), then the general solution of (9.1) is $f_1(t) + f(t)$.

The last two theorems lead to the familiar separation of the problem of solving (9.1) into two problems: (A) find the general solution of (9.2), i.e., n linearly independent solutions of (9.2); and (B) find any solution of (9.1). The sum of the answers to these two problems is the answer to the principal problem. On the assumption that the quantities a_i and b are constants, which will be tacitly made throughout the remainder of this section, we shall now give the solutions of these two problems.

First, problem (A). It was pointed out in Section 8 that the derivative of e^t is e^t itself; in other words, e^t is a solution of the simple homogeneous linear differential equation

$$f'(t) - f(t) = 0 .$$

Generalizing this result slightly, one can verify by direct substitution that $e^{-\left(\frac{a_1}{a_0}\right)t}$ is a solution of

$$a_0 f'(t) + a_1 f(t) = 0 .$$

Thus it appears (cf. Section 1) that functions of the form $e^{\lambda t}$ may play the same role here that the functions λ^t play in the theory of difference equations with constant coefficients. To pursue this possibility further, substitute $f(t) = e^{\lambda t}$ into (9.2). Since $f'(t) = \lambda e^{\lambda t}, f''(t) = \lambda^2 e^{\lambda t}$, and in general $f^{(k)}(t) = \lambda^k e^{\lambda t}$, the result of this substitution is

$$(9.4) \quad a_0 \lambda^n e^{\lambda t} + a_1 \lambda^{n-1} e^{\lambda t} + \ldots + a_n e^{\lambda t} = 0 .$$

Since $e^{\lambda t} \neq 0$, (9.4) is equivalent to the equation

$$(9.5) \quad a_0 \lambda^n + a_1 \lambda^{n-1} + \ldots + a_n = 0 .$$

Here again we have a polynomial equation for λ, and in view of its origin we may say that $e^{\lambda t}$ *is a solution of (9.2) if and only if λ is a solution of (9.5)*. Accordingly, (9.5) is called the *auxiliary equation* for (9.2) (or [9.1]). If the n roots $\lambda_1, \lambda_2, \ldots, \lambda_n$ of (9.5) are distinct, we thus obtain n different solutions $e^{\lambda_1 t}, e^{\lambda_2 t}, \ldots, e^{\lambda_n t}$ of (9.2). Not only are they different but they are linearly independent. For if one calculates the Wronskian $W(t)$, the value of $W(0)$ is exactly the Vandermonde determinant that appears in Section 3, and because the λ_i's are distinct, $W(0) \neq 0$. The linear independence of the given solutions of (9.2) therefore follows from Theorem 9.3.

In summary, we have Theorem 9.6.

Theorem 9.6. If the auxiliary equation (9.5) has n distinct roots λ_1, λ_2, ..., λ_n, the general solution of (9.2) is

$$(9.6) \quad c_1 e^{\lambda_1 t} + c_2 e^{\lambda_2 t} + \ldots + c_n e^{\lambda_n t}.$$

This result is strictly correct whether the roots λ_i are real or not; here again, however, the expression (9.6) is rather unsatisfactory if the original differential equation has real coefficients and one is interested only in real solutions, but some of the roots λ_i are not real. In this case the solution (9.6) may be put into a real form by means of Euler's formula (8.6). In fact, let $\lambda = \alpha + \beta i$ be a complex root of (9.5) ($\beta \neq 0$). Then $\bar{\lambda} = \alpha - \beta i$ is also a root of (9.5), since by assumption (9.5) has real coefficients. Thus (9.6) contains two terms which may be written $ce^{\lambda t} + de^{\bar{\lambda} t}$; and using the properties of exponents and Euler's formula, we obtain[4]

$$\begin{aligned}
ce^{\lambda t} + de^{\bar{\lambda} t} &= ce^{(\alpha + \beta i)t} + de^{(\alpha - \beta i)t} \\
&= ce^{\alpha t} e^{\beta i t} + de^{\alpha t} e^{-\beta i t} \\
&= e^{\alpha t}(ce^{\beta i t} + de^{-\beta i t}) \\
&= e^{\alpha t}[c(\cos \beta t + i \sin \beta t) + d(\cos \beta t - i \sin \beta t)] \\
&= e^{\alpha t}[(c + d) \cos \beta t + i (c - d) \sin \beta t].
\end{aligned}$$

For this to be real, the coefficients $(c + d)$ and $i(c - d)$ must themselves be real. To simplify the notation, we therefore denote them by A and B. This yields the desired real equivalent of the given pair of terms, namely,

$$e^{\alpha t}(A \cos \beta t + B \sin \beta t).$$

If the auxiliary equation (9.5) has multiple roots, Theorem 9.6 does not quite solve problem (A); but in this case one can resort to precisely the same expedient as was appropriate at the corresponding point in the theory of difference equations: if λ is a k-fold root of (9.5), in place of the solution $e^{\lambda t}$ repeated k times, one obtains the k truly distinct solutions $e^{\lambda t}$, $te^{\lambda t}$, $t^2 e^{\lambda t}, \ldots, t^{k-1} e^{\lambda t}$. Thus, precisely as in Section 5, one arrives at Theorem 9.7.

Theorem 9.7. If the auxiliary equation (9.5) has the distinct roots λ_i ($i = 1, 2, \ldots, r \leqslant n$), the multiplicity of λ_i being k_i, the general solution of (9.2) is obtained if one multiplies $e^{\lambda_i t}$ by the general polynomial of degree $k - 1$ and adds all of the resulting expressions together.

If there are repeated complex roots, the corresponding terms may still be put in a real form by the method described above.

Thus problem (A) is completely solved. Problem (B) is much easier.

---

[4] In the fourth line we also use the identity $\sin (-\theta) = -\sin \theta$, which may be verified by consulting the definition of the sine, Section 3.

The idea again is to use a constant trial solution, $f(t) \equiv c$. Substituting this into (9.1) gives simply

$$a_n c = b ,$$

since all the terms containing derivatives vanish. If $a_n \neq 0$, therefore, b/a_n is a solution of (9.1). If $a_n = 0$, (i.e., if $\lambda = 0$ is a root of the auxiliary equation), one should try a solution of the form $f(t) = ct$; and if that fails, of the form $f(t) = ct^2$; and so on. Sooner or later one will arrive at an integer m such that (9.1) has a solution of the form $f(t) = ct^m$, where the value of c may be determined by substitution.

EXERCISES

9.1. Find the general solution of each of the following differential equations:
  a) $f'(t) + f(t) = 0$
  b) $f''(t) - 5f'(t) + 6f(t) = 1$
  c) $f''(t) + f(t) = 2$
  d) $f^{(4)}(t) - 25f''(t) = 100$

9.2. The close parallelism between the theory of the differential equation (9.1) and that of the difference equation (1.4) has been alluded to frequently in this section. Taking this as a hint,
  a) Prove Theorem 9.2.
  b) Prove Theorem 9.3.
  c) Prove Theorem 9.4.
  d) Prove Theorem 9.5.

9.3. Devise a method for determining, simply by looking at the given differential equation, what the value of the exponent m mentioned in the last paragraph of this section should be.

10. Systems of Differential Equations. The extremely close analogy between the theory of difference equations and that of differential equations persists when one comes to the consideration of systems. Thus the account of *systems* of differential equations in the present section will be fairly brief, for the reader should be able to fill in the most important details by developing the analogues to the details in Section 6. Our discussion will nevertheless differ in two important respects from the discussion in Section 6: on the one hand, all differential equations concerned will be assumed to be *homogeneous;* on the other hand, we shall not confine our attention to systems involving only two equations.

Specifically, we shall consider the system of equations

$$(10.1) \quad f'_i(t) = a_{i1}f_1(t) + a_{i2}f_2(t) + \ldots + a_{in}f_n(t) \quad (i = 1, 2, \ldots, n) ,$$

where all of the coefficients a_{ij} are constants. The exclusive consideration of this system is not as restrictive as it may appear, since any system of linear differential equations with constant coefficients can be put into this form; an example of the process will be found in Chapter Four, Section 5.

A *solution* of (10.1) is a set of functions $f_1(t), \ldots, f_n(t)$ such that when they are substituted into (10.1), the system becomes identical in t. Following the lead suggested by Sections 6 and 9, we choose the trial solution $f_i(t) = e_i e^{\lambda t}$, $(i = 1, \ldots, n)$, where the e_i's and λ are constants to be determined. Substituting $e_i e^{\lambda t}$ for $f_i(t)$ in (10.1) gives

$$(10.2) \quad e_i \lambda e^{\lambda t} = a_{i1} e_1 e^{\lambda t} + a_{i2} e_2 e^{\lambda t} + \ldots + a_{in} e_n e^{\lambda t} \quad (i = 1, \ldots, n).$$

Removing the nonzero common factor $e^{\lambda t}$ and slightly rearranging terms, one obtains from (10.2) the system of equations

$$(10.3) \begin{cases} (a_{11} - \lambda)e_1 + a_{12}e_2 + \ldots + a_{1n}e_n = 0, \\ a_{21}e_1 + (a_{22} - \lambda)e_2 + \ldots + a_{2n}e_n = 0, \\ \ldots\ldots\ldots\ldots\ldots\ldots\ldots\ldots\ldots\ldots\ldots\ldots \\ a_{n1}e_1 + a_{n2}e_2 + \ldots + (a_{nn} - \lambda)e_n = 0. \end{cases}$$

This may be regarded as a homogeneous system of n linear equations in the n unknowns $e_1, e_2, \ldots, e_n$ containing the parameter λ. According to Theorems 6.2 and 6.3 of Chapter Eleven, this system has a nontrivial solution (i.e., a solution not consisting entirely of zeros) if and only if the determinant

$$(10.4) \quad \begin{vmatrix} a_{11} - \lambda & a_{12} & \ldots a_{1n} \\ a_{21} & a_{22} - \lambda & \ldots a_{2n} \\ \ldots\ldots\ldots\ldots\ldots\ldots\ldots\ldots\ldots \\ a_{n1} & a_{n2} & \ldots a_{nn} - \lambda \end{vmatrix} = 0.$$

This is a polynomial equation of degree n in λ, and therefore has n roots $\lambda_1, \lambda_2, \ldots, \lambda_n$. For each of these values of λ, say λ_i, the system (10.3) has nontrivial solutions. Let one such solution be $(e_{1i}, e_{2i}, \ldots, e_{ni})$. Since (10.3) is equivalent to (10.2), it follows that each of the sets of functions

$$(10.5) \quad f_{1i} = e_{1i}e^{\lambda_i t}, \, f_{2i} = e_{2i}e^{\lambda_i t}, \ldots, f_{ni} = e_{ni}e^{\lambda_i t} \quad (i = 1, \ldots, n)$$

constitutes a solution of (10.1). Moreover, if the roots λ_i are all distinct, the n solutions of (10.5) are essentially different; i.e., the *general* solution of (10.1) may be obtained by taking the general linear combination of the solutions (10.5):

$$(10.6) \quad f_1(t) = \Sigma_i c_i e_{1i}e^{\lambda_i t}, \ldots, f_n(t) = \Sigma_i c_i e_{ni}e^{\lambda_i t}.$$

If some of the roots of the auxiliary equation are repeated, or complex, or both, the usual qualifications should be made: if the coefficients a_{ij} are all real, and one is interested only in real-valued solutions, then in the presence of complex roots λ_i one can use Euler's formula to put the general solution in real form; and if some roots are repeated, some of the constants e_{ij} must be replaced by polynomials in t.

EXERCISES

10.1. Find the general solution of the system

$$\begin{cases} f_1'(t) = 4f_1(t) + 4f_2(t) , \\[2mm] f_2'(t) = 4f_1(t) + 2f_2(t) . \end{cases}$$

10.2. Write down the general solution of (10.1) if $a_{ij} = 0$ whenever $i \neq j$.

10.3. Show how one solution might be found for the nonhomogeneous system with constant coefficients

$$f_i'(t) = a_{i1}f_1(t) + a_{i2}f_2(t) + \ldots + a_{in}f_n(t) + c_i \quad (i = 1,2,\ldots,n),$$

assuming that 0 is not a root of the corresponding auxiliary equation (10.4).

10.4. Show that (10.1) has a constant solution other than $(0, 0, \ldots, 0)$ if and only if 0 is a root of the auxiliary equation (10.4).

11. Stability for Differential Equations. We have seen that the general solution of (9.1) is of the form[5] $f(t) + c$, and that the general solution of (10.1) is made up of functions $f_i(t)$, where the functions $f(t)$ and $f_i(t)$ are sums of terms of the type $kt^n e^{\lambda t}$, k being an arbitrary constant, n a nonnegative integer, and λ a root of the relevant auxiliary equation. Thus the constant (equilibrium) solution (c in the first case, $(0, 0, \ldots, 0)$ in the second) will be stable if and only if each of the terms $t^n e^{\lambda t} \to 0$ as $t \to \infty$. Since a quantity tends to zero if and only if its absolute value does so, this means that stability requires that

$$|t^n e^{\lambda t}| \to 0 \text{ as } t \to \infty$$

for each of the combinations $t^n e^{\lambda t}$ involved. If $\lambda = \alpha + \beta i$ (β may be zero) and $t > 0$ (as we may assume, since we are concerned with large values of t only),

$$|t^n e^{\lambda t}| = |t^n| \cdot |e^{\alpha t}| \cdot |e^{\beta i t}| = t^n e^{\alpha t},$$

since t^n and $e^{\alpha t}$ are positive and $|e^{\beta i t}| = 1$ (see Exercise 8.5).

Theorem 11.1. *Under the present assumptions, $t^n e^{\lambda t} \to 0$ as $t \to \infty$ if and only if $\alpha < 0$.*

This theorem may be proved along lines similar to those of the proof of Theorem 7.1.

Thus we have the fundamental stability criterion:

Theorem 11.2. *The equilibrium solution of (9.1) or of (10.1) is stable if and only if all roots of the associated auxiliary equation have negative real parts.*

Here again the equation (9.1) *will* have a (unique) constant solution if the stability condition is satisfied, for in the contrary case 0 must be a root

---

[5] Provided that (9.1) has a constant solution c; the contrary case will not concern us here.

of the auxiliary equation. The system (10.1) has a constant solution $(0, 0, \ldots, 0)$ in any case, but, likewise, the stability condition precludes the existence of any other constant solution (cf. Exercise 10.4). Thus, in any case, the stability condition of Theorem 11.2 not only guarantees the stability of a constant solution if it exists; it also guarantees the existence of such a solution.

Since the auxiliary equation is always a polynomial equation, the results of Chapter Eight, Section 7, are directly applicable to the problem of formulating explicit stability conditions in terms of the coefficients in (9.1) and (10.1).

A special result of importance in connection with the stability question for the system (10.1) is Theorem 11.3.

Theorem 11.3.   If the quadratic form $\Sigma_{ij}a_{ij}u_iu_j$ is negative definite, every root of the equation (10.4) has a negative real part.

PROOF: Let $\lambda = \alpha + \beta i$ be a root of (10.4). Then the system of equations (1.3) has a nontrivial solution, say $(e_1, e_2, \ldots, e_n)$, where $e_i = p_i + q_i i$ (p_i and q_i are real, $i = 1, \ldots, n$). Multiply the equations in (10.3) respectively by $\bar{e}_1, \bar{e}_2, \ldots, \bar{e}_n$, where $\bar{e}_i = p_i - q_i i$, and add; the result may be written

$$(11.1) \quad \Sigma_{ij}a_{ij}\bar{e}_ie_j - (\Sigma_i\bar{e}_ie_i)\lambda = 0 .$$

Since the complex number on the left side of this equation is zero, its real part must be zero; if one expands (11.1) in terms of the real numbers α, β, p_i, q_i, and discards all terms containing i, one therefore obtains

$$(\Sigma_i p_i^2 + \Sigma_i q_i^2)\alpha - (\Sigma_{ij}a_{ij}p_ip_j + \Sigma_{ij}a_{ij}q_iq_j) = 0 .$$

Since both the coefficient of α in this equation and the other term (because of the negative definiteness of $\Sigma_{ij}a_{ij}u_iu_j$) are positive, α can only be negative, as had to be proved.

COROLLARY: *The equilibrium solution of (10.1) is stable if the form $\Sigma_{ij}a_{ij}u_iu_j$ is negative definite.*

Similar stability conditions of a somewhat more special nature will be found in Chapter Four, Section 6.

EXERCISES

11.1. Formulate a set of specific stability conditions, in terms of the coefficients a_{ij}, for the system (10.1) when $n = 2$.

11.2. Prove Theorem 11.1.

SUGGESTIONS FOR FURTHER READING

For a somewhat more detailed introductory account of difference equations, see Tomlinson Fort, *Finite Differences* (Oxford: Clarendon Press, 1948), chap. vii; or F. B. Hildebrand, *Methods of Applied Mathematics* (New York: Prentice-Hall, Inc., 1952), chap. iii. Each of these works contains a list of more compendious works, of which C. Jordan's *Calculus of Finite Differences* (Budapest: Rottig & Romwalter, 1939) and L. M. Milne-Thompson's book of the same title (London: Macmillan Co., 1933) call for specific mention.

There are many introductory textbooks on differential equations, each with its peculiar merits; but we especially recommend Walter Leighton, *An Introduction to the Theory of Differential Equations* (New York: McGraw-Hill Book Co., Inc., 1952). A recent and rich treatise, to which we would send only readers with considerably more mathematical preparation than the present work can provide, is E. A. Coddington and N. Levinson, *Theory of Ordinary Differential Equations* (New York: McGraw-Hill Book Co., Inc., 1955).

Chapter Thirteen

MAXIMA AND MINIMA

In economic theory (as well as in many other subjects where mathematics plays a role) one frequently wants to know when a certain variable will attain its largest or smallest value. The variable is usually expressed as a function of certain other variables, say

$$x = f(t_1, \ldots, t_n),$$

and the problem more precisely is to determine which values should be assigned to the variables t_i in order to give x the largest or smallest values occurring in the range of the function. Sometimes it is further required that the domain of the function be restricted by a set of "constraints" or "side conditions" expressed in the form of equations

$$g_h(t_1, \ldots, t_n) = 0 \quad (h = 1, \ldots, m);$$

that is, the problem becomes that of making x as large (or as small) as possible by assigning values to the variables t_i which also satisfy these side conditions.

In economic theory problems of this kind are identified with the theory of consumer behavior and the theory of the firm, but of course once the relevant functions are given, whatever their source, the problem becomes a purely mathematical one. In this chapter we shall discuss problems of this type, beginning with the simplest case (that in which there is but one independent variable and no side conditions are imposed) and proceeding through the n-variable problem without side conditions to the full problem.

1. Extrema of a Function of One Variable. Let $f(t)$ be a given function of the real variable t, considered over a fixed interval of values of t: $T_1 \leqslant t \leqslant T_2$. The following basic definitions are in fair accord with everyday usage: A value t_0 of t $(T_1 \leqslant t_0 \leqslant T_2)$ is said to give $f(t)$ its *maximum* value over the fixed interval if

$$(1.1) \quad f(t) \leqslant f(t_0)$$

for all values of t in the interval, and its *minimum* value over the fixed interval if

$$(1.2) \quad f(t) \geqslant f(t_0)$$

for all values of t in the interval. Geometrically speaking, a given point on the graph of the function represents a maximum if there is no point on the graph (over the specified interval) higher than the given point, a minimum if there is none lower. Maxima and minima are thus defined relative to intervals; the maximum of a given function $f(t)$ over a specified interval may not remain maximum if the interval is expanded.

Sometimes it is convenient to allow for "infinite intervals." For instance, $f(t)$ is said to attain a maximum at t_0 relative to the semi-infinite interval $T_1 \leqslant t < +\infty$ if the inequality (1.1) is valid for every value of t satisfying $T_1 \leqslant t$, or relative to the infinite interval $-\infty < t < +\infty$ if (1.1) is true for any value of t whatever.[1] If no interval is specified, one may assume that the infinite interval is meant.

The word *extremum* is used to denote both maxima and minima.

A function may attain its maximum (or its minimum) at several points on a specified interval. The extreme example of this is provided by the constant functions: a function whose values are all equal attains its maximum (which is also its minimum) at every point of any specified interval. On the other hand, there may be no extrema at all, as in Example 1.1.

Example 1.1. Let $T_1 = -1$, $T_2 = +1$, and suppose that $f(t)$ is defined by the equations

$$f(t) = t \quad \text{if} \quad -1 < t < +1,$$
$$f(t) = 0 \quad \text{if} \quad t = -1 \text{ or } +1.$$

The graph of this function is indicated in Figure 1.1 (p. 316). The function attains values as near $+1$ as one wishes, but just fails to attain the value $+1$ itself; therefore $+1$, which is the most likely candidate for the maximum of $f(t)$, is not acceptable: there is no value t_0 of t such that $f(t_0) = +1$, but only such a value of t could give a maximum. The situation for a minimum is similar: -1 is almost a minimum for $f(t)$—no larger or smaller number could possibly do—but it fails because there is no value of t for which $f(t)$ actually equals -1.

The situation illustrated in Example 1.1 cannot occur when $f(t)$ is continuous. This fact is embodied in a basic theorem, Theorem 1.1, which we shall state without proof.

Theorem 1.1. If $f(t)$ is continuous on the finite interval $T_1 \leqslant t \leqslant T_2$, then $f(t)$ attains a maximum and a minimum on the interval.

This shows (as was already evident) that the trouble in Example 1.1 is due to the discontinuities of the given function at the ends of the interval.

Theorem 1.1 asserts the *existence* of extrema of continuous functions over finite intervals but gives not the slightest indication of how one should proceed in order to determine what the extrema are, or at what values of t they occur. Indeed, this is in general a rather difficult problem, and methods for solving it fall into two distinct classes: (a) special, direct methods extemporized to suit the particular function at hand—these methods tend

---

[1] Here again (cf. Chapter Nine, note 1) the symbols $-\infty$ and $+\infty$ should not be taken to stand for numbers but merely as inseparable constituents of the more complex symbols in which they occur.

to be basically arithmetical but often require a considerable amount of ingenuity; (*b*) general, indirect methods involving the notion of *relative* extrema and using the differential calculus. One example may serve to illustrate the methods of class (*a*), and therefore we shall limit our discussion to methods of the second class.

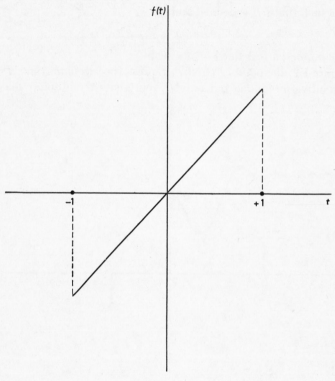

Fig. 1.1

Example 1.2. What is the maximum value (if any) of $f(t) = 5 + 8t - t^2$, and for what value(s) of t is it attained? Here one can use the method of "completing the square" introduced in elementary algebra:

$$f(t) = 5 + 8t - t^2$$
$$= 21 - 16 + 8t - t^2$$
$$= 21 - (16 - 8t + t^2)$$
$$= 21 - (4 - t)^2.$$

The last expression shows that the value of $f(t)$ may be regarded as the result of subtracting from 21 the nonnegative quantity $(4 - t)^2$. Thus the maximum value of the function is 21, and is attained only if this quantity is zero, i.e., $t = 4$.

Another instance of methods of class (*a*) was encountered in Example 6.1, Chapter Ten.

It is first necessary to define the concept of relative extrema. In order to preserve a clear distinction between these and the extrema defined above, we shall refer to the latter as *absolute* extrema. One says that a function $f(t)$ attains a *relative maximum* at t_0 if it attains an absolute maximum relative to some interval containing t_0 and contained in the domain of $f(t)$. More precisely, $f(t)$ attains a relative maximum at t_0 if there exists some positive number δ such that $f(t)$ is defined and

$$f(t) \leqslant f(t_0) \text{ whenever } t_0 - \delta \leqslant t \leqslant t_0 + \delta.$$

A *relative minimum* is defined analogously.

In Figure 1.2, the points P_1 and P_2 represent relative maxima, P_3 represents a relative minimum, but only P_1 represents the absolute maximum,

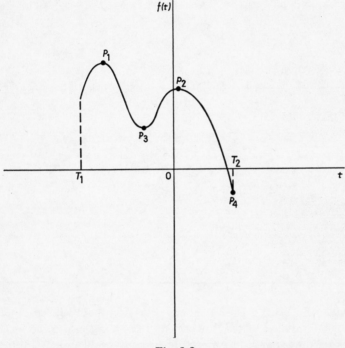

Fig. 1.2

and the absolute minimum is represented not by P_3, but by P_4, which is not a relative minimum at all.

Clearly, any absolute maximum must either be a relative maximum or occur at one end or the other of the interval. In order to determine the absolute maximum (if it exists) of a given function over a specified interval, it is therefore sufficient to determine all relative maxima and then, by simple arithmetical comparison, to see which of these is largest.[2] If the

---

[2] The process described may break down if there are infinitely many relative extrema, but this phenomenon (especially when the interval is finite) is definitely exceptional, and in particular cannot occur for rational functions, i.e., quotients of polynomials.

largest relative maximum is larger than the values of the function at the ends of the interval, it is the absolute maximum. Otherwise, the absolute maximum is attained at one end (or both ends) of the interval. If the function is discontinuous, these remarks require qualification, but in any case it should be clear that when one knows how to find relative extrema he is well equipped to find absolute extrema.

EXERCISES

1.1. Carefully formulate the definition of a relative minimum.

1.2. Using the method of Example 1.2, find the minimum value of the function $f(t) = t^2 - 6t - 20$, and find the value(s) of t for which the minimum is attained.

1.3. Find the absolute extrema of the function $f(t) = 1/(1 - t^2)$ on the interval $-1 \leqslant t \leqslant 0$.

1.4. Write out a detailed defense for the first statement in the last paragraph of Section 1.

2. *The Identification of Relative Extrema.* Further consideration of Figure 1.2 will suggest the geometrical significance of relative extrema; a relative maximum is a "peak" of the graph of the given function, while relative minima occur at the bottoms of "valleys." If a horizontal line is drawn through a point where a relative extremum occurs, then neighboring points on the curve will lie below (or on) the line if the extremum is a maximum, above (or on) the line if the extremum is a minimum. This in turn suggests that the concept of slope may be useful in identifying relative extrema. For instance, the relative maximum at P_1 in Figure 1.2 may be said to be one by virtue of the fact that the curve is upward sloping just to the left of P_1 and downward sloping just to the right: a point moving along the curve from left to right climbs just before reaching P_1 and falls just after. Relative maxima which are separated from other relative maxima (*isolated* relative maxima) will be characterized by this property, provided of course that one can speak of slopes on the curve in the neighborhood of the point.

In order to be able to pursue this point of view further, we shall assume that the function under investigation has a graph with a definite slope at every point; more precisely, we shall assume that the function has a continuous first derivative over the interval in question. It is hardly necessary to add that functions not satisfying this assumption may nevertheless have extrema of all kinds, and may at the same time be of great importance in some theoretical investigations. The assumption is being made merely to facilitate the analysis; our point of view can be extended to jagged and even discontinuous functions only with considerable awkwardness and but partial success.

The first theorem, Theorem 2.1, is basic.

Theorem 2.1.   If the function $f(t)$ has a relative extremum when $t = t_0$, then $f'(t_0) = 0$.

PROOF: We shall show that a relative extremum cannot occur at t_0 if $f'(t_0) \neq 0$. Using Taylor's formula with a remainder of order one we may write $f(t) = f(t_0) + f'(t')(t - t_0)$, or equivalently

$$(2.1) \quad f(t) - f(t_0) = f'(t')(t - t_0),$$

where t' lies between t and t_0. For the sake of argument, assume that $f'(t_0) > 0$. Since $f'(t)$ is continuous, $f'(t')$ will also be positive whenever t (and therefore t') is sufficiently close to t_0. But this means that the sign of the right side of equation (2.1) must change as t passes through t_0, for the first factor has an unvarying sign while the second changes sign at t_0. Therefore, by (2.1), $f(t) - f(t_0)$ is negative for values of t close to t_0 but smaller, positive for values of t close to t_0 but larger. This, however, cannot happen at a relative extremum; thus $f(t_0)$ is not a relative extremum of $f(t)$.

Theorem 2.1 may be paraphrased by saying that the vanishing of the first derivative is *necessary* for a relative extremum. That this condition is not sufficient is shown by a simple example, Example 2.1.

Example 2.1. Let $f(t) = t^3$. Then $f'(t) = 3t^2$, so that $f'(0) = 0$. The only value of t that could possibly give a relative extremum according to Theorem 2.1 is therefore zero; but it is easy to see that $f(t)$ does not attain a relative extremum at $t = 0$, for $f(t)$ is negative for all negative values of t and positive for all positive values of t. The function has no relative extrema.

A point at which the derivative is zero, but no relative extremum occurs, is sometimes called a *point of inflection*. It is characterized geometrically by the fact that the graph of the function crosses its own (horizontal) tangent at the point.

According to Theorem 2.1, if there are any relative extrema they must occur at points where $f'(t) = 0$. Points of this kind are called *critical points*, the corresponding values of t *critical values*. The first step in seeking relative extrema is therefore to differentiate the given function, set the resulting derivative equal to zero, and (if possible) find the real roots of the resulting equation. These roots will be the critical values of t, and what remains of the problem is to determine for each critical value whether it does not give a relative extremum at all (as in Example 2.1) or, if it does, whether the extremum is a relative maximum or a relative minimum. This problem is taken up in the next section.

EXERCISES

2.1. Illustrate the proof of Theorem 2.1 graphically.

2.2. Find all the critical values of t for each of the following functions:

(a) $6t^2 - 4t$,   (b) $t^3 + 6t^2 + 12t - 5$,   (c) t^4,

(d) $(1 + 2t)^2$,   (e) $\dfrac{t + 1}{t - 1}$,   (f) 12.

2.3. Find a condition on n such that the function $f(t) = t^n$ will attain a minimum at $t = 0$ if and only if the condition is satisfied. Consider only whole values of n.

2.4. Discuss the behavior as regards continuity, differentiability, and the existence of relative and absolute extrema of the function $f(t) = |t|$.

3. *The Classification of Relative Extrema.* In order to state the theorems of this section with both precision and a reasonable amount of simplicity, we shall find it convenient to use a new notation. Given any function $F(t)$ and any value t_0 of t, we shall write $F(t_0 -) < 0$ if there exists a positive number δ such that $F(t) < 0$ when $t_0 - \delta \leqslant t < t_0$, i.e., if $F(t)$ is negative for all values of t smaller, but not too much smaller, than t_0. Similarly, we shall write $F(t_0 +) < 0$ if there exists a positive δ such that $F(t) < 0$ for all values of t satisfying $t_0 < t \leqslant t_0 + \delta$; i.e., if $F(t)$ assumes negative values for all values of t close to but larger than t_0. The symbols

$$F(t_0 -) > 0, \quad F(t_0 -) \leqslant 0, \quad F(t_0 +) = 0, \text{ etc.,}$$

are to be defined analogously.

Theorem 3.1.   If $f'(t_0) = 0$, the nature of $f(t_0)$ (as a possible relative extremum) is given by Table 3.1.

TABLE 3.1

	$f'(t_0 +) < 0$	$f'(t_0 +) > 0$
$f'(t_0 -) < 0$	not a rel. ext.	relative minimum
$f'(t_0 -) > 0$	relative maximum	not a rel. ext.

This theorem completely takes care of the case in which t_0 is an *isolated* root of the equation $f'(t) = 0$, i.e., a root which lies inside some interval containing no other root of the same equation; for in this case one of the four combinations covered by Table 3.1 must occur.

The four combinations require separate proofs. However, the cases in which t_0 is asserted not to yield a relative extremum may be proved almost exactly as Theorem 2.1 was proved, and the other two cases are so much alike that it will suffice to prove one of them, say the case represented by the lower left-hand entry in the table.

Suppose, therefore, that $f'(t_0 -) > 0, f'(t_0 +) < 0$. We recall that this means that there exist two positive numbers δ_1 and δ_2 for which

$$f'(t) > 0 \quad \text{if} \quad t_0 - \delta_1 \leqslant t < t_0 ,$$
$$f'(t) < 0 \quad \text{if} \quad t_0 < t \leqslant t_0 + \delta_2 .$$

Then if δ denotes the smaller of the two numbers δ_1 and δ_2, it follows at once from the above relations that

$$(3.1) \quad f'(t) > 0 \quad \text{if} \quad t_0 - \delta \leqslant t < t_0 ,$$
$$f'(t) < 0 \quad \text{if} \quad t_0 < t \leqslant t_0 + \delta .$$

As in the proof of Theorem 2.1, we may write

$$(3.2) \quad f(t) - f(t_0) = f'(t')(t - t_0) ,$$

where t' lies between t_0 and t. Suppose that $t_0 - \delta \leqslant t \leqslant t_0 + \delta$; then t' lies in the same interval and (by (3.1) as applied to t') the factors on the right side of (3.2) will always have opposite signs (or both be zero if $t = t_0$). Therefore

$$f(t) - f(t_0) \leqslant 0 \quad \text{if} \quad t_0 - \delta \leqslant t \leqslant t_0 + \delta \,;$$

this, however, is precisely the condition for the occurrence of a relative maximum at t_0.

Example 3.1. We shall identify the relative extrema of the polynomial $f(t) = 3t^5 - 5t^3 + 7$. Differentiation gives $f'(t) = 15t^4 - 15t^2$, so the critical values of t are the roots of the equation $15t^4 - 15t^2 = 0$, which one may

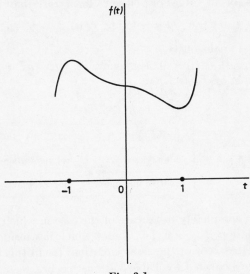

Fig. 3.1

readily find by factoring to be -1, 0 (a double root), and $+1$. Now $f'(t) > 0$ for all values of t less than -1; therefore $f'(-1-) > 0$. On the other hand, $f'(t) < 0$ for all values of t between -1 and 0; therefore $f'(-1+) < 0$. Consequently, by Table 3.1, -1 gives a relative *maximum* of the given function. As to the root 0, one may verify that $f'(t) < 0$ for

$$-1 < t < +1 \ (t \neq 0),$$

so that $f'(0-) < 0$ and $f'(0+) < 0$. Accordingly, 0 does not give a relative extremum at all. We leave it to the reader to verify that the root $+1$ yields a relative minimum. The relevant portion of the graph of this function is shown in Figure 3.1.

The various parts of Table 3.1 may be given simple geometrical interpretations, and the plausibility of the theorem appears. For instance, consider the case for which the proof was actually carried out above. The assumption $f'(t_0-) > 0$ means that the graph of $f(t)$ is rising as t increases towards t_0, while the assumption $f'(t_0+) < 0$ means that the graph is falling as t increases beyond t_0. Thus the graph rises just to the left of t_0, falls just to the right, and must therefore attain a peak of some kind at t_0—and this, of course, is the geometrical situation corresponding to the presence of a relative maximum.[3] All this is exhibited at the peak over $t = -1$ in Figure 3.1.

A simpler criterion for the classification of relative extrema is provided by the next theorem.

Theorem 3.2.   *If $f(t)$ has a continuous second derivative at the critical value t_0 of t, then*

a) t_0 *gives a relative minimum if $f''(t_0) > 0$,*
b) t_0 *gives a relative maximum if $f''(t_0) < 0$.*

PROOF: We shall actually prove part (a); part (b) may be proved in the same way. We assume, therefore, that $f''(t_0) > 0$, and apply Taylor's formula with a remainder of order two:

$$f(t) = f(t_0) + f'(t_0)(t - t_0) + \tfrac{1}{2}f''(t')(t - t_0)^2 \,,$$

or, since by assumption $f'(t_0) = 0$,

$$(3.3) \quad f(t) - f(t_0) = \tfrac{1}{2}f''(t')(t - t_0)^2 \,,$$

where t' lies between t and t_0. Since $f''(t_0) > 0$, and $f''(t)$ is continuous at t_0, there exists a positive number δ such that $f''(t)$ is positive throughout the interval $t_0 - \delta \leqslant t \leqslant t_0 + \delta$. Then if t lies in this interval, the t' of (3.3) must also; thus $f''(t') > 0$, and the right side of (3.3) is positive unless $t = t_0$, for this is true of $(t - t_0)^2$. Consequently,

$$f(t) - f(t_0) \geqslant 0 \quad \text{if} \quad t_0 - \delta \leqslant t \leqslant t_0 + \delta \,,$$

and a relative minimum evidently occurs. Moreover, the minimum is isolated.

Example 3.2.   Let us analyze the same function as in Example 3.1, but now by the use of Theorem 3.2. As before, the values of t which might give relative extrema are -1, 0, $+1$. At the same time, $f''(t) = 60t^3 - 30t^2$. Therefore $f''(-1) = -90 < 0$, $f''(0) = 0$, $f''(+1) = 30 > 0$. From the first and third of these relations we may conclude, by Theorem 3.2, that -1 gives a relative maximum and $+1$ gives a relative minimum. However, Theorem 3.2 gives us no information about the case $t_0 = 0$.

It is not hard to find reasons for believing Theorem 3.2 on intuitive grounds. As regards (a), for example, if $f''(t_0) > 0$ then $f'(t)$ must be increasing at and near t_0. Since its value is zero *at* t_0, its values must therefore be negative for values of t slightly smaller than t_0 and positive for values slightly larger than t_0; i.e., $f'(t_0-) < 0$, $f_0(t_0+) > 0$. But this in turn implies, as we have seen, that $f(t)$ must have a minimum at t_0.

It is not true (as one might be tempted to conjecture on the basis of Example 3.2, for instance) that when both the first and the second derivatives

---

[3] Properly speaking, the presence of an *isolated* relative maximum.

of $f(t)$ are zero, no relative extremum can occur. This may be verified by examining the function $f(t) = t^4$, for which $f'(0) = 0$, $f''(0) = 0$, but 0 nevertheless gives a relative (indeed, absolute) minimum. As a direct generalization of Theorem 3.2 one obtains a theorem, Theorem 3.3, which deals with situations of this kind when the function concerned has continuous derivatives of sufficiently high orders.

Theorem 3.3.   If $f^{(k)}(t_0) = 0$ $(k = 1, \ldots, n - 1)$ and $f^{(n)}(t_0) \neq 0$, $f^{(n)}(t)$ being continuous at t_0, then

(a) if n is odd, $f(t)$ does not attain a relative extremum at t_0;
(b) if n is even and $f^{(n)}(t_0) > 0$, t_0 gives a relative minimum;
(c) if n is even and $f^{(n)}(t_0) < 0$, t_0 gives a relative maximum.

PROOF: Let δ be a positive number such that the Taylor formula

$$(3.4) \quad f(t) = f(t_0) + f'(t_0)(t - t_0) + \ldots + f^{(n)}(t') \frac{(t - t_0)^n}{n!}$$

is valid, and $f^{(n)}(t)$ has the same sign, for all values of t satisfying

$$t_0 - \delta \leqslant t \leqslant t_0 + \delta .$$

By the first assumption, (3.4) may actually be reduced to

$$f(t) - f(t_0) = f^{(n)}(t') \frac{(t - t_0)^n}{n!} ,$$

where t' is between t and t_0. Now if n is odd, $(t - t_0)^n$ changes sign at t_0, whereas $f^{(n)}(t_0)/n!$ has the same sign throughout the interval. Therefore $f(t)$ cannot have a relative extremum when $t = t_0$, and this proves (a). If n is even, however, $(t - t_0)^n$ is positive for all values of t but t_0, for which it is zero. Therefore $f(t) - f(t_0)$ has the same (unvarying) sign as $f^{(n)}(t')$ throughout the interval—always excepting t_0—so $f(t)$ attains a relative extremum at t_0, and in fact a relative minimum if $f^{(n)}(t_0) > 0$, a relative maximum if $f^{(n)}(t_0) < 0$. This proves (b) and (c). It should be noted that Theorems 2.1 and 3.2 may be regarded as corollaries of this theorem.

Example 3.3.   The function $f(t) = t^4 - 4t^3 + 6t^2 - 4t + 5$ has $f'(1) = 0$, $f''(1) = 0$, $f^{(3)}(1) = 0$, but $f^{(4)}(1) = 24$. Therefore, by part (b) of Theorem 3.3, $f(t)$ attains a relative minimum when $t = 1$. This can be verified directly by observing that $f(t) = (t - 1)^4 + 4$.

In applications one can frequently dispense with the tests developed in this section, and analogous tests to be developed later. In a particular maximum problem, for instance, it may be possible to see directly from the data that there must be an absolute maximum, and that this maximum must in fact be a relative maximum as well. In these circumstances, if differentiation reveals just one critical point, then that critical point must be the maximum point, and further classification is unnecessary. This accounts for the phenomenon, frequently observed in the literature, of the mere identification of a critical point as such being accepted as the complete determination of a maximum or a minimum. This approach, though laborsaving and frequently valid, must be used with caution.

Example 3.4. For what value of t does the function

$$f(t) = \frac{1 - t^2}{1 + t^2}$$

attain its absolute maximum? That an absolute maximum exists may be seen by noting that for values of t very near zero the values of the function are positive, but for values of t far from zero (precisely, values of t satisfying $|t| > 1$) the values of the function are negative. The fact that the derivative of $f(t)$ is $-4t/(1 + t^2)^2$ shows that the only critical value of t is zero; thus the function attains its maximum value at $t = 0$.

EXERCISES

3.1. For each of the following functions, determine all critical values of t and then classify them twice, first using Theorem 3.1 and then using Theorem 3.2.

(a) $f(t) = 8 + 3t - t^3$,

(b) $f(t) = t^3 - 3t^2 - 24t + 54$,

(c) $f(t) = \dfrac{4}{1 + t^2}$,

(d) $f(t) = \dfrac{1 + t^2}{1 + at^2}$ $(a > 1)$.

3.2. Find the absolute maximum and the absolute minimum of the function $f(t) = 2t^3 + 3t^2 - 12t + 5$ on the interval $0 \leqslant t \leqslant 2$. Draw a graph to illustrate your conclusions.

3.3. A critical value of t for the function

$$f(t) = t^5 + 10(t^4 + 4t^3 + 8t^2 + 8t - 3)$$

is -2. Does this critical value correspond to a relative maximum, a relative minimum, or neither?

4. *Extrema of Functions of Several Variables.* To a certain extent, the results obtained in the last two sections have analogues when the function concerned depends on at least two independent variables. More specifically, we shall see that Theorems 2.1 and 3.2 carry over in a most natural way to the several-variable case. The gap in Theorem 3.2 (occurring when $f''(t_0) = 0$) was filled very nicely by Theorem 3.3 in the one-variable case, but when functions of several variables are considered this gap widens disturbingly, and despite the fact that it can sometimes be bridged (as by Theorem 4.4 below), it has never been completely filled. Our criteria for extrema in the several-variable case must therefore remain incomplete, even when it is possible to assume that the function under investigation has as many continuous derivatives as one may wish. Before the relatively simple criteria that are available are derived, however, the basic terms should be redefined in this more general setting.

The function $f(t_1, \ldots, t_n)$ is said to attain an *absolute maximum* relative to a set G of points $(t_1, \ldots, t_n)$ at the point $(\bar{t}_1, \ldots, \bar{t}_n)$ of G if

$$(4.1) \quad f(t_1, \ldots, t_n) \leqslant f(\bar{t}_1, \ldots, \bar{t}_n)$$

whenever $(t_1, \ldots, t_n)$ belongs to G. Absolute *minima* are defined in the same way, but with the inequality (4.1) replaced by

$$(4.2) \quad f(t_1, \ldots, t_n) \geqslant f(\bar{t}_1, \ldots, \bar{t}_n) \; ;$$

and an absolute *extremum*, as before, is an absolute maximum or an absolute minimum.

Theorem 1.1, which may be thought of as having provided a working basis for the investigations of Sections 2 and 3, is a special case of the next theorem, which plays the same role in the study of extrema problems for functions of several variables. The theorem involves the use of two new terms: a set G of points $(t_1, \ldots, t_n)$ is said to be *bounded* if there exists a positive constant K such that $|t_i| < K$ for all indices i and all points in G. Roughly speaking, a bounded set is one whose points can get only so far from the origin $(0, \ldots, 0)$. Secondly, the set G is said to be *closed* if it includes its boundary.[4]

Theorem 4.1. If the function $f(t_1, \ldots, t_n)$ is continuous at every point of a bounded closed set G, then there exists a point in G at which the function attains an absolute maximum relative to G and one at which it attains an absolute minimum relative to G.

This theorem is one of the basic instruments of mathematical analysis, but a proof is out of the question here. A specialization of Theorem 4.1 which bears a closer resemblance to Theorem 1.1 is the following corollary:

COROLLARY: *If G is the set of points $(t_1, \ldots, t_n)$ satisfying the conditions $T_i \leqslant t_i \leqslant T'_i$ $(i = 1, 2, \ldots, n)$, where T_i and T'_i are any constants such that $T_i \leqslant T'_i$, and if the function $f(t_1, \ldots, t_n)$ is continuous at all points of G, then it attains an absolute maximum and an absolute minimum in G.*

When $n = 1$ (so that there is no need for indices), G is an interval with the endpoints included, and we have Theorem 1.1; when $n = 2$, G is a rectangle with the sides (which are parallel to the t_1 and t_2 axes) included; and so on.

These theorems should give comfort to the searcher for maxima and minima, for they assure him that under frequently prevailing conditions his quest is not for nothing; but they provide no constructive help. As in the case of one independent variable, it is expedient to fall back on a concept of relative extrema, for which somewhat more specific criteria can be given and from a knowledge of which the absolute extrema may often be found.

The function $f(t_1, \ldots, t_n)$ is said to attain a *relative maximum* at the point $(\bar{t}_1, \ldots, \bar{t}_n)$ if there exists a positive number δ such that the inequality (4.1) is satisfied at all points $(t_1, \ldots, t_n)$ whose co-ordinates satisfy the inequalities $|t_i - \bar{t}_i| < \delta$ $(i = 1, 2, \ldots, n)$, a *relative minimum* if the in-

---

[4] It may be hoped that the term *boundary* is sufficiently self-explanatory; but here is a precise definition: A point $(\bar{t}_1, \ldots, \bar{t}_n)$ is said to belong to the boundary of G if and only if for any positive number ϵ, however small, there exist points $(t_1, \ldots, t_n)$ in G and also points not in G satisfying the n inequalities
$$|t_i - \bar{t}_i| < \epsilon \quad (i = 1, 2, \ldots, n).$$

equality (4.2) is satisfied under the same conditions. Relative extrema are therefore characterized by the fact that the quantity

$$f(t_1, \ldots, t_n) - f(\bar{t}_1, \ldots, \bar{t}_n)$$

does not change sign for nearby points: it is nonpositive if the function attains a relative maximum at $(\bar{t}_1, \ldots, \bar{t}_n)$, nonnegative if a relative minimum. Still another way of putting the matter is to say that relative extrema are absolute extrema relative to a sufficiently small "box" defined by the set of inequalities $|t_i - \bar{t}_i| < \delta$.

The generalization of Theorem 2.1 is given by the next theorem.

Theorem 4.2. If the function $f(t_1, \ldots, t_n)$ has continuous first derivatives at a point $(\bar{t}_1, \ldots, \bar{t}_n)$ where it attains a relative extremum, then $\partial f/\partial t_i = 0$ $(i = 1, 2, \ldots, n)$ at that point.

PROOF: In the function $f(t_1, \ldots, t_n)$, replace all of the variables but t_i by their barred values, thus getting $f(\bar{t}_1, \ldots, \bar{t}_{i-1}, t_i, \bar{t}_{i+1}, \ldots, \bar{t}_n)$. This is a function of the single variable t_i, and it follows at once from the definitions of relative extrema and the fact that the given function attains a relative extremum at $(\bar{t}_1, \ldots, \bar{t}_n)$ that this function of t_i must have a relative extremum of the same kind when $t_i = \bar{t}_i$. By Theorem 2.1, its derivative there must therefore be zero: but this derivative is exactly $\partial f/\partial t_i$ evaluated at $(\bar{t}_1, \ldots, \bar{t}_n)$.

Thus, according to Theorem 4.2, in order to find the relative extrema of $f(t_1, \ldots, t_n)$ one might first try to solve the system of n equations

$$(4.3) \quad \frac{\partial f}{\partial t_i} = 0 \quad (i = 1, 2, \ldots, n) \; ;$$

for only points simultaneously satisfying these equations can yield relative extrema. The system (4.3) may be inconsistent; in this event there can be no relative extrema. But even when the system (4.3) has solutions, some or all of them may fail to represent relative extrema. This again raises the problem of distinguishing those solutions of (4.3) which do not yield extrema from those that do, and then classifying the latter into maximum-yielding and minimum-yielding points. The major theorem which applies to this problem is Theorem 4.3.

Theorem 4.3. If all first and second derivatives of the function $f(t_1, \ldots, t_n)$ exist and are continuous at a point $(\bar{t}_1, \ldots, \bar{t}_n)$ satisfying the equations (4.3), then the function attains a relative maximum, a relative minimum, or neither at that point, according as the quadratic form $\Sigma a_{ij} u_i u_j$ is negative definite, positive definite, or indefinite, a_{ij} being the value of the derivative $\partial^2 f/\partial t_i \partial t_j$ at $(\bar{t}_1, \ldots, \bar{t}_n)$.

This theorem should be compared with Theorem 3.2, of which it is a generalization. The widened gap referred to in the first paragraph of the present section occurs just at this point, for Theorem 4.3 leaves the classification unsolved if the form $\Sigma a_{ij} u_i u_j$ happens to be semidefinite. All attempts to analyze this marginal case lead to formidable difficulties, and we shall have more to say about it only in the very special subcase that occurs when the quadratic form is identically zero.

The conditions in Theorem 4.2 are frequently called the *first-order conditions* for relative extrema, while those in Theorem 4.3 are called the *second-order conditions*. The word "order" here refers, of course, to that of the partial derivatives involved. Before embarking on the proof of Theorem 4.3, we shall use an example to illustrate how these two sets of conditions are used to find and classify relative extrema.

Example 4.1. We shall investigate the relative extrema of the polynomial

$$f(t_1,t_2) = 5t_1{}^2 + 6t_1t_2 + 5t_2{}^2 - 32t_1 - 32t_2 + 40 .$$

The first partial derivatives with respect to t_1 and t_2 are, respectively, $10t_1 + 6t_2 - 32$ and $6t_1 + 10t_2 - 32$; therefore the equations (4.3) become

$$\begin{cases} 10t_1 + 6t_2 - 32 = 0, \\ 6t_1 + 10t_2 - 32 = 0. \end{cases}$$

The only solution of this system of equations is $\bar{t}_1 = \bar{t}_2 = 2$; thus, by Theorem 4.2, the point $(2,2)$ is the only one at which the function might attain a relative extremum. The second derivatives of $f(t_1,t_2)$ are all constants, so the calculation of the quadratic form in Theorem 4.3 is a simple matter; it is

$$10t_1{}^2 + 6t_1t_2 + 6t_2t_1 + 10t_2{}^2, \quad \text{or} \quad 10t_1{}^2 + 12t_1t_2 + 10t_2{}^2 .$$

According to Theorem 3.1 of Chapter Eleven, this form is definite, since $12^2 - 4 \cdot 10 \cdot 10 < 0$; and since all of the coefficients are positive, it must be positive definite. Thus, finally, Theorem 4.3 asserts that the given function attains a relative *minimum* at the point $(2,2)$. Further investigation using other methods would show that this is in fact the absolute minimum of the function.

Proof of Theorem 4.3.[5] According to Taylor's formula with a remainder of order two, we may write

$$(4.4) \quad f(t_1, \ldots, t_n) = f(\bar{t}_1, \ldots, \bar{t}_n) + \tfrac{1}{2}\Sigma_{ij}\frac{\partial^2 f}{\partial t_i \partial t_j}(t_i - \bar{t}_i)(t_j - \bar{t}_j) ,$$

the second derivatives being evaluated at some point between $(\bar{t}_1, \ldots, \bar{t}_n)$ and $(t_1, \ldots, t_n)$ (see Chapter Ten, Section 8). Since a_{ij} is the value of $\partial^2 f/\partial t_i \partial t_j$ at $(\bar{t}_1, \ldots, \bar{t}_n)$, and these derivatives are continuous at this point, we may write

$$(4.5) \quad \frac{\partial^2 f}{\partial t_i \partial t_j} = a_{ij} + b_{ij} ,$$

where $b_{ij} \to 0$ as $t_i \to \bar{t}_i$ ($i = 1, 2, \ldots, n$), and it is to be understood that the partial derivatives on the left-hand side in (4.5) are evaluated at the

---

[5] This proof, which is given here mainly because it is not easily accessible elsewhere, goes somewhat deeper than most of the other proofs in this volume, and the reader whose mathematical self-confidence is fragile may be well advised to pass it up. It is adapted from a proof given by Curtiss in his monograph, cited at the end of the chapter.

same point as those in (4.4). The equation (4.4) may therefore be put in the form

$$(4.6) \quad f(t_1, \ldots, t_n) - f(\bar{t}_1, \ldots, \bar{t}_n)$$
$$= \tfrac{1}{2}\Sigma_{ij}a_{ij}(t_i - \bar{t}_i)(t_j - \bar{t}_j) + \tfrac{1}{2}\Sigma_{ij}b_{ij}(t_i - \bar{t}_i)(t_j - \bar{t}_j) \, .$$

We now define new variables r and x_i $(i = 1, 2, \ldots, n)$ by the formulas

$$(4.7) \quad r = \sqrt{\Sigma_i(t_i - \bar{t}_i)^2}$$

and

$$(4.8) \quad x_i = \frac{t_i - \bar{t}_i}{r} \, .$$

In order to avoid division by zero at this step, we shall assume that $t_i \neq \bar{t}_i$ for at least one value of the index i; since we are concerned only with points *near* $(\bar{t}_1, \ldots, \bar{t}_n)$, this assumption is quite safe. An easy calculation based on (4.7) and (4.8) shows that

$$(4.9) \quad \Sigma_i x_i^2 = 1 \, ,$$

and that the right-hand side of (4.6) may now be written

$$(4.10) \quad \tfrac{1}{2}r^2(\Sigma_{ij}a_{ij}x_ix_j + \Sigma_{ij}b_{ij}x_ix_j) \, .$$

Now suppose that the quadratic form $\Sigma a_{ij}u_iu_j$ is negative definite. For values of the variables x_i satisfying (4.9)—which defines a closed bounded set in the space of points $(x_1, \ldots, x_n)$—the continuous function $\Sigma_{ij}a_{ij}x_ix_j$ must attain a certain maximum value, by Theorem 4.1; and since the form $\Sigma a_{ij}u_iu_j$ is negative definite, this maximum value must be negative, say $-m$ $(m > 0)$. Since $b_{ij} \to 0$ as $r \to 0$ (cf. [4.5], [4.7]), for all values of r smaller than a certain value r_0 it must be that

$$(4.11) \quad |\Sigma_{ij}b_{ij}x_ix_j| < m \, .$$

Therefore, for such values of r, the expression (4.10) must be negative for all possible x_i's, for the first sum is at most $-m$ and the second sum is less than m. Now take δ to be any positive number smaller than $r_0/\sqrt{n}$; then if $|t_i - \bar{t}_i| < \delta$ $(i = 1, 2, \ldots, n)$,

$$\Sigma_i(t_i - \bar{t}_i)^2 < n\delta^2 < n \cdot \frac{r_0^2}{n} = r_0^2 \, ,$$

so that by (4.7), $r < r_0$, and in turn (4.10), and therefore both sides of (4.6), are negative. This shows that $f(t_1, \ldots, t_n)$ attains a relative maximum at $(\bar{t}_1, \ldots, \bar{t}_n)$.

If the quadratic form $\Sigma a_{ij}u_iu_j$ is positive definite, a closely similar line of reasoning shows that the function attains a relative minimum at the given point.

Finally, if the quadratic form $\Sigma a_{ij}u_iu_j$ is indefinite, there exist points $(x_1, \ldots, x_n)$ and $(y_1, \ldots, y_n)$ satisfying (4.9) such that

$$X = \Sigma_{ij}a_{ij}x_ix_j < 0 \quad \text{and} \quad Y = \Sigma_{ij}a_{ij}y_iy_j > 0 \, .$$

Let m be the smaller of the two positive numbers $-X$ and Y, and again let r_0 be such that (4.11) is satisfied when $0 < r < r_0$. Consider the point $(t_1, \ldots, t_n)$ whose co-ordinates are given by the formulas $t_i = \bar{l}_i + \frac{1}{2}\delta x_i$ $(i = 1, 2, \ldots, n)$, where δ is an arbitrarily small positive number subject to the sole condition $\delta < r_0$. On the one hand, we have

$$|t_i - \bar{l}_i| = \tfrac{1}{2}\delta|x_i| \leqslant \tfrac{1}{2}\delta < \delta,$$

since by (4.9) $|x_i| \leqslant 1$; but on the other hand, it follows from (4.7) and the fact that $(x_1, \ldots, x_n)$ satisfies (4.9) that the value of r for this point is $\tfrac{1}{2}\delta$, which is less than r_0, so that by the choice of r_0 the expression (4.10) is negative: the first term is at most $-m$, and the second term is less than m. This shows that within an arbitrarily small "box" $|t_i - \bar{l}_i| < \delta$ centered at $(\bar{l}_1, \ldots, \bar{l}_n)$ there exists at least one point such that the value of the expression

$$(4.12) \quad f(t_1, \ldots, t_n) - f(\bar{l}_1, \ldots, \bar{l}_n)$$

is negative. In the same way, working with the y_i's instead of the x_i's, one can show that within any such box there is at least one point at which this quantity is positive. Since a relative extremum occurs at $(\bar{l}_1, \ldots, \bar{l}_n)$ only if there is some box centered at the point within which (4.12) does not change sign, this shows that a relative extremum is not attained at the point, and the third and last part of the theorem is proved.

The methods used in this proof require very little modification to give a proof of the following somewhat more general theorem, whose relation to Theorem 4.3 is that of Theorem 3.3 to Theorem 3.2 in the case of one independent variable.

Theorem 4.4. *If all derivatives of* $f(t_1, \ldots, t_n)$ *of orders up to and including* p $(p \geqslant 1)$ *exist and are continuous at the point* $(\bar{l}_1, \ldots, \bar{l}_n)$, *and if all of the derivatives of orders less than p are zero at this point while at least one derivative of order p is not zero at the point, then the function attains a relative maximum, relative minimum, or neither at the given point according as the form* $\Sigma a_{ij} \ldots {}_s u_i u_j \ldots u_s$ *is negative definite, positive definite, or indefinite, $a_{ij} \ldots {}_s$ being the value of the pth-order derivative* $\partial^p f/\partial t_i \partial t_j \ldots \partial t_s$ *at* $(\bar{l}_1, \ldots, \bar{l}_n)$.

This theorem again leaves undecided the case in which the form is semidefinite, as it may easily be if p is even (if p is odd, the form is necessarily indefinite; see Theorem 2.1 in Chapter Eleven).

EXERCISES

4.1. Find and classify the points at which relative extrema are attained by each of the following functions:

a) $f(t_1, t_2) = 1 + 3t_1 + t_1 t_2 + t_1^2 + t_2^2$,

b) $f(t_1, t_2) = t_1^3 - 4t_2^2 + t_1 t_2^2$

c) $f(t_1, t_2) = 1 - t_1^4 - t_2^4$

d) $f(t_1, t_2) = \dfrac{1}{1 + (t_1 + t_2)^2}$

4.2. Find the absolute maximum of the function $f(t_1,t_2) = t_1 - t_1^2 - t_2^2$ on the set defined by $0 \leqslant t_1 \leqslant 1$, $0 \leqslant t_2 \leqslant 1$.

4.3. Show that Theorems 2.1, 3.2, 3.3, 4.2, and 4.3 may all be regarded as special cases of (or corollaries to) Theorem 4.4. Example: If $n = 1$ and $p = 1$ in Theorem 4.4, the form

$$\Sigma a_{ij} \ldots {}_s u_i u_j \ldots u_s$$

is simply $f'(\bar{t}) \cdot u$ (the subscript 1 is omitted); and unless $f'(\bar{t}) = 0$, this form is indefinite and, by Theorem 4.4, a relative extremum is not attained at $\bar{t}$. In other words, if a relative extremum is attained at t, it must be that $f'(\bar{t}) = 0$; and this is logically equivalent to Theorem 2.1.

4.4. Using Theorems 4.2 and 4.3 together with the appropriate theorems from Chapter Eleven, formulate directly, i.e., in terms of the first and second derivatives, and without reference to quadratic forms, criteria for identifying and classifying the points at which a function of two independent variables attains relative extrema.

5. Conditioned Extrema. When in an extremum problem for a function $f(t_1, \ldots, t_n)$ the variables $t_1, \ldots, t_n$ are required to satisfy certain "side conditions" of the form

$$(5.1) \quad g_k(t_1, \ldots, t_n) = 0 \quad (k = 1, 2, \ldots, m) \, ,$$

the extrema are called *conditioned extrema*. More precisely, one says for instance that the function $f(t_1, \ldots, t_n)$ attains *a relative minimum subject to the conditions* (5.1) at a point $(\bar{t}_1, \ldots, \bar{t}_n)$ if there is some positive number δ such that $f(t_1, \ldots, t_n) \geqslant f(\bar{t}_1, \ldots, \bar{t}_n)$ whenever the point $(t_1, \ldots, t_n)$ satisfies the inequalities

$$|t_i - \bar{t}_i| < \delta \quad (i = 1, 2, \ldots, n)$$

and the conditions (5.1). Corresponding definitions for the other types of conditioned extrema may be obtained by modifying the basic definitions for unconditioned (or, as we shall say, *free*) extrema as given in Section 4 in the same way.

Needless to say, a given function may or may not attain a conditioned relative extremum at a certain point, depending on the functions g_k occurring in the side conditions (5.1). One usually requires that $m < n$ (the number of side conditions is less than the number of independent variables), for in the contrary case ($m \geqslant n$) the system of equations (5.1) would normally have a finite number of solutions or none at all, and the problem of finding conditioned extrema would be trivial or meaningless.

A crude but sometimes effective method for finding conditioned extrema is that of using the equations (5.1) to eliminate m variables from the function $f(t_1, \ldots, t_n)$, and then finding the free extrema of the resulting function of $n - m$ variables. It would be an excellent practical method were it not for the fact that the elimination process involved in it is usually difficult or practically impossible. We shall conclude this chapter with a description of a method which is vastly superior on theoretical grounds, although from the standpoint of the practical calculation of answers there may be only minor advantages on either side. Throughout the argument it will be assumed that the functions f and g_k $(k = 1, \ldots, m)$ have continuous second derivatives.

The identification problem may be made a matter of applying to a certain auxiliary function the criterion for *free* relative extrema. The auxiliary function is defined as follows: Let $\lambda_1, \ldots, \lambda_m$ be m new independent variables, and put

$$(5.2) \quad F(t_1, \ldots, t_n; \ \lambda_1, \ldots, \lambda_m) = f(t_1, \ldots, t_n) + \sum_{k=1}^{m} \lambda_k g_k(t_1, \ldots, t_n) \,.$$

It should be noticed that at points satisfying the conditions (5.1), this function coincides with the given function $f(t_1, \ldots, t_n)$; for when the conditions (5.1) are fulfilled, all of the terms following the summation sign on the right side of (5.2) are zero, and, in effect, the variables λ_k drop out.

Now, according to Theorem 4.2, the function F can have a relative extremum at a point $(t_1, \ldots, t_n; \ \lambda_1, \ldots, \lambda_m)$ only if each of its first partial derivatives $\partial F/\partial t_i$ $(i = 1, \ldots, n)$ and $\partial F/\partial \lambda_k$ $(k = 1, \ldots, m)$ is equal to zero at that point. Thus the function F can have a relative extremum at $(t_1, \ldots, t_n; \ \lambda_1, \ldots, \lambda_m)$ only if the $n + m$ equations

$$(5.3) \quad \frac{\partial F}{\partial t_i} = \frac{\partial f}{\partial t_i} + \sum_{k=1}^{m} \lambda_k \frac{\partial g_k}{\partial t_i} = 0$$

and

$$(5.4) \quad \frac{\partial F}{\partial \lambda_k} = g_k(t_1, \ldots, t_n) = 0$$

are satisfied at that point. But the equations (5.4) are precisely the conditions (5.1); and this means that F can have a relative extremum only when the conditions (5.1) are satisfied. The equations (5.3) are new; and it can be shown that these equations are necessary conditions for the existence of conditioned relative extrema of the original function f. More precisely,

Theorem 5.1.   If the function $f(t_1, \ldots, t_n)$ attains at a point $(t_1, \ldots, t_n)$ a relative extremum subject to the conditions (5.1), there must exist numbers $\lambda_1, \ldots, \lambda_m$ such that the equations (5.3) are satisfied at that point.[6]

The numbers $\lambda_1, \ldots, \lambda_m$ are usually called *Lagrange* (or *Lagrangean*) *Multipliers*.

The procedure for finding possible conditioned relative extrema is therefore this: given the functions $f, g_1, \ldots, g_m$, one sets up the equations (5.3) and (5.4), and then solves for $t_1, \ldots, t_n, \lambda_1, \ldots, \lambda_m$. The values of $(t_1, \ldots, t_n)$ occurring in these solutions give the points at which f *may* have relative extrema subject to the conditions (5.1).

---

[6] Strictly speaking, this is true only if the rank of the matrix whose typical element is $a_{ij} = \partial g_i/\partial t_j$ $(i = 1, \ldots, m; j = 1, \ldots, n)$ is m; but this stipulation, which in a way expresses the independence of the conditions (5.1), is usually satisfied more or less automatically in practical problems.

Example 5.1. For what values of t_1 and t_2 might the function

$$f(t_1,t_2) = t_1 + t_2 - 4$$

attain relative extrema subject to the condition $t_1{}^2 + t_2{}^2 = 1$? Here $n = 2$, $m = 1$, and the equations (5.3) become

a) $1 + \lambda_1(2t_1) = 0$,
b) $1 + \lambda_1(2t_2) = 0$,

while (5.4) may be written

c) $t_1{}^2 + t_2{}^2 - 1 = 0$.

Solving the equation (*a*) for t_1 and the equation (*b*) for t_2, we get

d) $t_1 = -\frac{1}{2}\lambda_1, \quad t_2 = -\frac{1}{2}\lambda_1$.

Squaring both sides and adding gives

$$t_1{}^2 + t_2{}^2 = \frac{1}{2}\lambda_1{}^2 ;$$

but this compared with (*c*) shows that $2\lambda_1{}^2 = 1$, or

$$\lambda_1 = \pm\frac{1}{\sqrt{2}} .$$

Putting this in (*d*) gives finally

$$t_1 = \pm \sqrt{2}/4, \quad t_2 = \pm \sqrt{2}/4.$$

Thus the conditioned relative extrema can occur only at the points

$$(\sqrt{2}/4, \ \sqrt{2}/4), \quad (-\sqrt{2}/4, -\sqrt{2}/4).$$

Whether extrema actually do occur at these points is another question (the answer to which is that they do).

With the same approach as that used in the theory of free extrema, but with some modification of the details, one can prove the classification theorem, Theorem 5.2.

Theorem 5.2. The function $f(t_1, \ldots, t_n)$ attains a relative maximum subject to the conditions (5.1) at a point $(\bar{l}_1, \ldots, \bar{l}_n)$ satisfying (5.3) and (5.4) if the inequality

$$(5.5) \quad \Sigma_{ij}a_{ij}u_iu_j < 0 ,$$

where a_{ij} is the value of $\partial^2 f/\partial t_i \partial t_j$ at $(\bar{l}_1, \ldots, \bar{l}_n)$, is satisfied by all values of $(u_1, \ldots, u_n)$ other than $(0,0, \ldots, 0)$ which satisfy the m linear equations

$$(5.6) \quad \Sigma_i b_{ki}u_i = 0 \quad (k = 1,2, \ldots, m)$$

where b_{ki} is the value of $\partial g_k/\partial t_i$ at $(\bar{l}_1, \ldots, \bar{l}_n)$. Reversing the inequality in (5.5) gives an analogous sufficient condition for relative minima.

There exist determinantal criteria for the "conditioned" negative or positive definiteness involved in this theorem; these may be found in the monograph by Hancock cited below.

SUGGESTIONS FOR FURTHER READING

The only book in English devoted entirely to the subject of this chapter is H. Hancock, *Theory of Maxima and Minima* (Boston: Ginn & Co., 1917). Nevertheless, nearly all books on the calculus, including all those cited at the end of Chapter Nine, deal at some length with the subject, if only in the one-variable case. An exceptionally full account will be found in T. Chaundy, *The Differential Calculus* (Oxford: Clarendon Press, 1935), chap. ix. See also P. A. Samuelson, *Foundations of Economic Analysis* (Cambridge: Harvard University Press, 1947), Mathematical Appendix A; and D. H. Curtiss, "Maxima and Minima of Functions of Several Variables," *Mathematical Monographs I* (Evanston and Chicago: Northwestern University, 1941), pp. 1–43.

Anyone intending to consult these works should be warned beforehand that the terminology is by no means uniform: for example, what we call a relative extremum is called by Chaundy a "turning value" and by Hancock (for whom the word "relative" has quite a different meaning) an "extreme."

LIST OF SPECIAL SYMBOLS

Symbol	Examples at Pages	Meaning or Use
α (alpha)	32, 59, 60, 136, 295	parameter; adjustment coefficient
β (beta)	34, 90, 295	parameter; adjustment coefficient
δ (delta)	178, 303, 317	planned market demand function; "sufficiently small" number
ϵ (epsilon)	178, 247	"arbitrarily small" number
θ (theta)	108, 291	angle; measure of angle
λ (lambda)	71, 114, 262, 294, 331	root of, or variable in, auxiliary equation; Lagrange multiplier; parameter
μ (mu)	147	Lagrange multiplier
π (pi)	144, 291	profit or net revenue; the constant 3.1415. . . .
σ (sigma)	91	real part of a complex number
τ (tau)	91, 136	imaginary part of a complex number; distance parameter
ϕ (phi)	138, 157, 162	transformation function; decision function
Δ (cap. delta)	118, 119, 265	determinant; cofactor; discriminant
Σ (capital sigma)	28, 79, 198	summation sign
$-$ (over a variable)	55, 256	"equilibrium (or fixed) value of"
$\dashv$	105	"is inferior to"
$\sim$	105	"is indifferent to"
$\int$	69, 86, 238, 244	integral sign
∂	33, 230, 233	partial derivative sign
$\equiv$	201	"is identical with"
∞	55, 216 n, 315	"infinity"
$\rightarrow$	55, 216	"approaches"
$||$	56, 216 n, 292	absolute value
$[. . .]$	59, 60	nonlinear terms in Taylor series
$\{. . .\}$	89	nonconstant terms in Taylor series
* (superscript)	176	"observable value of"

Index

INDEX

*This book has been set on the Monotype in 10 and 9
point Bodoni No. 175, leaded 2 points. Chapter
numbers are in 30 point Liberty and chapter titles
in 14 point Bodoni No. 175 italic caps. The size of
the type page is 27 by 46½ picas.*